Quantitative Organic Analysis

Quantitative Organic Analysis

JAMES S. FRITZ & GEORGE S. HAMMOND

Department of Chemistry,
Iowa State College
and The Ames Laboratory
of The Atomic Energy Commission

NEW YORK · JOHN WILEY & SONS, INC.

London · Chapman & Hall, Ltd.

This book is dedicated to Marian Hammond and Joan Fritz, whose encouragement, tolerance, and ability to filter family responsibility have made the writing possible.

PREFACE

This book has been written as a consequence of the conviction of
the authors that analysis of organic compounds by selective, functional
group reactions is a powerful and expanding field of analytical chemistry. Chemical industry in all its phases continually presents problems in the analysis of organic materials for which elegant and
convenient solutions may be found in functional group assays. Research in university laboratories can be similarly implemented by
frequent recourse to these methods. We are by no means alone in this
sentiment, very valuable books having already appeared in the field.
The pioneering work of Siggia, *Quantitative Organic Analysis via
Functional Groups,*[1] provides a collection of useful and versatile procedures. The collected work, *Organic Analysis,*[2] of which two volumes
have already appeared, seems destined to become indispensable to the
professional analyst. However, neither of these works answers the
need for a teaching text for use in the presentation of courses at the
later undergraduate or beginning graduate level of instruction. That
there is a need for such a textbook is emphasized by the fact that little

[1] S. Siggia, *Quantitative Organic Analysis via Functional Groups,* 2nd edition,
John Wiley & Sons, New York, 1954.

[2] J. Mitchell, I. M. Kolthoff, E. S. Proskauer, and A. Weissberger, Editors,
Organic Analysis, Interscience Publishers, New York, Vol. 1, 1953; Vol. 2, 1954.

attention has been accorded the teaching of quantitative organic analysis in colleges and universities, despite the fact that many schools offer excellent courses in inorganic quantitative analysis.

It is our opinion that such a course should acquaint the student with two types of information. First, it should familiarize him with typical established procedures and, to some extent at least, with their limitations. In addition, he should learn as much as possible about the best approaches to the problems of setting up new methods and adapting old ones to specific applications. Considerable emphasis has been placed upon the development of the latter subject. The fantastic variation in the structure of organic compounds and in their reactivities makes it folly to attempt to establish universal methods for all compounds of a class. In principle, each problem should be considered in its own right. In practice, at least passing attention must be given to the specific reactivity of each new compound which is to be determined and to possible interferences from other constituents of the reaction mixture.

One of the most intriguing aspects of the field devolves from the possibility of setting up selective methods that will allow the determination of the individual constituents of mixtures of compounds that contain the *same* functional groups. It is here that extreme variations in reactivity, which doom to failure any attempt to establish general methods for all members of a class, can be put to work by the analyst. In order to take advantage of such phenomena, it is necessary to utilize data concerning reaction rates or to be able to make educated guesses concerning the expected differences in the rates of the reactions of the compounds involved. We have attempted to illustrate the use of kinetic data in the planning of analytical procedures. The basis for prediction of relative reactivities lies in the field of theoretical organic chemistry. Anything more than occasional generalizations and allusions to that field would lead us far beyond the intended scope of this book. Although the book is intended for students who are well grounded in elementary quantitative analysis and organic chemistry, it will be evident that the concepts developed will become increasingly useful as the student's understanding of the theory of organic chemistry is increased by other experiences.

In keeping with the philosophy that a successful analyst in this field will be the individual who can approach a new problem in a constructive and imaginative manner, we have devoted considerable space to discussion of the reasoning that can be applied to the choice of methods and the proper planning of trial experiments. We have, furthermore, made frequent brief suggestions as to possibilities for the development of new procedures. Since we make no claim to omniscience, we thoroughly anticipate that some such suggestions will, if studied, prove to be of little use. The value of such material is, therefore, to be judged by its success in stimulating creative thinking by the students.

Since frequent reference is made to kinetics, a student will feel more at home in reading the text if he has had a course in elementary physical chemistry. However, such a course need not be a necessary prerequisite to the intelligent study of this book. Presentation of the material to students who have had no physical chemistry can be made on the basis of the qualitative generalizations concerning the influence of concentrations and temperature on reaction rates which are a part of all courses in general chemistry. The translation of these concepts into the few kinetic equations needed to utilize rate data as it appears in the chemical literature can be made on a purely *ad hoc* basis. Such an explanation can be presented in no more than a few minutes' lecture time.

Since the main purpose of the book is the presentation of principles, we have made methods and techniques—rather than organic structural classification—the basis of the organization. We hope, however, that a good index and the liberal use of cross references will help to answer needs of the practicing chemist who wishes to compare the various methods for determining a particular functional group.

The purpose of the laboratory section is to provide tested procedures for a basic college course. We have chosen these so as to illustrate a variety of principles and have included a sufficient number to allow some choice of experiments in a brief laboratory course. At Iowa State College it is our practice to offer the course for variable credit. Those who take more than the minimum number of credits devote a considerable fraction of their time to the extension of methods to compounds with which they have not been tested and to exploratory work with new procedures.

JAMES S. FRITZ
GEORGE S. HAMMOND

Ames, Iowa
April, 1957

ACKNOWLEDGMENTS

We wish to express our sincere thanks to William Allen (American Cyanamid Co.), Richard Bowers, Donald De Ford (both of Northwestern University), Charles De Puy, and Robert Hansen (both of Iowa State College), who read sections of the manuscript and furnished valuable suggestions. Figure 40 is based on data kindly supplied us by Dr. Sidney Siggia (General Aniline & Film Co.). To Carol Collins goes credit for writing some of the laboratory procedures. We also gratefully acknowledge the help of the graduate students who aided in the presentation of our own course in quantitative organic analysis: Carol Collins, Joe Dietrich, George Schenk, Stanley Yamamura, and especially Robert Johnson without whose aid our first course offering could not have been successful.

J. S. F.
G. S. H.

CONTENTS

CONTENTS

1.

INTRODUCTION

The analysis of mixtures of organic compounds is a field as complex as that of organic chemistry itself. It has been estimated that the number of known organic compounds has passed the million mark, and the number seems to be increasing almost without limit. It is quite obvious that organic analytical chemistry will never be able to aspire to the objective of compiling a sufficient number of methods for the determination of each individual compound to permit its assay in mixtures of all conceivable types. Two considerations limit this sort of possibility. The first is constant expansion of the number of compounds known. The second is the impossibility of tabulating methods *and interferences* without making serious inroads on the world's supply of paper.

When the field is considered in this light, it becomes evident that the formulation of principles and stimulation of the creative faculties of the student in the field are fully as important as the description of methods. Furthermore, in the realm of methodology it is quite as important to develop an appreciation for methods of evaluating procedures for applicability to a particular problem as it is to become familiar with established methods of analysis. It is no exaggeration to state that a chemist could commit to memory the details of each of the many excellent analytical procedures that have been developed and

still be of only limited value in the analytical research department of
an industrial concern that was primarily interested in the manufacture
of organic chemicals. Each new type of sample is likely to present its
own unique problems which call for adaptation of established methods
or the devising of new ones.

Many methods are discussed in this textbook, but none of them
should be considered *the method* for determination of anything. A
student should bend his efforts toward two main objectives—first, to
understand the chemistry of the methods as they are described; and,
second, to attempt to imagine the types of problems to which the particular method would or *would not* be applicable. An additional chal-
lenge is also worth keeping in mind. A most interesting aspect of this
field is the myriad of new and useful methods that can be invented.
Every serious student should try his hand at such invention. One
of the very satisfying features of the study of analytical chemistry
is the ease with which many such ideas can be tried out and given at
least preliminary evaluation. Furthermore, in the field of organic
analysis, so much remains to be done that it is not at all out of the
question for even a thoughtful neophyte to make a genuine contribution
to the field. In the course that the authors offer, it is their practice
to encourage students to substitute variations or completely original
methods for prescribed experiments in the laboratory.

Since such an aggressive approach to the course is urged upon the
student, it is appropriate to point out some of the various uses to which
organic analysis may be put. Major analytical problems are to be
found in all fields of organic chemistry. The farmer who wishes to
determine whether he should spray his apple orchard after a brief
shower and the spectroscopist who wishes to ascertain whether a weak
absorption band in benzene is due to a previously undetected, forbidden transition or to a trace impurity are both in need of analytical
methods. Neither has a problem that would be considered trivial by
any analyst. The following summary is far from complete but will
serve to illustrate some specific applications in a variety of fields.

Synthetic Organic Research

The conventional approach to synthetic research is to carry out
reactions and then isolate and characterize the products. If the results appear to be less than optimum, the procedure is repeated with
a variation in reaction conditions. Each such product isolation step
is in actuality a gravimetric analysis of a particularly tedious and
inaccurate sort. In the search for optimum reaction conditions, the

experimenter may speed up his work enormously and, at the same time, conserve starting materials if he can develop a specific and rapid assay for the desired reaction product and, perhaps, for expected by-products. It is true that the worker will ordinarily have to develop a procedure for product isolation sooner or later. However, this aspect of the work can profitably be delayed until it is assured that the reaction mixture actually contains as good a yield of the desired product as can be readily obtained. Many workers have adopted the practice of examining crude reaction products by infrared spectrophotometry with excellent results. The fact that the judicious use of burets can accomplish similar economies of time and action is much less widely recognized.

Characterization Studies

Since time immemorial, organic chemists have routinely included neutralization and saponification equivalents in the characterization of acids, bases, and esters. The usefulness of these analyses is so well recognized that we are at a loss to account for the common reluctance to adopt the fine methods for the determination of other functional groups for similar purposes. There seems to be little reason to expect that quantitative determination of unsaturation, carbonyl equivalent, etc., cannot become an integral part of characterization studies.

Kinetics

Every kinetic study depends upon some type of analysis, and it is hardly necessary to point out that a certain amount of spadework to develop an adequate analytical procedure must precede even the most exotic kinetic measurements. It is interesting to note that many of the best methods of quantitative analysis were actually first worked out in the course of kinetic studies of reaction mechanisms. Anyone who wishes to do kinetic studies should develop *an interest* in analytical methods since they will be the principal tools of the trade.

Process Control

The importance of rapid analytical procedures for following industrial production is widely recognized. Highly elaborate instrumental programs are developed to follow the course of production processes and to establish reliable criteria for evaluating product quality. It is quite likely that rapid volumetric determinations can frequently be used in the same way. Much ingenuity is usually demanded in the devising of new control analyses for new products or even to keep up with changes in established processes.

Biochemical Work

Specific methods for the determination of a particular constituent are invaluable in biochemical work but are among the most difficult to work out in a really reliable manner. The difficulty arises from the complexity of mixtures derived from natural origins. There are always many substances present that are unknown or nonisolable. This precludes the thorough study of interferences and makes the general area a most challenging field for analytical research.

Product Analysis

A common necessity arises in industrial laboratories to learn as much as possible about the nature of a successful product from a competitive company. This demands an analysis of composition. Furthermore, the identification of trace impurities may reveal key facts concerning the manufacturing process.

Applications

The poor farmer who was concerned about the retention of an insecticide on his tree may or may not have been a good example of a man with a problem demanding field testing. Despite the fact that the authors are exceedingly naive about this type of work, it is often stated—and seems self-evident—that fast, simple analytical methods would be of great service in controlling the wise use of organic chemicals. One thing is certain. Technical service representatives are naturally reluctant to burden themselves with gross instruments whenever they call on customers. It is not beyond the realm of possibility, however, to imagine their carrying with them small kits containing a carefully chosen set of standard solutions in bottles fitted with medicine droppers. With such an outfit and a very minimum amount of equipment, such as a few stoppered flasks and a hot plate, our trouble shooter could do a remarkably large number of useful semiquantitative determinations with a minimum of ceremony. The comfort and perhaps the utility to his customer could be substantial.

It may seem that instrumental analyses are treated with undue levity in the preceding discussion. If this is so, it is a consequence of overdrawing for the sake of emphasis. The authors are duly impressed with the great power of the various spectroscopic methods of analysis. They have been as excited as anyone by the development of a new and unique spectrophotometric method.* They are also much impressed with the ease and utility of many of the new methods of volumetric or electrochemical analysis. For the chemist, the latter type of analysis has an added appeal because it still leaves the analyst in complete command of the situation. It is a rare individual who can really claim to have mastered a complicated instrument, such as a mass spectrometer, as well as a nontechnical laboratory helper can master the principles of the buret in a very brief period of instruction.

Since this book attempts to deal with the broad area of organic analysis, a chapter on spectroscopic methods is included. It would not be correct to say that this arrangement relegates such methods to their proper relative importance. Spectroscopy is, and will remain, one of the finest and most versatile servants of the analytical chemist.

* Nuclear magnetic resonance spectrophotometry.

2.

DETAILS

OF

A METHOD

INTRODUCTION

The problems of designing and utilizing an analytical method based upon a functional group reaction are far more complex than those encountered in most elementary analyses. This is a consequence of the wide variation in chemical behavior encountered among members of a functional class and the overlapping of the chemical reactions of various classes of compounds. These complications in the planning of a specific method are, of course, related closely to the amazing versatility of the general method. In order to illustrate the point, we have chosen to carry out a detailed examination of a single, well-known procedure. It would not be practical to do so with a large number of methods but it is often necessary for an individual analyst to carry out an analysis of a particular problem along lines similar to those illustrated by the following discussion.

The oximation of carbonyl compounds according to equation 1 has been rather arbitrarily chosen for discussion. The method has been

$$(1) \qquad \underset{R}{\overset{R}{\diagdown}}C{=}O + NH_2OH \rightleftharpoons \underset{R}{\overset{R}{\diagdown}}C{=}NOH + H_2O$$

used widely for determination of both aldehydes and ketones and, under suitable circumstances, can be made highly precise and agreeably convenient to carry out. It would be presumptuous to imply that the lines of reasoning presented below were applied in detail to the development of the excellent procedures which are in use.[1-6] However, the problems that are discussed have been taken care of by one approach or another.

The two principal problems that must be considered are (1) the equilibrium limitations and (2) the kinetic considerations. Knowledge of the equilibrium constant for the particular reaction tells one whether there is any prospect of utilizing it as an analytical method. The rate of the reaction determines whether one can achieve the maximum conversion in a practical period of time and in many cases dictates the choice of reaction conditions.

Factors such as the effects of varying solvents, temperature, and especially the influences of acids and bases can be conveniently discussed in connection with the equilibrium and rate problems. Lastly, one must always consider interfering side reactions which consume either the reagent or the compound that is being determined.

THERMODYNAMIC CONSIDERATIONS

The equilibrium conversion constant for reaction 1 can be formulated in the conventional manner.

$$(2) \qquad K = \frac{[\text{$>$C}{=}\text{NOH}][\text{H}_2\text{O}]}{[\text{$>$C}{=}\text{O}][\text{NH}_2\text{OH}]}$$

For analytical purposes the quantity of significance is the degree of conversion of the carbonyl compound to the derived oxime. If the analytical method is to be serviceable, the ratio of product to reactant at equilibrium should be at least 100 and preferably much larger.

$$(3) \qquad c = \frac{[\text{$>$C}{=}\text{NOH}]}{[\text{$>$C}{=}\text{O}]} = \frac{K[\text{NH}_2\text{OH}]}{[\text{H}_2\text{O}]} \gg 100$$

[1] C. T. Bennett and M. S. Salamon, *Perfumery Essent. Oil Record,* **18**, 511 (1927).

[2] M. E. Martin, K. L. Kelley, and M. W. Green, *J. Am. Pharm. Assoc.,* **35**, 220 (1946).

[3] J. G. Malby and G. R. Prinavesi, *Analyst,* **74**, 498 (1949).

[4] A. J. Feuell and J. H. Skellon, *Analyst,* **78**, 135 (1953).

[5] J. J. Perret, *Helv. Chim. Acta,* **34**, 1531 (1951).

[6] S. Siggia, *Quantitative Organic Analysis via Functional Groups,* Wiley, New York, 1954, p. 21.

There are only a few equilibrium constants in the literature for oximation reactions, and it is therefore necessary to depend largely upon
inference in gathering working information. First, it is common experience that excellent yields are frequently obtained in the preparation of oximes from aldehydes and ketones. This is promising in that
it indicates that side reactions do not occur regularly. It does not
guarantee that the equilibrium constants for reaction 1 are large
enough to be suitable for analytical purposes. The conversion ratio,
c, depends upon the concentration of hydroxylamine, and the concentrations employed in preparative experiments may be much larger
than those that are most desirable in analytical work.

It is possible to estimate the order of magnitude of the required
equilibrium constants by borrowing a powerful tool from the field
of theoretical organic chemistry. Quantitative information is available concerning related reactions, and, in particular, semicarbazone
formation has been the subject of detailed study.[7]

(4) $H_2NCONHNH_2 + {>}C{=}O \rightleftharpoons {>}C{=}NNHCONH_2 + H_2O$

Both the oximation and semicarbazone formation are reactions of the
type,

(5) ${>}C{=}O + H_2NX \rightleftharpoons {>}C{=}NX + H_2O$

in which X is an electron-accepting group. It is anticipated that the
equilibrium constants for reactions 1 and 4 will respond in a similar
manner to changes in the structure of the carbonyl compounds. This
hypothesis may break down for ketones that contain very bulky groups
because steric hindrance to semicarbazone formation will be greater
than in oximation. However, this effect will make the semicarbazone
relatively less stable than the oxime. Therefore, if consideration of
the formation constant for the semicarbazone indicates that a particular oximation reaction should be satisfactory, it is almost certain that
this will be true in actual practice. Thus the knowledge of one or
two oximation constants and a series of formation constants for semi-
carbazones can be coupled by means of a well-designed guess to yield
a considerable amount of presumptive information concerning oximation. Table 1 shows data for semicarbazone formation in water solution.

Conant and Bartlett calculated the formation constant for acetoxime
as 1.1×10^4 in water solution. This value is nearly 350 times as large

[7] J. B. Conant and P. D. Bartlett, *J. Am. Chem. Soc.*, **54**, 2881 (1932).

TABLE 1

Formation Constants for Semicarbazones in Water Solution at 25.0° [7]

Carbonyl Compound	K_{aq} * $\times 10^4$
Furfural	1.3
Acetaldehyde	0.33
Benzaldehyde	3.3
Trimethylacetaldehyde	0.54
Pyruvic acid	2.0
Acetone	0.0031
Cyclohexanone	0.0047
Pinacolone	0.00086

$$* K_{aq} = \frac{K}{[H_2O]} = \frac{[{>}C{=}NNHCONH_2]}{[{>}C{=}O][H_2NCONHNH_2]}.$$

as the formation constant for acetone semicarbazone. A *conservative* estimate of the oximation constants may be made by multiplying the semicarbazone constants by 300. Since ordinary analytical work will not involve the use of reagents in solutions more dilute than 0.01 M, we have calculated the estimated values of the conversion ratio in the presence of 0.01 M hydroxylamine. These values and the estimated oximation constants are tabulated in Table 2.

TABLE 2

Estimated Equilibrium Constants and Conversion Ratios in Oximation Reactions

Carbonyl Compound	K_{aq} * est.	$[{>}C = NOH]/[{>}C = O]$ in 0.01 M NH$_2$OH
Furfural	10^6	10^4
Acetaldehyde	10^5	10^3
Benzaldehyde	10^7	10^5
Trimethylacetaldehyde	10^5	10^3
Pyruvic acid	10^6	10^4
Acetone	10^4	10^2
Cyclohexanone	10^4	10^2
Pinacolone	10^3	10

$$* K_{aq} = \frac{K}{[H_2O]} = \frac{[{>}C{=}NOH]}{[NH_2OH][{>}C{=}O]}.$$

pH Effects

The conversion ratios will be raised correspondingly if the concentration of the reagent is increased. The results indicate that the determination of ketones by oximation *in water solution* would be, at

best, a marginal procedure. Moreover, the calculations are made on
the assumption that the reagent is actually present as *free* hydroxylamine. Since hydroxylamine has a basicity constant of 1.2×10^{-8} in
aqueous solution, it will be extensively ionized in acid solutions,
thereby reducing the concentrations of free hydroxylamine much below
the total concentrations of the reagent. At pH 4 the ratio of $[\overset{+}{N}H_3OH]$
to $[NH_2OH]$ will be approximately 100, and so the free hydroxylamine
concentration will be reduced to very small values. The oximes are
also measurably basic but their basicity constants are of the order of
10^{-11} so that the conversion ratios may be reduced by as much as a
factor of 1000 in acid solution. The estimates in Table 2 show that
under these conditions even the oximation of some aldehydes would be
subject to serious error because of the failure of the reaction to approach completion at equilibrium.

Solvent Effects

All the data that have been considered relate to aqueous solution.
Since water is a product of oximation reaction, it follows that equilibrium conversions should be higher in nonaqueous solutions. This
improves the situation considerably. The aqueous solution oximation
constants are related to the thermodynamic equilibrium constants as
follows:

$$(6) \qquad K_{thermo} = \frac{a_{\rangle C=NOH}\, a_{H_2O}}{a_{\rangle C=O}\, a_{NH_2OH}}$$

$$(7) \qquad K_{thermo} = \frac{K_{aq} a_{H_2O}\, \gamma_{\rangle C=NOH}}{\gamma_{\rangle C=O}\, \gamma_{NH_2OH}}$$

The a's represent activities and the γ's are degenerate activity coefficients [8] that relate the activity of the various compounds in the
medium under consideration to the activity in dilute aqueous solution.
Activity comparisons between media are tedious to carry out, and
activity coefficients change considerably as solvents are varied. However, it is reasonable to expect that none of the variations will out-
weigh the effect on conversions of changing the activity of water from
that in the pure liquid to that in an anhydrous solvent. Other complications may arise in some solvents such as the equilibration of the
carbonyl compounds with the corresponding hemiacetal and acetal in
alcohol solutions according to equations 8 and 9.

[8] E. Grunwald and B. J. Berkowitz, *J. Am. Chem. Soc.*, **73,** 4939 (1951).

(8) $\quad \text{C=O} + C_2H_5OH \rightleftharpoons \overset{OH}{\underset{OC_2H_5}{C}}$

(9) $\quad \overset{OH}{\underset{OC_2H_5OH}{C}} + C_2H_5OH \rightleftharpoons \overset{OC_2H_5}{\underset{OC_2H_5}{C}}$

These reactions, or others, that involve interaction with solvent could decrease the effective concentration of the carbonyl compound and thereby decrease the conversion. Fortunately, those compounds, such as sterically hindered ketones, that have small oximation constants are not likely to be extensively involved in addition reactions. In accord with wide practical experience, it seems fairly certain that almost any aldehyde or ketone can be determined in nonaqueous solution by oximation if the reactions can be made sufficiently rapid and if side reactions do not intervene.

THE KINETIC PROBLEM

It is little comfort to the analytical chemist to know that equilibrium conditions are favorable for a good determination unless he can guarantee that this conversion can be accomplished within a reasonable period of time. Like many organic reactions, oximations are measurably slow, and the rates of the reactions vary even more than the equilibrium constants. The reaction rates are normally quite slow in neutral, aqueous media but the reactions are known to be catalyzed by both acids and bases.[9] Conditions for determination are ordinarily chosen so as to take advantage of these catalytic effects. A reasonable amount of kinetic data on oximation and related reactions is found in the literature and provides enough of a guide to indicate to the analyst where his troubles will arise.

Acid Catalysis

In acid catalysis, there are two major problems. The first is the effect due to the basicity of the reagent, and the second is the variation in catalytic effects as the nature of the catalyzing acid is varied. In the presence of strong mineral acids such as sulfuric and perchloric,

[9] L. P. Hammett, *Physical Organic Chemistry*, McGraw-Hill Book Co., New York, 1940, Chapter 11.

the kinetic effects are due entirely to the hydrogen ion and can be treated analytically with ease. The specific rate of the reaction is given by equation 10, where x is the concentration of product formed.

(10) $$\frac{dx}{dt} = k[{>}C{=}O][NH_2OH][H^+]$$

However, the free hydroxylamine concentration is decreased in the presence of acid, and at high acidities the reaction rate becomes independent of the hydrogen ion concentration.

This conclusion can be demonstrated quantitatively as shown in equations 11 through 14.

(11) $$[NH_2OH] = \frac{K_w[\overset{+}{N}H_3OH]}{K_b[H^+]}$$

(12) $$T_H = [NH_2OH] + [\overset{+}{N}H_3OH]$$

(13) $$[NH_2OH] = \frac{K_w T_H}{K_b[H^+] + K_w}$$

(14) $$\frac{dx}{dt} = v = \frac{k K_w T_H[H^+][{>}C{=}O]}{K_b[H^+] + K_w}$$

At low pH, $K_b[H^+]$ becomes much larger than K_w so that the numerator becomes approximately equal to $K_b[H^+]$ and the rate law reduces to equation 15.

(15) $$v = \frac{k K_w T_H[{>}C{=}O]}{K_b}$$

The value of K_b for hydroxylamine is 1.2×10^{-8}, so that the product, $K_b[H^+]$, becomes approximately equal to K_w at about pH 6. Since the rates are practically independent of the hydrogen ion concentration at higher pH, strong acids are essentially useless as catalysts and their only effect will be to repress the equilibrium conversion.

It has been found, however, that *in buffer solutions* the rates of oximation of acetone [10] and acetophenone and its derivatives [11] go through maxima at acidic pH's. This is due to the fact that the oximation reaction is subject to *general acid catalysis*. This means that the reaction is catalyzed not only by hydrogen ions but also by each of the

---

[10] A. Orlander, *Z. physik chem.*, **129**, 1 (1927).
[11] P. Anziana, *Bull. soc. chim. France*, **6**, 949 (1939).

acidic species in solution. It is possible and also very practical to use acid catalysis to speed up the oximation reactions in solutions whose pH is high enough to prevent a large fraction of the hydroxylamine from being tied up as the hydroxylammonium ion.

General acid catalysis implies that the rate law of equation 16 is followed.

$$(16) \quad v = [\text{>C=O}][\text{NH}_2\text{OH}]\{k_{\text{H}^+}[\text{H}^+] + k_{\text{HA}}[\text{HA}] + K^+_{\text{NH}_3\text{OH}}[\overset{+}{\text{NH}_3\text{OH}}]\}$$

In the cases of interest, catalysis by hydrogen and hydroxylammonium ions will become negligible in comparison to that by HA because of the relatively high concentration of the latter in buffered solutions. For the usual case the rate law approaches equation 17.

$$(17) \quad v = k_{\text{HA}}[\text{>C=O}][\text{NH}_2\text{OH}][\text{HA}]$$

Since the buffer ratio, $[\text{HA}]/[\text{A}^-]$, determines the hydrogen ion concentration, it also determines the fraction of the hydroxylamine which is tied up as the hydroxylammonium ion, as shown in equation 18,

$$(18) \quad \frac{[\overset{+}{\text{NH}_3\text{OH}}]K_w}{[\text{NH}_2\text{OH}]K_b} = \frac{K_i[\text{HA}]}{[\text{A}^-]}$$

where K_i is the ionization constant of the buffer acid, HA. If equation 18 is solved for the concentration of the free hydroxylamine in terms of T_{H}, the total reagent concentration, we obtain equation 19.

$$(19) \quad [\text{NH}_2\text{OH}] = \frac{T_{\text{H}}K_w}{K_w + \dfrac{K_iK_b[\text{HA}]}{[\text{A}^-]}}$$

and the rate expression becomes

$$(20) \quad v = k_{\text{HA}}[\text{>C=O}] \left\{ \frac{T_{\text{H}}K_w[\text{HA}]}{K_w + \dfrac{K_iK_b[\text{HA}]}{[\text{A}^-]}} \right\}$$

It is easily verified that, if the pH is varied by altering the buffer ratio while maintaining the total buffer concentration ($[\text{HA}] + [\text{A}^-]$) constant, the reaction rate will pass through a maximum. The catalytic constants, k_{HA}, for neutral acids, HA, increase as the strength of the acids is increased,[12] and as a generalization it is safe to say that one should use a buffer such that

$$(21) \qquad\qquad K_w \gg \frac{K \cdot K_b [\text{HA}]}{[\text{A}^-]}$$

If the concentrations of HA and A$^-$ are about equal, the useful buffers will be those made from acids whose ionization constants are about 10^{-6} (since K_b is about 10^{-8}). This condition may be altered somewhat in nonaqueous solutions since the values of K_i and K_b will both be decreased in media of low dielectric constant. It is not surprising to find that acetate buffers ($K_i = 1.8 \times 10^{-5}$) give good results in alcoholic solutions.

> If one wishes to carry out an easy check on his semiintuitive choice of a buffer system for a particular nonaqueous solvent, this can be done conveniently by carrying out a potentiometric titration of hydroxylamine with the buffer acid in that solvent. If the titration curve shows a break of one pH unit or more, the acid is too strong to be effective. For best results the curve should be just detectably different from that obtained by adding a solution of the buffer acid to the solvent containing no hydroxylamine.

Base Catalysis

It may seem trivial to examine in great detail the delicate problem of acid catalysis of oximation since, as has been previously mentioned, the reaction is also subject to base catalysis. Although the rates obtainable by base catalysis are not general as high as those that are obtainable by acid catalysis, it would be profitable to consider the development of a general method for a strongly basic medium if it were not for the complications arising from base-catalyzed reactions such as self-condensation of the carbonyl compounds. It does seem entirely possible that, for certain unreactive ketones which do not give good results in the usual procedures, the scope of the general method may be extended by carrying out the oximation under alkaline conditions. This possibility has not been investigated, but the line of approach is fairly obvious. The only effect of strong bases on the equilibrium conversion will be to increase the conversion since oximes are stronger acids than hydroxylamine. This will not be of much significance in aqueous solution except at the very highest alkalinities. Optimum assay conditions will be the highest concentrations of base that do not lead to rapid deterioration of the carbonyl compound *at*

[12] L. P. Hammett, *Physical Organic Chemistry*, p. 222.

the concentrations chosen for the assay. Since the condensation reactions of the carbonyl compounds are bimolecular, their rates will be slower in more dilute solutions. The conditions for base-catalyzed destruction of the aldehyde or ketone will vary widely with the structure of the compounds. If an individual compound of known structure is to be determined, a reasonable check on its stability in the assay medium may be made by observing the ultraviolet spectrum of a solution of the compound in the medium since condensation products ordinarily have different spectra from that of the parent compound. In hydroxylic solvents this procedure may give deceptive results because of the slow formation of hemiacetals and similar adducts. These adducts, which are formed reversibly, may be convertible to the oximes by way of the free carbonyl compound. Since hydroxylamine decomposes slowly under alkaline conditions, controls must be run to establish proper corrections.

TEMPERATURE EFFECTS

As with most reactions that are measurably slow, oximation rates can be increased by raising the temperature. The rates of the side reactions are also increased so it is possible for the stoichiometric relationship to become unsatisfactory at high temperatures. However, if a specific determination gives incomplete conversion, it is always worth while to try raising the temperature.

SIDE REACTIONS

The common experience of the synthetic organic chemist has led to the view that the yields in preparative experiments seldom approach the theoretical very closely. In many instances this is due more to the failure of isolation procedures than it is to the occurrence of side reactions. However, it is an inescapable fact that side reactions do occur frequently. Their occurrence is often of paramount importance to the analytical chemist who is able to avoid problems in isolation by using volumetric procedures. Most, but not all, side reactions cause the degeneration of the stoichiometric relationships which are the basis of analysis. In the oximation reaction, interference from aldol condensations has already been noted, as have the complications due to the formation of acetals and hemiacetals in hydroxylic solvents. The contrast between these two types of reactions is interesting since the latter are usually rapidly reversible under the conditions of the determination whereas self-condensations are reversed only very slowly.

The rapid equilibration of either the reagent or the compound being determined with other constituents of the solution does not necessarily harm the analytical procedure. If, on the other hand, either material is tied up in some species from which it is recovered very slowly, the method usually becomes valueless.

The consumption of the reagent by constituents of the assay mixture other than the material to be determined is the most common source of inaccuracy in functional group determinations. The reactions of a particular functional group are not, in general, really unique. In the case under discussion, the reaction of compounds other than aldehydes and ketones with hydroxylamine warrant careful scrutinizing. Conditions can be found for effecting the acylation of hydroxylamine by nearly any substance of the general structure RCOX, as shown in equation 22.

$$(22) \qquad RCOX + NH_2OH \rightarrow RC \overset{\displaystyle O}{\underset{\displaystyle NHOH}{\big\langle}} \quad + HX$$

The rates of formation of hydroxamic acids from various acylating agents vary a great deal. Carboxylic acids and amides react so slowly as to render them noninterfering except in the case of unreactive ketones which require very drastic conditions for oximation. In contrast, the acylation by acid chlorides and anhydrides is exceedingly rapid. Esters form an intermediate group. It is generally stated that alkyl esters do not interfere with oximation whereas aryl esters give trouble. Since the reactivity of the two classes of compounds does not differ by any wide margin in other acylation reactions such as ester hydrolysis, it follows that any ester must be considered as a potential source of interference in oximation. This will be especially true if the aldehyde or ketone reacts rather slowly itself or if the ester is present in the unknown mixture in large excess (as the solvent, for example) over the compound to be determined.

Circumventing these interferences also varies in difficulty. Acid chlorides and anhydrides present no serious problem if their presence is recognized. Because of their high reactivity, it is ordinarily a relatively simple matter to convert them to less reactive derivatives under conditions that do not harm the aldehyde or ketone. Unless the mixture is very insoluble in water, the offending constituents can ordinarily be hydrolyzed to the corresponding carboxylic acids in pyridine-water or dioxane-water solutions. If quantitative hydrolysis can be carried out, the interference can be avoided; but the acid produced must be taken into account in adjusting the acidity of the oximation solution. If unknown amounts of acids are present either in the sample or in a hydrolyzed product, the sample or an aliquot portion should be titrated with a strong base to determine the amount of acid that must be neutralized. In the determination of normally reactive aldehydes and ketones, a satisfactory procedure consists of dissolving the sample in ethanol and allowing the solution to stand for a short period of time to permit ethanolysis of the acid chloride or anhydride to the ester. The acidity of the solution can then be adjusted, and a standard solution of hydroxylamine hydrochloride can be added to complete the determination.

The interference from reactive esters in the determination of unreactive ketones may be much more troublesome. In most cases it will probably be possible to hydrolyze the ester without causing unwanted condensation reactions of the carbonyl compound.

Hydroperoxides are known to interfere with the oximation reaction, and no entirely satisfactory method has been found for avoiding the interference. The reduction of the offending species has been attempted with only limited success, but this approach seems to be a logical one; and it would appear that in time a suitable scheme involving prereduction can be developed.

Interference by reactive alkylating agents such as allylic halides has not been reported but might easily become a problem. If the determination is to be carried out in aqueous or alchoholic solvent, these compounds should be removable by allowing them to solvolyze to the corresponding alcohols or esters. If the determination is to be carried out in a solvent such as pyridine, the corresponding pyridinium salt will be formed. The pyridinium ions are reactive as alkylating agents,

$$(23) \quad RX \ + \ \text{(pyridine)} \longrightarrow \text{(N-R pyridinium)} \ X^-$$

and interference from the alkylation of hydroxylamine could easily occur. Even so, the presence of a small amount of alkylating agent should not be troublesome if the reaction is monitored by an acid-base titration since either an O- or an N-alkyl hydroxylamine would have close to the same basicity as the parent compound. Large amounts of the reactive alkylating agent would be a more serious matter since their presence would necessitate the use of large excesses of the reagent, thereby reducing the precision of the method.

THE ULTIMATE ANALYSIS

Possible Methods

In principle it is possible to complete the determination by measuring the decrease in the concentration of the reagent, hydroxylamine, or the amount of either of the products, water and the oxime, that has been formed.

In general, the properties of the oxime are not enough different from those of the carbonyl compound to encourage one to look to their determination as an ultimate analysis. Oximes are weakly acidic and can be titrated as acids in nonaqueous media (see p. 36). However, it is not easy to develop a convenient method to take advantage of this property. It is interesting to note that, if oximes were stronger acids by only two or three pK units, the reactions would quite likely be followed by titration of the reaction product. In the special case of α-diketones the vicinal dioximes produced could be estimated by virtue of their ability to react with Ni^{II}. The method would require careful calibration since only one of the three possible stereoisomeric modifications of the dioximes gives the characteristic reaction with nickel ions.

If the oximation is carried out in an anhydrous medium, the water produced can be determined satisfactorily by the Karl Fischer titration (see p. 102). This might be the method of choice if it were not for the inconvenience of protecting the system from atmospheric moisture throughout the determination. Modest amounts of water in the sample can be tolerated if a blank determination is carried out. In view of the complications involved in the determination of hydroxylamine, the water titration certainly ranks as a method well worth consideration.

Titration of Hydroxylamine As a Base

The procedures usually adopted involve the determination of unreacted hydroxylamine by either an acid-base or a redox titration. Since solutions of hydroxylamine are conveniently made up from its salts, it is frequently stated that the mineral acid liberated in the oximation reaction is determined by titration with excess base. The hydroxylammonium ion is instantaneously equilibrated with a proton and the free base according to equation 24. Therefore, if one starts

$$(24) \qquad NH_2OH + H_2O \overset{K_b}{\rightleftharpoons} \overset{+}{N}H_3OH + OH^-$$

with a solution of a hydroxylammonium salt and titrates the "liberated" strong acid, the end point is the same as if one began with a solution of the free base and titrated the excess with strong acid. The only distinction between the two methods therefore lies, not in the principle of the ultimate analysis, but in operational convenience and, more important, in the influence of pH upon the reaction rate and the equilibrium conversion.

The acid-base titration would be routine if it were not for the kinetic advantages to be gained by carrying out the reaction in a buffered solution. If buffers are to be used, interference in an acid-base titration as an ultimate analysis is inevitable. Much research has been directed toward the proper choice of an indicator for the titration in particular buffer systems. In order to obtain good stoichiometry, it is necessary to choose an end point such that the hydroxylamine will be stoichiometrically converted to $\overset{+}{N}H_3OH$ without alteration of the buffer ratio, $[HA]/[A^-]$. This requires that the hydroxylamine must be a considerably stronger base than A^-. Since the kinetic considerations alone (see p. 13) indicated that optimum rates could be obtained if the buffer base was stronger than hydroxylamine, it is evident that the choice of the acid-base titration forces one to compromise himself in the choice of conditions for the oximation reaction. It is interesting to examine the details of a highly recommended procedure in the light of these considerations. Pyridine has been used successfully as a reaction medium, and the acid-base titration can be carried out by the careful choice of an indicator and by conscientious control of the composition of the titration medium.[13] In this case the buffer system is as shown in equation 25. The analysis is completed by

titrating the liberated acid, which means that the pyridinium ion is a much stronger acid than hydroxylammonium ion *in pyridine solution.* The basicity constants of hydroxylamine and pyridine in water solution are fairly close together, being respectively 1.2×10^{-8} and 1.4×10^{-9}.

[13] S. Siggia, Reference 6, p. 7.

This indicates that there is a remarkable solvent effect on the relative basicity constants of the two bases. It is not surprising that the accuracy of the final titration is seriously affected if too much water or methanol is allowed to accumulate in the reaction mixture. The advantages of oximation in pyridine as compared to alcohol are probably due more to the catalytic effect of pyridine as a base than to the influence of pyridine in "driving the reaction to completion" by consuming the acid liberated. For the latter to be a significant effect it would be necessary that the equilibrium constant for reaction 25 be reasonably large. The success of the final titration assures that this is not the case. The reaction is then carried out in effect in an unbuffered solution in a solvent that is capable of functioning as a basic catalyst with the success of the final analysis depending upon an unexpected (but very useful) solvent effect upon the basicities of the two neutral bases.

An attractive variation of the usual acid-base titration has apparently not been investigated carefully. This consists of carrying out the oximation in a buffer of concentration chosen to give good kinetic performance followed by separation of the buffer from the mixture by an ion exchange technique. For example, if the reaction solution were buffered with a $H_2PO_4^- - HPO_4^=$ buffer, passage of the solution through an anion exchanger would permit the exchange of the phosphate ions for nonbasic anions such as halide or sulfate. The hydroxylamine, being neutral, would remain in solution and could be titrated with standard acid without complication.

Oxidation of Hydroxylamine

Since hydroxylamine is a powerful reductant, a redox titration to estimate the unreacted reagent is an attractive alternative to the acid-base titration. Such methods have been used in connection with various kinetic studies of oximation reactions but have not been commonly utilized in standard analytical procedures. There are two principal limitations inherent in the oxidative methods. First, hydroxylamine does not form reversible couples in the electrochemical sense. Its reactions with many common oxidants are slow and stoichiometrically complicated. The method of choice for the determination of hydroxylamine in aqueous solution is oxidation with ferric ion. However, the method is useless in oximation because of the slowness of the oxidation. Since oximation is reversible with the rates of hydrolysis of many oximes being faster than the rate of the oxidation reaction, large errors would result from the use of the method. On the other hand, permanganate oxidation is rapid but gives a mixture of nitrogen and nitrous oxide with the relative amounts of the two products varying with concentrations of the reactants. Permanganate oxidation has been used in a clever procedure in which the total volume of gaseous products was measured manometrically.[14] The total volume of gas is independent of the relative amounts of N_2 and N_2O formed. In a laboratory in which manometric apparatus is maintained, this method probably deserves serious consideration.

Hydroxylamine has been determined by titration with iodine; and in the course of his classic study of the oximation of acetone, Olander worked out the conditions necessary for obtaining reliable results.[15] The stoichiometry varies with pH, and conditions must be rigidly controlled.

The discussion of the problem of analyzing for hydroxylamine leads to another interesting observation. The literature affords an ample number of comparisons between procedures for the determination of hydroxylamine and semicarbazide. It is certainly much easier to assay the latter since it reacts stoichiometrically with several oxidants including periodate,[16] iodine cyanide,[16] and iodine.[17] Although hydroxylamine, despite its drawbacks, is certainly the reagent of choice for the determination of the less reactive carbonyl compounds because it reacts more rapidly and completely, it may be well worth while to consider semicarbazide as a convenient alternative for the determination of aldehydes and the more reactive ketones.

SUMMARY

An attempt has been made to illustrate the kinds of problems that may be encountered in setting up a typical functional group analysis. It is not implied that consideration in such great detail is always a necessary prerequisite to devising a new method or adapting an old one to a particular purpose. However, there will be many instances in which examination of such details will provide time-saving guides or indispensable clues.

[14] R. Jacquemain and P. Galliot, *Ann. chim.* [12], **1**, 262 (1955).

[15] A. Olander, *Z. physik Chem.*, **129**, 1 (1927).

[16] A. J. Feuell and J. H. Skellon, Reference 4, p. 7.

[17] J. B. Conant and P. D. Bartlett, Reference 7, p. 8; F. H. Westheimer, *J. Am. Chem. Soc.*, **56**, 1962 (1934).

PROBLEMS

1. Comment on the relative merits of oximation and semicarbazone formation as methods for the determination of carbonyl compounds.

2. Devise a method for the determination of acetone in the presence of a comparable amount of benzophenone.

3. Devise in detail a procedure for estimation of the yield of product formed in the acetylation of benzene by the Friedel-Crafts reaction.

$$C_6H_6 + CH_3COCl \xrightarrow[AlCl_3]{} C_6H_5COCH_3 + HCl$$

4. What difficulties would be encountered in estimating the amount of cyclohexanone present in a solution that also contained large amounts of aniline? How might these problems be overcome?

3.

ACID-BASE TITRATIONS

IN

NONAQUEOUS SOLVENTS

INTRODUCTION

Several organic functional groups have acidic or basic properties. Determination of such groups by acid-base titrations is attractive because neutralization is one organic reaction that proceeds instantly and quantitatively. Unfortunately, the scope of such titrations in aqueous solution is limited, first by the slight solubility of many organic compounds in water, and second by the fact that many organic acids and bases are too weak to be titrated in aqueous solution. Use of alcohol or alcohol-water mixtures as the solvent solves the solubility problem in most cases but does not appreciably increase the scope of acid-base titrations. By choosing suitable nonaqueous solvents, the number of organic acids and bases that can be titrated is increased tremendously. For example, in water it is possible to titrate only amines having a pK_b of 7 or less; but in nonaqueous media, bases having a pK_b (in water) as great as 12 or 13 can be determined. Hundreds of amines that are much too weak to be titrated in water can thus be accurately titrated in glacial acetic acid or other suitable nonaqueous solvents.

Although titration of acids and bases is much more versatile in organic solvents than in water, the technique is relatively simple. The titration can be carried out using visual indicators or it can be followed potentiometrically using an ordinary pH meter. Most of the useful titrants are easily prepared and can be standardized readily against common primary standards such as potassium acid phthalate and benzoic acid. The precision and accuracy are excellent, often exceeding that attainable in titrimetry in aqueous solutions.

ACID-BASE THEORIES

Some knowledge of the leading acid-base theories is essential if acid-base behavior in nonaqueous solvents is to be understood.

The Arrhenius theory stressed dissociation into ions. An acid was defined as a compound that ionized in water to give hydrogen ions and a base as one that gave hydroxyl ions. Neutralization always involved the formation of a salt and water. These definitions were widely adopted and are still used by many even though they are largely inadequate for reactions in nonaqueous solvents.

The theory of solvent systems, begun by Franklin [1] in 1905 and extended by Germann [2] in 1925 is of some importance. It was reasoned that, if water ionizes to form oxonium and hydroxyl ions, then the self-ionization of liquid ammonia must produce ammonium and amide ions, and other ionizable solvents would behave in similar fashion.

(1) $$2H_2O \rightleftharpoons H_3O^+ + OH^-$$

(2) $$2NH_3 \rightleftharpoons NH_4^+ + NH_2^-$$

(3) $$2HOCH_3 \rightleftharpoons H_2OCH_3^+ + OCH_3^-$$

(4) $$2HAc \rightleftharpoons H_2Ac^+ + Ac^-$$

According to this theory, any solute that increases the solvent cation (lyonium ion) concentration is an acid, whereas any substance that increases the anion (lyate ion) concentration is a base. Thus, in liquid ammonia, ammonium nitrate is a strong acid just as nitric acid is a strong acid in water. In glacial acetic acid, sodium acetate is a strong base analogous to sodium hydroxide in water.

The theory of solvent systems seems to be fairly satisfactory for ionizable solvents but is not applicable to acid-base reactions in dioxane, benzene, and other aprotic solvents.

According to the Bronsted theory, an acid is any substance that can

[1] E. C. Franklin, *J. Am. Chem. Soc.*, **27**, 820 (1905).
[2] A. F. O. Germann and C. R. Timpany, *J. Am. Chem. Soc.*, **47**, 2275 (1925).

give up a proton. A base is any compound that can accept a proton. These definitions lead to the relationship:

(5) $Acid = H^+ + Base$

Just as free electrons cannot exist in solution, it has also been calculated that free, uncombined protons also cannot exist in solution. Since this is true, no reaction takes place unless a base is added to accept the proton from the acid. With this in mind, the following expression can be derived:

(6) $A_1 \qquad = H^+ + B_1$

(7) $B_2 + H^+ = A_2$
                       $\overline{}$

(8) $A_1 + B_2 = A_2 + B_1$

It will be noted that this is analogous to adding two redox half-reactions to obtain a complete reaction. According to Bronsted, in all acid-base reactions an acid reacts with a base to form a new acid and a new base.

One consequence of the Bronsted theory is that acids are not limited to cations nor bases to anions. Thus an acid may be a neutral molecule such as hydrogen chloride, a cation ($C_6H_5NH^+$, H_3O^+, etc.), or an anion (HCO_3^-, $H_2PO_4^-$, etc.). A base may also be neutral (NH_3, C_5H_5N, etc.), an anion (OH^-, $OC_2H_5^-$), or even a cation ($Co[OH][NH_3]_5^{++}$, $Al[OH]_2^+$).

The fact that a substance cannot act as an acid unless a base is present to accept the proton leads to the prediction that a neutral acid will not be ionized unless the solvent in which it is dissolved has some basic properties. Bronsted reported an experiment that confirms this.[3] A solution of picric acid in benzene is colorless, and the conductance is negligible. This shows that in the inert solvent, benzene, picric acid is not ionized. If a solution of aniline in benzene is now added to the picric acid solution, the solution becomes yellow (owing to the formation of picrate ions) and the conductance increases.

G. N. Lewis defined an acid as an electron pair acceptor and a base as an electron pair donor. The striking part of this theory is that boron fluoride, aluminum chloride, stannic chloride, and several other substances that do not contain hydrogen are included as acids. Typical

---

[3] J. N. Bronsted, *Ber.*, **61**, 2049 (1928).

bases are the hydroxyl and alkoxyl ions, amines, ethers, and even carboxylic acid anhydrides.[4]

Lewis defends his inclusion of boron chloride and similar compounds as acids by pointing out that they have all the properties commonly associated with acids. In chlorobenzene, for example, boron chloride will change crystal violet indicator to the acid color. Addition of a base then returns the indicator to the basic color. Aluminum chloride is a Lewis acid but is insoluble in carbon tetrachloride. If a mixture of aluminum chloride and carbon tetrachloride is shaken and then filtered, a clear filtrate is obtained which does not give an acid reaction to crystal violet indicator. This indicates that no hydrolysis to hydrogen chloride takes place owing to traces of moisture. Addition of crystal violet indicator to a suspension of aluminum chloride in carbon tetrachloride, however, gives an acid reaction because of the acidic nature of the aluminum chloride *molecule*.

According to Lewis, acid-base reactions may be classified either as neutralization or as displacement reactions. Neutralization is defined as the formation of a coordinate covalent bond. The product of neutralization may be a covalent compound, or the formation of a coordinate covalent bond may be followed or be accompanied by ionization so that the product is a salt.

The product of neutralization is not necessarily neutral in the sense that it is neither acidic nor basic. In fact, according to this theory, hydrogen chloride is merely the neutralization product of a proton and an anion base. Kolthoff [5] believes this to be one of the weaknesses of the Lewis theory.

Displacement reactions take place when a stronger acid displaces a weaker acid from combination with a base or when a stronger base liberates a weaker base bound to an acid. The guiding principle in this type of reaction is that a weaker coordinate bond is broken to form a stronger one. The examples given below illustrate this.

1. In acetone:

---

[4] For a thorough discussion of the G. N. Lewis theory, see W. F. Luder and S. Zuffanti, *The Electronic Theory of Acids and Bases*, Wiley, New York, 1946.

[5] I. M. Kolthoff, *Chem. Eng. News,* **27**, 835 (1949).

2. In water:

$$(10) \qquad HCl + H_2O \rightarrow H_3O^+ + Cl^-$$

(The stronger base, water, displaces the weaker base, chloride, from combination with the proton.)

Virtually all the reactions involved in acid-base titrimetry are displacement reactions. For example, the titration of sodium hydroxide with hydrochloric acid in water, although it is often written

$$(11) \qquad H^+ + OH^- \rightarrow H_2O$$

it is more correctly written

$$(12) \qquad H_3O^+ + OH^- \rightarrow 2H_2O$$

indicating that the strong base (OH^-) displaces the proton from combination with the much weaker base (H_2O).

ACID-BASE BEHAVIOR IN NONAQUEOUS SOLVENTS

Unlike redox reactions, which proceed with measurable velocity, most acid-base reactions occur almost instantaneously. Lewis and Seaborg[6] noted that acids such as hydrogen chloride and boron chloride react instantly with certain indicator bases even at $-70°$ C. Several compounds were found that behaved like typical acids and bases except that they reacted slowly, especially at low temperatures. These substances were termed "secondary" acids and bases. This concept is useful in explaining why some indicator acids and bases respond rapidly whereas others are only slowly reversible.

Ionization in solution can occur by one of two mechanisms. Salts are often ionized in the solid state. Dissolution in an appropriate solvent merely permits the ions more freedom than in the solid state. Nonionized solids must react with the solvent for ionization to take place in solution. In order for a neutral acid to ionize, the solvent must possess some basic properties. Likewise, a base will ionize only in an acidic solvent. Everything else being equal, the more strongly basic (or acidic) a solvent is, the more completely will a given acid (or base) be ionized in that solvent.

The dielectric constant of a solvent affects ionization. Solvents having a high dielectric constant facilitate charge separation and promote ionization. If the dielectric constant of the solvent is low, positive

[6] G. N. Lewis and G. T. Seaborg, *J. Am. Chem. Soc.*, **61**, 1894 (1939).

and negative ions have a greater attraction for each and ion pair formation is promoted.

It should be emphasized that ionization of an acid is not required for a successful titration with a standard base. In 1912, Folin and Flanders [7] used conductivity measurements to show that solutions of carboxylic acids in benzene were essentially nonionized but, nevertheless, could be titrated quantitatively with sodium ethoxide. Very sharp end points were obtained, using phenolphthalein indicator. When increasing amounts of alcohol were added to the original solution, the conductance increased but the end points became less sharp.

DETERMINATION OF TOTAL BASE

General Conditions for Titrations

Any solvent used for acid-base titrations should meet several requirements:

1. It must dissolve the substance to be titrated.

2. It should be readily available at a reasonable price. Preferably, the solvent should require no purification.

3. The products of titration should be either soluble or crystalline precipitates. Highly adsorptive, gelatinous precipitates cause low results and fading end points.

4. There should be no disturbing side reactions with either the substance to be titrated or the titrant.

5. It should permit titration of weak bases (or acids).

To titrate a weak base successfully, the solvent should possess, at the most, only weakly basic properties. Table 3 shows the over-all reactions for the titration of a given base, B, in water, ethanol, and acetic

TABLE 3

Reactions for the Titration of a Weak Base in Various Solvents

Solvent	(Acid) + (Base) = (Acid) + (Base)
H_2O	$H_3O^+ + B = BH^+ + H_2O$
EtOH	$EtOH_2^+ + B = BH^+ + EtOH$
HAc	$H_2Ac^+ + B = BH^+ + HAc$
	(Titrant) (Solvent)

[7] O. Folin and F. F. Flanders, *J. Am. Chem. Soc.* **34**, 774 (1912).

acid. Because the solvent is present in tremendous excess over the other species present, even a very slightly basic solvent will partially reverse the reaction and cause a poor end point. Water and alcohol are thus unsatisfactory solvents for the titration of a weak base because of their basic properties. A nonbasic solvent such as glacial acetic acid is an excellent choice for such a titration. A number of other solvents including benzene, chlorobenzene, nitrobenzene, nitromethane, acetonitrile, chloroform, carbon tetrachloride, and 1,4-dioxane are also very satisfactory for the titration of a weak base.[8]

The equilibrium will also be favored if the titrant employed is a very strong acid (see Table 3). In aqueous solution perchloric, hydrochloric, and nitric acids are equally suitable titrants from the standpoint of acid strength because each reacts essentially completely with water to form H_3O^+. In this case, water acts as a "leveling" solvent because it reduces the strength of the three acids to a common level. In glacial acetic acid, a "nonleveling" solvent for strong acids, the order of acid strength is perchloric$>$hydrochloric$>$nitric.[9] For this reason, perchloric acid is almost always chosen as the titrant for weak bases in nonaqueous solvents.

Both potentiometric and visual indicator techniques are available for the detection of the end point. Methyl violet and crystal violet are extensively used as indicators in nonaqueous media. These give vivid, reversible end points in many types of solvents but, unfortunately, do not have a simple color change.

The ionization of crystal violet as the acidity of the medium is increased is represented by equations 13–15.

$$(13) \quad \left(Me_2N-\!\!\left\langle\;\right\rangle\!\!-\right)_3 COH + H^+ \rightleftharpoons$$

$$\left(Me_2N-\!\!\left\langle\;\right\rangle\!\!-\right)_3 C^+ \leftrightarrow Me_2\overset{+}{N}=\!\!\left\langle\;\right\rangle\!\!=C\left(-\!\!\left\langle\;\right\rangle\!\!-NMe_2\right)_2$$

$$\updownarrow$$
etc.

A-violet

$$(14) \quad A + H^+ \rightleftharpoons Me_2\underset{+}{N}-\!\!\left\langle\;\right\rangle\!\!-\overset{H}{\underset{+}{C}}\left(-\!\!\left\langle\;\right\rangle\!\!-NMe_2\right)_2 \leftrightarrow \text{etc.}$$

B-green

[8] J. S. Fritz, *Anal. Chem.*, **22**, 1028 (1950).
[9] I. M. Kolthoff and A. Willman, *J. Am. Chem. Soc.*, **56**, 1007, 1014 (1934).

(15) $\quad \text{B} + \text{H}^+ \rightleftharpoons \left(\underset{+}{\overset{\text{H}}{\text{Me}_2\text{N}}}\!\!-\!\!\bigcirc\!\!-\right)_2\!\!\overset{+}{\text{C}}\!\!-\!\!\bigcirc\!\!-\text{NMe}_2 \leftrightarrow$ etc.

C-yellow

Methyl violet has a formula very similar to crystal violet and behaves in an analogous manner. Most amines can be titrated successfully, using methyl violet or crystal violet indicator if the first complete disappearance of a violet tinge is taken as the end point. For the best accuracy, however, it is advisable to first titrate each type of sample potentiometrically in order to select the proper indicator or end-point color. Some of the indicators that have been used for titration of bases in nonaqueous media are listed in Table 4.

TABLE 4

Indicators for Titration of Weak Bases

Indicator	Solvents Used for the Titration
Methyl violet 1-Naphtholbenzein *	Acetic acid, acetonitrile, benzene, nitromethane, nitromethane-acetic anhydride, etc.
Methyl red	Dioxane,† glycol-isopropanol
Modified methyl orange Dibenzalacetone Triphenylmethanol	Dioxane † Nitromethane-acetic anhydride, acetic acid-acetic anhydride

* G. F. Nadeau and L. E. Branchen, *J. Am. Chem. Soc.*, **57**, 1363 (1935).
† J. S. Fritz, *Anal. Chem.*, **22**, 578 (1950).

Very weak bases do not give sharp end points when visual indicators are used. Such compounds should always be titrated potentiometrically. Potentiometric titrations in nonaqueous solvents are carried out, using an ordinary pH meter or other type of direct-reading potentiometer. If a pH meter is used, the measurements should be made on the millivolt scale because the pH scale set up for water has no significance in acetic acid. Furthermore, potentials measured in nonaqueous solvents often go off the aqueous pH scale. A standard glass electrode is usually employed as the indicator electrode. The classical potentiometric titrations in glacial acetic acid were carried out by Conant and Hall [10] using a chloranil indicator electrode. This consists of a

[10] N. F. Hall and J. B. Conant, *J. Am. Chem. Soc.*, **49**, 3047, 3062 (1927). N. F. Hall and T. H. Werner, *J. Am. Chem. Soc.*, **50**, 2367 (1928). J. B. Conant and T. H. Werner, *J. Am. Chem. Soc.*, **52**, 4436 (1930).

bright platinum wire dipping into the solution being titrated. A small amount of chloranil and tetrachlorohydroquinine is added to set up a redox system sensitive to changes in the acidity of the solution.

A standard fiber-type calomel electrode is a convenient and satisfactory reference electrode for use in acetic acid and in other solvents having a higher dielectric constant than acetic acid. This electrode works best if kept in water except when in use. The purpose of this is to prevent potassium chloride from crystallizing in the capillary, thus partially blocking the contact and causing unsteady potential readings. Improved contact between the electrode and solution can be obtained by using a sleeve-type calomel electrode, but the amount of potassium chloride introduced into the non-aqueous solvent becomes excessive for certain titrations. A silver wire coated with silver chloride serves as a reference electrode and does not require a salt bridge. It has been found, however, that better results are obtained if the silver-silver chloride electrode is used in conjunction with a salt bridge of lithium chloride dissolved in glacial acetic acid.[11] A convenient form of this electrode is shown in Fig. 1. This has the advantage that no water is introduced into the titration by the salt bridge.

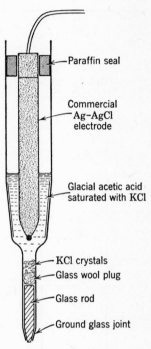

Figure 1. Calomel reference cell for use in acetic acid. (Reprinted from *Analytical Chemistry* with permission.)

Potentiometric titrations have proved satisfactory in all solvents except those having very low dielectric constants. With solvents such as benzene, toluene, chloroform, and ethers, the very high resistance encountered makes potentiometric titrations difficult. Potentiometric titrations in chloroform or dioxane can be carried out, however. Ordinary glass and calomel electrodes are used but the electrodes are placed close together.[12] One electrode is inserted, in a horizontal position, through an opening in the side of the titration vessel, and the other electrode is in the usual perpendicular position. This arrangement decreases the resistance of the circuit and permits steady potential readings.

[11] R. A. Glenn, *Anal. Chem.*, **25**, 1916 (1953).
[12] C. W. Pifer, E. G. Wollish and M. Schmall, *Anal. Chem.*, **25**, 310 (1953).

Scope and Limitations

The most widely applicable method for organic bases involves titration with standard perchloric acid dissolved in either glacial acetic acid or 1,4-dioxane. The base to be titrated is dissolved in acetic acid, nitromethane, acetonitrile, chlorobenzene, benzene, chloroform, carbon tetrachloride, or some other nonbasic solvent. The end point is determined either potentiometrically or by a visual indicator such as methyl violet.

By this method, primary, secondary, and tertiary amines and amino acids can be determined. Some amino acids are difficult to dissolve in acetic acid and are, therefore, dissolved in acetic acid containing a

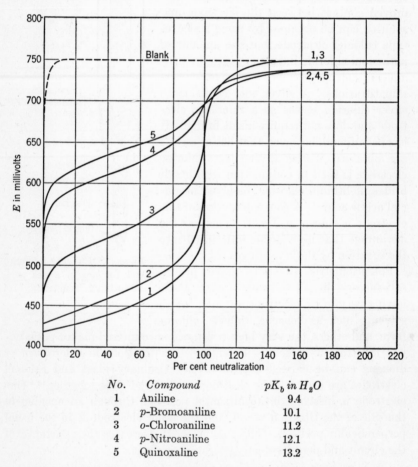

No.	Compound	pK_b in H_2O
1	Aniline	9.4
2	p-Bromoaniline	10.1
3	o-Chloroaniline	11.2
4	p-Nitroaniline	12.1
5	Quinoxaline	13.2

Figure 2. Titration of amines in acetic acid with 0.1 M perchloric acid.

measured amount of perchloric acid. The excess perchloric acid is then back-titrated with a standard base such as potassium acetate in glacial acetic acid.

Aromatic amines are quite weak bases in water (pK_b in water for aniline is 9.4) but can be accurately titrated in acetic acid. Chloro, bromo, nitro, and certain other electron-withdrawing groups decrease the basic strength of aromatic amines, especially if the substituents are in the ortho or para positions. Alkyl substituents tend to enhance the basic strength of amines slightly. Figure 2 shows the effect of various substituents on the titration of aromatic amines. It will be noted that amines having a pK_b in water less than 12.0 to 12.5 are strong enough to be titrated potentiometrically in glacial acetic acid. In Table 5 are

TABLE 5

Effect of Various Substituents on the Basic Strength of Aniline

Substituent	pK_b in Water	ΔpK_b
None	9.4	0.0
o-NO$_2$	13.9	+4.5
o-X (Cl, Br)	11.3	+1.9
m-X (Cl, Br)	10.5	+1.1
p-NO$_2$	12.1	+2.7
p-SO$_2$NH$_2$	11.7	+2.3
p-COCH$_3$	11.3	+1.9
p-X (Cl, Br)	10.1	+0.7

listed the pK_b values for a number of aniline derivatives together with the number of units that each group raises the pK_b. If, as a rough approximation, the effect of each group is assumed to be additive, it is possible to predict whether a given amine can be titrated. For example, by adding 1.9 pK units for an ortho halogen and 0.7 unit for a para halogen to the pK_b for aniline (9.4), the pK_b for 2,4-dichloroaniline is calculated to be 12.0. The measured pK_b is 12.2. From this it would be predicted that 2,4-dichloroaniline is a sufficiently strong base to be titrated in acetic acid. This procedure and its limitations are presented in detail in discussions of the Hammett equation.[13, 14]

Substitution of electron-withdrawing groups on the basic nitrogen has a much greater effect on the basicity of amines than does substitution in the ring. Thus, acetanilide is too weakly basic to be titrated

---

[13] L. P. Hammett, *Physical Organic Chemistry*, McGraw-Hill Book Co., New York, 1940, pp. 186–194.

[14] H. H. Jaffe, *Chem. Revs.*, **53**, 191 (1953).

in nonaqueous solvents, and diphenylamine gives only a faint inflection at the end point. Schiff bases of the type ArCH=NAr and ArCH=NR are less basic than the free amine but still give sharp potentiometric end points.[15] Amides, azo compounds, imides, nitriles, oximes, sulfonamides, thioureas, and ureas are too weakly basic to be titrated but do not in general interfere with the titration of stronger bases.

Many nitrogen heterocyclics are sufficiently basic to be titrated in nonaqueous solvents. Pyridine, quinoline, acridine, and related compounds give excellent visual or potentiometric end points. Thiazoles, oxazoles, pyridones, quinolines, and purines (such as caffeine and theobromine) are weaker bases but can be titrated potentiometrically in nitromethane-acetic anhydride or acetic acid-acetic anhydride (see p. 37). Pyrrole, indole, carbazole, and similar compounds cannot be successfully titrated as bases.

The salt of a weak acid will react with a strong acid, the weaker acid (HA) being formed as the neutralization product.

$$(16) \qquad\qquad A^- + H^+ \rightarrow HA$$

Such a salt can be titrated successfully if the titrant is a much stronger acid than the acid liberated in the titration. In water, comparatively few salts can be determined by this scheme. In glacial acetic acid, however, the alkali metal, ammonium, and amine salts of carboxylic and some inorganic acids can be titrated with accuracy. Salts of divalent metals give less satisfactory results, and the salts of tri- and tetravalent metals cannot be titrated at all. Pifer and Wollish [16] showed that better results are obtained for amine salts if the salt is titrated in a mixture of acetic acid and 1,4-dioxane. This is accomplished by dissolving the salt in acetic acid and titrating with perchloric acid in dioxane. Amine nitrates and sulfates can be titrated potentiometrically.

$$(17) \quad RNH_3^+NO_3^- + H^+ClO_4^- \rightarrow RNH_3^+ClO_4^- + H^+NO_3^-$$

(18)

$$(RNH_3^+)_2SO_4^= + H^+ClO_4^- \rightarrow RNH_3^+HSO_4^- + RNH_3^+ClO_4^-$$

Halides can be titrated if excess mercuric acetate is first added. The halide is tied up as undissociated HgX_2, and the acetate ion liberated can be titrated as a base with perchloric acid.

[15] S. K. Freeman, *Anal. Chem.*, **25**, 1750 (1953).
[16] C. W. Pifer and E. G. Wollish, *Anal. Chem.*, **24**, 300 (1952).

$$(19) \qquad 2RNH_3{}^+X^- + HgAc_2 \xrightarrow{\text{(excess)}} 2RNH_3{}^+Ac^-$$

$$(20) \quad RNH_3{}^+Ac^- + H^+ClO_4{}^- \longrightarrow RNH_3{}^+ClO_4{}^- + HAc$$

Mercuric acetate is essentially undissociated in acetic acid and, therefore, does not interfere if a modest excess is employed. This titration is widely used in the pharmaceutical industry to determine the total alkaloid content of various preparations since it is equally applicable to the free bases and their salts.

In addition to the quantitative determination of known bases in mixtures, titration in nonaqueous solvents is a very useful aid in the identification of unknown amines. If the pure amine is available, the equivalent weight can be calculated from the results of the titration. If the sample is in a mixture, it is often convenient to isolate the amine in some weighable form such as the picrate. Both the melting point and the equivalent weight of the amine picrate as determined by acidimetric titration aid in the identification of the amine.[17] In a similar manner alcohols can be isolated as xanthates and the equivalent weights determined by titration with perchloric acid in glacial acetic acid.[18]

$$(21) \qquad RO\overset{\displaystyle S}{\overset{\displaystyle \|}{C}}\!\!-\!\!S^- + H^+ \rightarrow ROH + CS_2$$

Acid-base titrations in nonaqueous solvents are commonly carried out with 0.1 N perchloric acid as the titrant. Smaller amounts of organic bases and salts can be titrated using 0.01 N titrant. Typical applications are the determination of basic impurities in refined hydrocarbons and hydrocarbon oils,[19] determination of vitamins in capsules, and the microdetermination of the equivalent weight of pure amines. If necessary, 0.001 N titrant can be used. With this procedure, as little as 15 to 20 micrograms of most amines can be titrated with an accuracy of about 2%.[20] Sharp visual end points are obtained, but only if a minimum amount of indicator is used. A centrifuge tube as the titration vessel permits observation through a comparatively great depth of solution and thus permits a very low indicator concentration.

[17] J. R. Clark and S. M. Wang, *Anal. Chem.*, **26**, 1230 (1954).

[18] J. Berger, *Acta Chem. Scand.*, **6**, 1564 (1952).

[19] H. N. Wilson, *J. Soc. Chem. Ind. (London)*, **67**, 237 (1948). G. Whittmann, *Angew. Chem.*, **A60**, 330 (1948).

[20] R. T. Keen and J. S. Fritz, *Anal. Chem.*, **24**, 564 (1952).

Effect of Water

Most amines can be titrated in acetic acid containing up to 2 or 3% water. If more water is present, the end point is not sharp and the results are somewhat inaccurate. Alcohol has a similar effect but can be tolerated in somewhat larger amounts because it is less basic than water. An aqueous solution of a base can be handled in one of two ways. If the solution is sufficiently concentrated, a small measured portion can be diluted with about a fifty fold excess of acetic acid and titrated directly. Another method is to extract the base with an

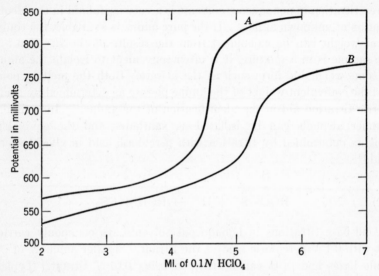

Figure 3. Titration of caffeine. (*A*) In nitromethane-acetic anhydride; (*B*) in nitromethane. (Reprinted from *Analytical Chemistry* with permission.)

immiscible solvent such as benzene or chloroform. Automatic continuous extractors are available which make this a convenient operation.[21] The base is then titrated directly in the extracting solvent.

Although ordinary amines can be titrated in the presence of some water, the successful titration of many very weak bases requires that as little water as possible be present. When the titrant is being prepared, it is rather standard practice to add enough acetic anhydride to combine with most of the water introduced by the perchloric acid. Some water is still present during the titration, however, because

[21] M. Schmall, C. W. Pifer and E. G. Wollish, *Anal. Chem.*, **24**, 1446 (1952); **26**, 1670 (1954).

reagent-grade acetic acid commonly contains 0.2 to 0.5% water. A convenient technique for avoiding water is to carry out the titration in a solvent mixture containing excess acetic anhydride.[22] Very striking improvement in the end point can be obtained by titrating a weak base in acetic acid or nitromethane which contains 5 to 20% by volume of acetic anhydride. Typical titration curves are shown in Fig. 3, and a list of some very weak bases that have been titrated with this technique is given in Table 6.

TABLE 6

Potentiometric Titrations in 4-to-1 Nitromethane-Acetic Anhydride

Compound	Purity Found, %
Benzothiazole	97.8
	97.7
Caffeine	99.8
	99.6
5,7-Dichloro-8-hydroxyquinoline	95.8
	96.2
1-Methyl-2-pyridone	95.1
	96.1
Nicotinamide	99.8
	99.6
8-Nitroquinoline	95.1
	94.5
	94.5
Quinoxaline	97.8
	97.5
Theobromine	99.3
	100.0
	100.0
Theophylline	99.2
	99.2
Triphenylmethanol	100.5
	100.2
	100.0

[22] J. S. Fritz and M. O. Fulda, *Anal. Chem.*, **25**, 1837 (1953).

It is believed that the complete removal of water by acetic anhydride causes the improvement in end points. When water is present, at least some of the titrant is probably converted from $H_2Ac^+ClO_4^-$ to $H_3O^+ClO_4^-$, which is a considerably weaker acid. Support for this argument is given in Fig. 4. It will be noted that the addition of a

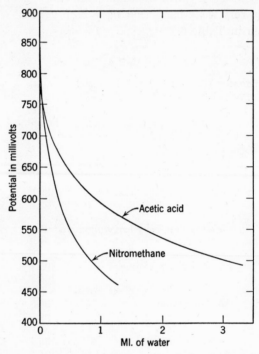

Figure 4. Addition of water to perchloric acid solutions. (Reprinted from *Analytical Chemistry* with permission.)

small amount of water to perchloric acid in nearly anhydrous acetic acid or nitromethane causes a considerable drop in potential. Titration in acetic anhydride solvent mixtures increases the end point "break" 100 to 150 millivolts in most instances. Some very weak bases can be titrated which give no break at all when titrated in the absence of acetic anhydride.

One limitation of this technique is that it is applicable only to tertiary amines and salts that do not have their basic properties destroyed by acetylation. Gremillion [23] has shown that in certain cases

[23] A. F. Gremillion, *Anal. Chem.*, **27**, 133 (1955).

the acylation of primary and secondary amines may be prevented by carrying out the titration at 0° C.

Other Solvent Effects

Varying the solvent so that the product of titration will be insoluble is sometimes a useful technique. For example, theobromine is too weakly basic to be titrated in acetic acid but can be titrated in carbon

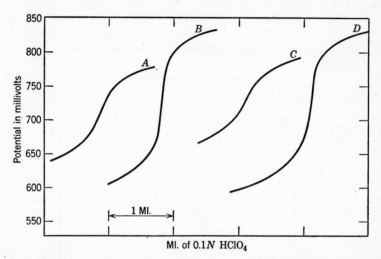

Figure 5. Titration curves for 1-methyl-2-pyridone and caffeine. (*A*) 1-Methyl-2-pyridone in acetic acid-acetic anhydride. (*B*) 1-Methyl-2-pyridone nitromethane-acetic anhydride. (*C*) Caffeine in acetic acid-acetic anhydride. (*D*) Caffeine in nitromethane-acetic anhydride. (Reprinted from *Analytical Chemistry* with permission.)

tetrachloride because theobromine perchlorate is insoluble.[24] Removing most of the perchlorate salt from solution gives a much more favorable relationship, and a satisfactory end point can be obtained. Many nitrogen heterocyclic bases form crystalline, insoluble perchlorates in solvents of low dielectric constant.

Some organic bases can be titrated much more sharply in nitromethane than in other organic solvents commonly used for the titration of weak bases.[22] Figure 5 illustrates this effect for 1-methyl-2-pyridone and for caffeine. Most other bases exhibit almost identical behavior in acetic acid and in nitromethane. This is not an effect attributable to the dielectric constant because other solvents of similar

[24] A. Poulos, *Anal. Chem.*, **24**, 1858 (1952).

dielectric constant (nitrobenzene and acetonitrile) do not cause any improvement over acetic acid for the above bases. It is likely that the protonated bases are selectively solvated by nitromethane, thus causing a favorable shift in the equilibria.

In the titration of certain metal salts as bases, a definite solvation effect by acetonitrile is noted.[25] In acetic acid or in mixtures of acetic acid and another solvent, very poor breaks are obtained for the titration of most divalent and trivalent metal acetates with perchloric acid, because of the high degree of association of such compounds in acetic acid. If some acetonitrile is present, however, several of the divalent metal acetates can be titrated sharply. Figure 6 illustrates this effect

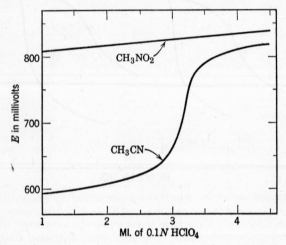

Figure 6. Titration of cupric acetate. (Reprinted from *Analytical Chemistry* with permission.)

for cupric acetate. Similar effects are observed for nickel, cobalt, cadmium, zinc, and mercury; but little if any improvement is noted in the case of manganese, lead, and magnesium acetates. Apparently the metal forms a complex with the solvent, thus freeing the acetate ion for reaction with the acidic titrant.

$$(22) \qquad MAc_2 + xCH_3CN \rightarrow M(CH_3CN)_x^{++} + 2Ac^-$$

$$(23) \qquad Ac^- + H^+ \rightarrow HAc$$

It appears significant that the metals that exhibit this effect are known to form strong cyanide complexes in aqueous solution.

[25] J. S. Fritz, *Anal. Chem.*, **26**, 1701 (1954).

DIFFERENTIATING TITRATIONS OF AMINES

Two approaches are available for the quantitative differentiation of various types of amines. One possibility is to employ the classical chemical reactions which distinguish primary, secondary, and tertiary amines. The other possibility is to do a differentiating titration based on differences in basic strength of various amines.

In water the pK_b of aliphatic amines is of the order of 4 or 5 whereas the pK_b of aromatic amines is 9 or 10 (except for negatively substituted aromatic amines, which may have pK_b values of 10 to 14). This difference in pK is sufficient to allow observation of separate end points on titrating a mixture of aliphatic and aromatic amines. Because aromatic amines are too weakly basic to be titrated in water, a nonaqueous solvent must be used for the differentiating titration. When an amine mixture such as butylamine and pyridine is titrated potentiometrically in glacial acetic acid, however, only a single end point is obtained corresponding to the titration of the sum of the two amines. This may be attributed to the leveling effect of acetic acid. Butylamine reacts with the solvent (acetic acid) to form butylammonium acetate.

$$C_4H_9NH_2 + HAc \rightarrow C_4H_9NH_3{}^+Ac^-$$

It is the acetate ion that is then titrated with perchloric acid. The acetate ion is a weaker base than butylamine and is about the same basic strength as pyridine; hence, only one end-point break is observed.

To avoid this difficulty, the solvent chosen for differentiating titrations should not have appreciable acidic properties. At the same time, the solvent should not have appreciable basic properties in order that a satisfactory end point can be obtained for the titration of the weakly basic aromatic amine. Acetonitrile [26] and chloroform [27] are suitable solvents for this purpose. Figure 7 shows the two sharp breaks that are obtained when a mixture of butylamine and pyridine is titrated in acetonitrile. In order to avoid introduction of any acetic acid during the titration, perchloric acid in dioxane is used as the titrant. (Perchloric acid in acetonitrile is relatively unstable on standing.) The titration curve for cinchonine shows separate end points for the two basic nitrogens in the cinchonine molecule.

It appears that this is a general method for the differentiating titration of aliphatic-aromatic amine mixtures. Aromatic amines of differ-

[26] J. S. Fritz, *Anal. Chem.*, **25**, 407 (1953).

[27] C. W. Pifer, E. G. Wollish and M. Schmall, *Anal. Chem.*, **25**, 310 (1953).

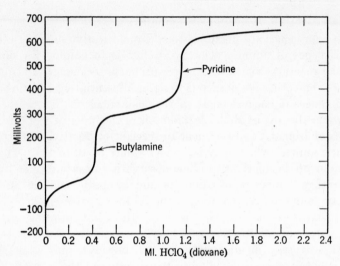

Figure 7. Titration of butylamine + pyridine in acetonitrile. (Reprinted from *Analytical Chemistry* with permission.)

ent basic strength can be differentiated by this same method. Better results are obtained, however, with perchloric acid in acetic acid as the titrant since aromatic amines are too weak to be leveled by acetic acid. Figure 8 shows curves for the titration of several mixtures of aromatic amines. The breaks are not extremely sharp where the

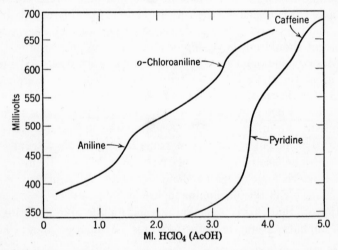

Figure 8. Titration of mixtures in acetonitrile. (Reprinted from *Analytical Chemistry* with permission.)

difference in basic strength of the two amines is not large. For example, the pK_b values (in water) for aniline and o-chloroaniline are 9.4 and 11.2, respectively ($\triangle pK = 1.8$). In water a $\triangle pK$ of at least 3 or 4 is required to obtain separate, distinguishable breaks for two amines.

The potential (in millivolts) at the mid point of the titration of amines in acetonitrile plotted against the aqueous pK_b values of various amines gives essentially a straight line.[26] The theoretical slope of this line is 59 millivolts per pK unit. This means that less difference in basic strength is required to obtain separate end points in acetonitrile.

Primary, secondary, and tertiary amines can be distinguished quantitatively by acidimetric methods. Tertiary amines are determined by first acetylating the primary and secondary amines with acetic anhydride-acetic acid.[28] Most of the basic strength of primary and secondary amines is destroyed, but tertiary amines are unaffected and can be titrated with perchloric acid. The excess acetic anhydride does not interfere with the titration; in many cases it actually makes the end point sharper.

Primary amines react with salicylaldehyde to form Schiff bases which are weaker bases than the primary amine. The basicity of secondary and tertiary amines is essentially unaffected by the salicylaldehyde reagent. This permits the determination of primary amines in the presence of other amines. By titrating aliquots of a mixture with perchloric acid in the presence and absence of salicylaldehyde, the primary amine content can be determined by difference. A method by Wagner, Brown, and Peters [29] which uses benzene-isopropanol as the solvent is applicable for mixtures of aliphatic amines. Ethylene glycol-isopropanol solvent, used by Siggia, Hanna, and Kervenski,[30] is said to be applicable for either aromatic or aliphatic amine mixtures.

TITRATION OF ORGANIC ACIDS

Conditions for Titration

The ideal solvent for the titration of acids should dissolve readily a large variety of acidic compounds but should have no acidic properties itself. The titrant should be a strong base dissolved in a nonacidic

[28] K. G. Blumrich and G. Bandel, *Angew. Chem.*, **54**, 374 (1941). C. D. Wagner, R. H. Brown and E. D. Peters, *J. Am. Chem. Soc.*, **69**, 2609 (1947).

[29] C. D. Wagner, R. H. Brown and E. D. Peters, *J. Am. Chem. Soc.*, **69**, 2611 (1947).

[30] S. Siggia, J. G. Hanna and I. R. Kervenski, *Anal. Chem.*, **22**, 1295 (1950).

solvent and should be stable on standing. The titration of a weak acid (HA) with a strong base (RO^-) can be represented as shown in equation 24. Because the amount of solvent is very great compared

$$(24) \qquad\qquad HA + RO^- \rightleftharpoons A^- + ROH$$
$$\text{(acid)} \quad \text{(base)} \quad\;\; \text{(base)} \quad\;\; \text{(acid)}$$

to the other species present, even a very weakly acidic solvent will partially reverse this reaction near the stoichiometric point and thus cause a poor end point. An acidic solvent also limits the strength of the base used as the titrant in the same manner that water limits the strength of acids used to titrate bases (page 29).

Because water is a relatively acidic solvent, titration of acids in aqueous solution is limited to those stronger than approximately pK 7. Another limiting factor is that many organic acids are not soluble in water. Alcohol is a good solvent for most organic acids and has found extensive use. It is somewhat less acidic than water but still cannot be used for the titration of very weak acids. Mixtures of alcohols and nonacidic solvents such as benzene, anisole, or acetone are better than alcohol alone because the concentration of the acidic solvent (alcohol) is decreased.[31] The G-H (glycol-hydrocarbon) solvent mixtures proposed by Palit [32] are still less acidic. These appear to be very useful media for titration of fairly weak acids.

Acetonitrile, pyridine, dimethylformamide, and ethylenediamine * are probably the best solvents available for the titration of acidic organic compounds. Acetone and butylamine are also useful. Dimethylformamide and ethylenediamine are especially powerful solvents, dissolving almost all organic acids, including many polymers. Ethylenediamine is a good medium for titration of very weakly acidic compounds, but for the titration of most acids a less basic solvent is more convenient to use and will usually give a sharper end point. The reason for this is that ethylenediamine exerts a leveling effect on acids and thus reduces the magnitude of the end-point break for all but very weak acids. Pyridine is an excellent solvent for the potentiometric titration of all types of acidic compounds. However, because of their higher dielectric constants (which permits use of a greater variety of indicators and gives steadier potential readings) and lack

---

[31] A. E. Ruehle, *Ind. Eng. Chem., Anal. Ed.*, **10**, 130 (1938).

[32] S. R. Palit, *Ind. Eng. Chem., Anal. Ed.*, **18**, 246 (1946).

* Anhydrous (95 to 100%) ethylenediamine should be used instead of the more common 70 to 76% material.

of offensive odor, acetonitrile, dimethylformamide, or acetone is frequently the solvent of choice for alkalimetric titrations.

All these solvents are available commercially and can be used without purification provided the acidic impurities do not cause an excessively high solvent blank. A simple way to remove the acidic impurities in acetonitrile or dimethylformamide is to pass the solvent through a column containing mixed, air-dried cation and anion exchange resins, then through a second column containing activated alumina. Reagent-grade pyridine and acetone usually do not require purification.

Sodium, potassium, or lithium methoxide in benzene-methanol is an excellent titrant. A 0.1 N solution of potassium methoxide contains 1 volume of methanol to about 10 volumes of dry benzene, this being the minimum amount of alcohol required to produce a homogeneous solution. This titrant generally gives sharper end points than does potassium methoxide in methanol alone, because less alcohol is introduced into the solution by the titrant itself. Potassium methoxide is a slightly stronger base than either sodium or lithium methoxide. A methoxide solution, unlike the alkali metal salts of many higher alcohols, remains colorless on long standing. The solution must, however, be protected from carbon dioxide and water vapor. Sodium aminoethoxide is widely used for the titration of weak acids in ethylenediamine and appears to be reasonably satisfactory.

Solutions of tetrabutylammonium hydroxide in benzene-methanol or isopropanol, and triethyl-n-butylammonium hydroxide in benzene-methanol are now receiving considerable attention as titrants. These have at least two major advantages over other titrants. In virtually every case the tetraalkylammonium salt of the titrated organic acid is soluble in the solvents commonly used. Sodium and potassium salts of organic acids frequently precipitate during a titration. The other point in favor of tetraalkylammonium hydroxides is that excellent potentiometric curves are obtained with a readily available glass-calomel electrode system.

Preparation of this titrant may be accomplished by shaking a solution of tetrabutylammonium iodide in methanol with a suspension of silver oxide. The excess silver oxide is filtered off, and the solution is diluted to the desired volume with benzene. An alternate preparation is to pass a solution of tetrabutylammonium iodide in isopropanol through a rather large anion exchange column in the —OH form.[33]

[33] G. A. Harlow, C. M. Noble, and G. E. A. Wyld, *Anal. Chem.*, **28**, 787 (1956).

Detection of the End Point

Titrations of organic acids can usually be followed potentiometrically except when the titration medium has a very low dielectric constant. A conventional glass-calomel electrode system * is very satisfactory when a tetraalkylammonium hydroxide is the titrant and a neutral or weakly basic solvent medium is employed. Excellent curves for a wide variety of acidic compounds have been obtained in pyridine, dimethylformamide, acetone, and acetonitrile. This electrode system is not very satisfactory for titration of weakly acidic compounds with sodium alkoxides, especially if the solvent is somewhat basic. In very basic solvents such as butylamine and ethylenediamine, this system should not be employed because the glass electrode fails to function as a satisfactory indicator electrode. A glass electrode has actually been used as a reference electrode for titrations in butylamine with sodium methoxide as the titrant. When a weak acid is titrated with a potassium alkoxide and a glass-calomel electrode system is used, the end point is sharper than when a sodium alkoxide is the titrant, but not as sharp as with a tetraalkylammonium hydroxide titrant. A tentative explanation is that the glass electrode is subject to a considerable "alkali error" in basic solutions containing the sodium ion. The larger potassium ion causes less trouble, whereas the very large tetrabutylammonium ion is apparently free from this difficulty.

Platinum electrodes have been used successfully for titrations with sodium or potassium titrants.[34] The indicator electrode is anodically polarized for 1 minute in dilute sulfuric acid before each titration. A platinum wire in the titrant stream serves as the reference electrode.

Antimony is a good indicator electrode and can be used in several solvents. In ethylenediamine[35] and dimethylformamide it is used in conjunction with the fiber-type calomel reference electrode; in butylamine it is used with the glass electrode as the reference. In ethylenediamine an ingenious antimony-antimony electrode system may also be used. The indicator electrode is an antimony rod dipping into the solution being titrated, and the reference electrode is an antimony rod mounted in the buret below the stopcock. The buret tip is immersed in the solution being titrated, thus making contact between the two

---

* When weak acids are being titrated the end point is usually sharper if the aqueous potassium chloride solution in the calomel electrode is replaced with a saturated methanolic solution of potassium chloride.

[34] G. A. Harlow, C. M. Noble, and G. E. A. Wyld, *Anal. Chem.*, **28**, 784 (1956).

[35] M. L. Moss, J. H. Elliott, and R. T. Hall, *Anal. Chem.*, **20**, 784 (1948).

electrodes. This arrangement permits continual flushing of the reference electrode to avoid diffusion (Fig. 9).

It is often convenient to determine the end point by means of visual indicators. Thymol blue gives an excellent end point (yellow to blue) for titrations carried out in benzene, dimethylformamide, butylamine, and several other solvents. It cannot be used in ethylenediamine. Azo violet (*p*-nitrobenzeneazoresorcinol) is a less acidic indicator than thymol blue and is used in the titration of acids too weak to give a sharp thymol blue end point. Azo violet gives a very sharp end point (red to blue) in ethylenediamine, butylamine, pyridine, and dimethylformamide. No satisfactory color change is observed in benzene or other hydrocarbon solvents. *o*-Nitroaniline is a still weaker indicator acid and is used for the titration of phenol and other acids too weak to be titrated by means of either thymol blue or azo violet. This indicator gives a fairly sharp change (yellow to orange-red) in dimethylformamide or ethylenediamine but does not appear to function as an indicator in butylamine, benzene, or alcohol.

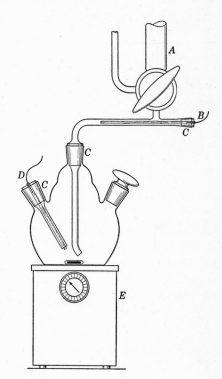

Figure 9. Titration assembly. A, 50 ml. buret; B, antimony reference electrode; C, $^{10}\!/_{30}$ joints; D, antimony indicator electrode; E, magnetic stirrer.

Scope

The following discussion is intended to serve as a general guide to the scope and most convenient methods for alkalimetric titration in nonaqueous solution.

Carboxylic Acids. The acidic strength of most carboxylic acids is sufficiently great to make titration a comparatively simple matter. Titration in alcohol with an aqueous solution of sodium hydroxide, using phenolpthalein indicator, is a familiar procedure. When this method is used, however, fatty acids form objectionable soaps, and polyfunctional acids often give poorly defined end points. Titration in benzene-methanol or dimethylformamide with potassium methoxide is generally more satisfactory, but in many cases precipitation of a jelly-like alkali metal carboxylate cannot be avoided. Titration in dimethylformamide or acetonitrile with a tetraalkylammonium hydroxide is almost never accompanied by objectionable precipitate formation, and is therefore the method most highly recommended.

In benzene-methanol, acid halides, and anhydrides can be titrated directly with potassium methoxide, both behaving as monobasic acids in the absence of water. Ethylene glycol has also been used with

$$
(25) \qquad RC{\overset{O}{\overset{\|}{}}}{-}X + CH_3OK \rightarrow RC{\overset{O}{\overset{\|}{}}}{-}OCH_3 + KX
$$

$$
(26) \qquad RC{\overset{O}{}}{-}O{-}{\overset{O}{}}CR + CH_3OK \rightarrow RCOCH_3 + RCOK
$$

considerable success as a solvent for the titration of carboxylic acids.[32]

Enols and Imides.[36] Most enols and imides can be titrated potentiometrically in dimethylformamide, acetonitrile, acetone, or pyridine with a tetraalkylammonium hydroxide, or with potassium methoxide with thymol blue or azo violet as the indicator. Very weakly acidic enols and imides can usually be titrated in ethylenediamine, with o-nitroaniline as the indicator.

Enols of the type A—CH$_2$—A′ are acidic enough to be titrated provided A and A′ are groups possessing suitable electron-withdrawing properties. If A and A′ are any combination of $-\overset{O}{\overset{\|}{C}}-R$, $-\overset{O}{\overset{\|}{C}}-H$, $-\overset{O}{\overset{\|}{C}}-OR$, $-\overset{O}{\overset{\|}{C}}-NHAr$, or $-C{\equiv}N$, accurate titration in dimethylformamide is possible. The amide group, $-\overset{O}{\overset{\|}{C}}-NH_2$, has weaker electron-withdrawing properties. This is shown by the fact that malononitrile gives a good azo violet end point but cyanoacetamide gives a very poor end point and malonamide is not at all acidic toward azo violet. Cyanoacetamide does give a satisfactory end point in ethylenediamine,

[36] J. S. Fritz, *Anal. Chem.*, **24**, 674 (1952).

with o-nitroaniline as the indicator; malonamide is slightly acidic toward this indicator.

The carboxyl groups in cyanoacetic acid and malonic acid can be titrated but these compounds apparently have no further acidic properties. Compounds of the type $A—CH_2CH_2—A'$ are not acidic toward azo violet even if A and A' are strong electron-attracting groups. Examples of some enols that have been titrated are listed in Table 7.

TABLE 7

Titration of Some Enols

Compound	Solvent	Indicator
Acetoacetanilide	DMF *	Azo violet
1-Acetyl-2-thiohydantoin	DMF	Thymol blue
Cyanoacetamide	En †	o-Nitroaniline
Dibenzoylmethane	DMF	Thymol blue
Ethyl cyanoacetate	DMF	Azo violet
Ethyl malonate	DMF	Azo violet
Malononitrile	DMF	Azo violet
Methone	DMF	Azo violet
1-Phenyl-3-carbethoxy-5-pyrazolone	DMF	Azo violet
1-Phenyl-3-carboxy-5-pyrazolone	DMF	Azo violet

* Dimethylformamide.
† Ethylenediamine.

Compounds having the configuration A—NH—A' can be titrated accurately as acids if A and A' are any combination of the accompany-

$$\overset{O}{\overset{\|}{-C}}-R, \quad \overset{O}{\overset{\|}{-C}}-H, \quad \overset{O}{\overset{\|}{-C}}-OR, \quad \overset{O}{\overset{\|}{-C}}-NHAr$$

ing groups. If either A or A' is the $\overset{O}{\overset{\|}{-C}}-NH_2$ or $\overset{O}{\overset{\|}{-C}}-NHR$ group, the success of the titration is uncertain. For example, acetylurea gives a very poor end point; yet hydantoin, which is essentially the cyclic equivalent of acetylurea, gives an excellent visual (azo violet) or potentiometric end point. Although the electron-attracting properties of aryl groups are somewhat less than the above listed groups, a phenyl group in the proper position will noticeably increase the acidity of an imide. This is illustrated by the fact that acetylacetanilide ($CH_3COCH_2CONHPh$) gives a much sharper end point than acetylurea ($CH_3CONHCONH_2$) and that oxanilide ($PhNHCOCONHPh$)

can be titrated as a monobasic acid whereas oxamide ($NH_2COCONH_2$) does not even react acidic to azo violet.

TABLE 8

Titration of Some Imides and Thioureas

Compound	Solvent	Indicator
1,3-Diphenylthiourea	DMF *	Azo violet
Dithiobiuret	DMF	Azo violet
Dithiooxamide	DMF	Azo violet
Hydantoin	DMF	Azo violet
1-Phenyl-3-cyclohexylthiourea	En †	o-Nitroaniline
1-Phenyl-3-naphthylthiourea	DMF	Azo violet
1-Phenyl-3-(2-pyrimidyl)thiourea	DMF	Azo violet
Phthalimide	DMF	Azo violet
Succinimide	DMF	Azo violet
Theobromine	Pyridine	Azo violet
Thiobarbituric acid	DMF	Thymol blue

* Dimethylformamide.
† Ethylenediamine.

Imides containing a thiocarbonyl group are considerably stronger acids than the analogous compounds containing a carbonyl group. Thus s-diphenylthiourea can be titrated in dimethylformamide (azo violet) and phenylthiourea in ethylenediamine (o-nitroaniline), but neither s-diphenylurea or phenylurea can be determined by either procedure. Even thiourea is weakly acidic toward o-nitroaniline in ethylenediamine although no definite end point is obtainable.

Sulfonamides. The $ArSO_2NH-$ group is acidic and can be titrated in nonaqueous solvents. The sulfonamides of primary aromatic amines give very sharp visual end points in dimethylformamide, acetonitrile, or acetone. Sulfonamides of aliphatic amines are less acidic, but can be titrated potentiometrically in acetonitrile or pyridine with a tetra-alkylammonium hydroxide.

The nonaqueous titration of 21 sulfonamides has been reported,[37] including 8 commonly used sulfa drugs. Samples of pure sulfathiazole, sulfadiazine, sulfapyridine, sulfamerazine, sulfasuxidine, and sulfa-thalidine have been assayed with an accuracy of ±0.2%. Sulfanil-amide is not acid to thymol blue but can be titrated accurately in butylamine, with azo violet as the indicator. Potentiometric titration in acetonitrile or acetone makes possible the quantitative determina-

[37] J. S. Fritz and R. T. Keen, *Anal Chem.*, **24**, 308 (1952).

tion of each constituent in sulfathiazole-sulfanilamide and sulfathia-zole-sulfapyridine mixtures.

Phenols. Alkalimetric titration of phenols has long been an inviting prospect, but the very weakly acidic nature of phenols has made this difficult. Potentiometric titration in anhydrous ethylenediamine with sodium aminoethoxide, suggested in 1948 by Moss, Elliott, and Hall [35] is a satisfactory and widely applicable method. Sterically hindered phenols present no problem. Dark-colored resins can be titrated, separate breaks being obtained for the carboxylic acid and phenolic constituents. Monohydric phenols give good end points but resorcinol gives two gradual breaks. Three slight but distinct breaks are obtained in the titration of boric acid. Even phenolic esters of carboxylic acids can be titrated.[38] Apparently these esters undergo aminolysis at room temperature in the ethylenediamine solvent, producing phenols and carboxylic acid amides of ethylenediamine.

$$(27) \quad RCOOAr + NH_2CH_2CH_2NH_2 \rightarrow$$

$$RCOONHCH_2CH_2NH_2 + ArOH$$

The carboxylic acid may be either aliphatic or aromatic, and the phenol may be a derivative of either benzene or naphthalene. Lactones of phenols can be titrated in the same manner as phenolic esters. Examples of some phenolic esters that have been determined by this procedure are listed in Table 9.

TABLE 9

Phenolic Esters Titrated in Ethylenediamine

Acetylsalicylic acid	Phenyl chloroacetate
Coumarin	Phenyl propionate
6-Dibenzopyrone	Phenyl salicylate
Diphenyl phthalate	Phenyl succinate
Diphenyl succinate	Phenyl stearate
1-Naphthyl acetate	o-Tolyl acetate
Phenyl acetate	m-Tolyl acetate
Phenyl benzoate	p-Tolyl benzoate

Phenols can be titrated potentiometrically in pyridine, acetonitrile, or acetone with a tetraalkylammonium hydroxide. Some typical examples of phenols that have been titrated are listed in Table 10. From the curves obtained it is found that electron-withdrawing groups increase the acidity of phenols in the order: $-NO_2 > -CHO > -COR$

[38] R. A. Glenn and J. T. Peake, *Anal. Chem.*, **27**, 205 (1955).

> —Cl, —Br > —C_6H_5. A group in the ortho or para position affects the acidity more than in the meta position. The increase in acidity attributable to electron-withdrawing groups is frequently substantial. Thus phenol is a very weak acid, but 2,4-dinitrophenol is approximately equal in acidic strength to a carboxylic acid.

TABLE 10

Titration of Some Phenols with Triethylbutylammonium Hydroxide

o-, m-, and p-Bromophenol	Methyl salicylate
Catechol	β-Naphthol
2,6-Dibromophenol	o-, m-, and p-Nitrophenol
2,4-Dinitrophenol	α-Nitroso-β-naphthol
Ethyl vanillin	Phenol
Hydroquinone	o-Phenylphenol
o- and p-Hydroxyacetophenone	Resorcinol
o-, m-, and p-Hydroxybenzaldehyde	Vanillin

Salts.[39] A salt of the type BH^+A^- can be titrated as an acid provided that it is soluble in a suitable organic solvent, that HA is a sufficiently strong acid, and that B is not too strong a base.

Ethylenediamine and dimethylformamide are the most satisfactory media for the titration of salts. Ethylenediamine is an excellent solvent for most salts of organic bases although sulfates, phosphates, oxalates, and carbonates do not dissolve in this solvent. Sharp end points are obtained, using sodium or potassium methoxide as the titrant and azo violet as the indicator. Aqueous salt solutions can be analyzed by adding a large excess of ethylenediamine to the sample before carrying out the titration. Solid samples, such as ammonium sulfate, that do not dissolve readily in ethylenediamine directly may be dissolved in a small amount of water. Ethylenediamine is then added, and the titration is carried out with the formation of a precipitate.

Dimethylformamide is almost as good a solvent for salts as ethylenediamine and is somewhat more convenient to use. One disadvantage with dimethylformamide is that water interferes, causing high results. If the sample is essentially anhydrous, however, use of dimethylformamide is highly recommended.

Salts of aromatic amines are easily titrated in either aqueous or nonaqueous media. Salts of ammonia or aliphatic amines are too weakly acidic to be titrated in water but can be titrated very accurately in ethylenediamine or dimethylformamide. Guanidine salts give

[39] J. S. Fritz, *Anal. Chem.*, **24**, 306 (1952).

very poor end points even in ethylenediamine since the highly reso-nance-stabilized guanidinium ion is very weakly acidic. Quaternary ammonium salts are not acidic to azo violet in either dimethylformam-ide or ethylenediamine. This would be expected, of course, since they have no acidic protons.

Alcohols. Although not commonly regarded as such, alcohols actu-ally are very weak acids and can be titrated as such under the proper conditions. Higuchi, Concha, and Kuramoto [40] showed that alcohols may be titrated in tetrahydrofuran with a very strong base such as a lithium aluminum amide. The titrant is prepared by reacting lithium aluminum hydride with a secondary amine in completely dry tetra-hydrofuran. The reaction for titration of an alcohol is

$$(28) \qquad ROH + R_2NM \rightarrow R_2NH + ROM$$

This method can also be used to determine several other types of very weak acids. Some examples, taken from the work of Higuchi *et al.*[40] are listed in Table 11. Because this method is simple and

TABLE 11

Titration with Lithium Amides

Compound	Classification	Equivalents of Amide/Mole
Ethanol	Alcohol	1
n-Pentanol	Alcohol	1
Acetamide	Amide	1.2 to 1.3
Acetanilide	Amide	1
Benzyl benzoate	Ester	1
Phenyl salicylate	Ester, phenol	2
Phthalimide	Imide	2.2 to 2.5
Acetophenone	Ketone	1
Benzophenone	Ketone	1
1-Naphthol	Naphthol	1
Carbazole	....	1

rapid, it should be useful in identification and characterization. It will first be necessary to do more extensive work showing the stoi-chiometry of reactions of lithium aluminum amides with carbonyl groups and active hydrogen groups.

[40] T. Higuchi, J. Concha, and R. Kuramoto, *Anal. Chem.*, **24**, 685 (1952).

Pyrroles. Sodium triphenylmethane in 1-to-1 diethyl ether-toluene has been used to titrate extremely weak acids such as pyrroles.[41] The

$$(C_6H_5)_3C^-Na^+ \; + \; \underset{\underset{H}{N}}{\bigcirc} \; \longrightarrow \; \underset{\underset{Na^+}{N^-}}{\bigcirc} \; + \; (C_6H_5)_3CH$$

end point of the titration can be very simply detected by observing the red color due to the first excess of deeply colored titrant. The success of this method depends upon the very careful purification of all solvents used and the complete exclusion of moisture, carbon dioxide, and oxygen.

Titration of Mixtures

Compounds that differ appreciably in their acidic strength can be determined separately in mixtures by a potentiometric titration. This can be best accomplished in a nonleveling solvent. For example, two sharp breaks are obtained on titrating a mixture of mandelic acid and 2-aceto-1-naphthol in acetonitrile.[42] Separate end points are also obtained in the titration of a carboxylic acid-phenol mixture in ethylenediamine, but the first end point is not very sharp because of the leveling effect of the ethylenediamine. Many mixtures can be titrated in pyridine,[43] acetone,[44] acetonitrile, or ethyleneglycol dimethylether, using a tetraalkylammonium hydroxide as the titrant. Some of the results are quite dramatic. For example, the two acidic hydrogens of sulfuric acid are usually considered to be almost indistinguishable, yet titration in pyridine produces separate end-point breaks of more than 300 millivolts for each hydrogen. As shown in Fig. 10, separate end points are obtained for titration of a mixture of 2,4-dinitrophenol (I), 2-nitrophenol (II), and methyl salicylate (III) ; also for titration of a mixture

41 A. H. Corwin and R. C. Ellingson, *J. Am. Chem. Soc.*, **64**, 2098 (1942).
42 J. S. Fritz and R. T. Keen, *Anal. Chem.*, **25**, 179 (1953).
43 R. H. Cundiff and P. C. Markunas, *Anal. Chem.*, **28**, 792 (1956).
44 J. S. Fritz and S. S. Yamamura, *Anal. Chem.*, in press.

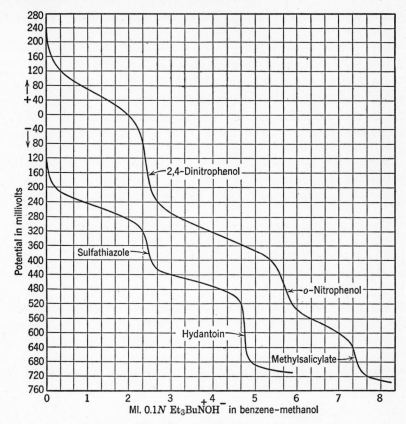

Figure 10. Titration of acid mixtures in acetone.

of sulfathiazole (IV) and hydantoin (V). The scope of differentiating

titrations of acid mixtures in nonaqueous solvents has not yet been worked out in detail, but by proper choice of conditions for titration it should be possible to analyze a variety of mixtures.

Interferences

Very weakly acidic substances such as water and alcohol can usually be tolerated in small amounts, but larger concentrations interfere. In ethylenediamine containing up to about 5% water or alcohol, very good results are obtained in the titration of carboxylic acids and other moderately strong acids. Weakly acidic compounds give sharp end points only in ethylenediamine, which is essentially free of alcohol or water. Moss et al.[35] found that phenol gives a sharp end-point break of 180 to 200 millivolts in 99 to 100% ethylenediamine but that the break amounts only to about 20 millivolts in 80% ethylenediamine. They recommend removal of even the last 1% moisture.

In dimethylformamide, high results are obtained in most titrations if much more than a trace of water is present. This is probably due to hydrolysis,

$$(29) \qquad HCON(CH_3)_2 + H_2O \rightarrow HCOOH + (CH_3)_2NH$$

the formic acid formed being titrated along with the sample. Dimethylformamide, ethylenediamine, butylamine, and pyridine readily absorb carbon dioxide from the air. Carbon dioxide is titrated as an acid, and the results will be seriously in error unless some provision is made to exclude carbon dioxide during the titration. It is usually sufficient to carry out the titration in a closed or covered container, although for highest precision it is best to work under nitrogen.

Although many acidic compounds containing an ester group can be titrated smoothly, some esters (such as ethyl acetate) cause high results and a fading end point. This is believed to be caused by condensation to form acidic enolic compounds.

$$2CH_3COOEt \xrightarrow{\text{(base)}} CH_3COCH_2COOEt + EtOH$$

Some halogen-containing compounds are dehydrohalogenated by bases. Such compounds interfere, causing high results and fading end points.

In a few cases the neutralization product precipitates in a gelatinous form, causing inaccurate results. This can usually be avoided by the proper choice of solvents for the titration.

Titrations using sodium triphenylmethane or lithium aluminum hydride are subject to many additional interferences. Among these are oxygen, aldehydes, ketones, and slight traces of water.

PRECISION AND ACCURACY

The accuracy and precision of acid-base titrations carried out in either aqueous or nonaqueous solvents depend chiefly on the sharpness of the end point and the precision with which the buret can be read. The temperature coefficient of cubic expansion of most organic solvents is much greater than for water, but error can usually be prevented by avoiding temperature changes during the titration. Under carefully controlled conditions, titration of amines in acetic acid has been shown to be precise and accurate to 0.1% or better. An error not exceeding 0.2 or 0.3% is usually considered satisfactory for any titration. For some differential titrations in nonaqueous solvents, the error is often around 1% because two end points must be determined, and the end point breaks are less than when amines are titrated separately.

Most compounds for which the use of sodium methoxide titrant and thymol blue or azo violet indicator is applicable can be titrated with an accuracy and precision of ±0.3% or better. Where o-nitroaniline must be employed as indicator, the accuracy drops to ±0.5 or 0.6%. Few data are available regarding the accuracy of potentiometric titrations in ethylenediamine, although such titrations should be at least as accurate as those using visual end points. Data given by Higuchi $et\ al.$ for titrations with lithium aluminum amides indicate accuracy of 2 or 3%. Even with careful technique, accuracy greater than about 5% is doubtful where sodium triphenylmethane is used as the titrant.

PROBLEMS

1. Devise a good method for determining quantitatively each constituent in each of the following mixtures:

(a) [benzene ring with COCH₃] and [benzene ring with COCH₃ and OH]

(b) $C_4H_9NH_2$ and $C_4H_9NH_3{}^+$ Cl^-.

(c) [benzene ring with —CO₂H and —OH] and [benzene ring with —CO₂CH₃ and —OH].

(d) Pyridine and caffeine.

(e) [benzene ring with N(CH₃)₂] and [benzene ring with CH₂N(CH₃)₂]

2. Explain how you would determine a primary aliphatic amine in the presence of both a secondary aliphatic and a secondary aromatic amine, using the salicylic acid method.

3. Consult a standard textbook on qualitative organic analysis, and prepare a list of derivatives of the common functional groups for which the equivalent weight could probably be determined by a nonaqueous acid-base titration.

4. A method is described on page 74 for the determination of isocyanates and isothiocyanates. Devise an acid-base method for distinguishing quantitatively between phenyl isocyanate and phenyl isothiocyanate.

5. The potentiometric titration of urea in glacial acetic acid with perchloric acid gives only a faint inflection at the end point. In acetic acid containing 10 to 20% acetic anhydride, a very sharp potential break is observed when perhaps 60 to 80% of the theoretical amount of perchloric acid has been added. Explain.

4.

INDIRECT

ACID-BASE METHODS

INTRODUCTION

Many important methods are based on indirect acid-base titrations. If a certain functional group reacts with an acidic or basic reagent, the amount of reagent consumed in the reaction may be measured by a titration of the excess. Another general technique is to titrate the acid or base formed in the reaction of a compound to be assayed with a suitable reagent.

ACYLATION

Acetylation and phthalation are widely employed for the quantitative determination of alcoholic hydroxyl groups. Phenols, primary amines, and many secondary amines may also be determined by acetylation. Alcohols react with acetic anhydride to give 1 mole of ester and 1 mole of acetic acid. When this reaction is complete, excess water is added to react with the excess acetic anhydride. This reaction gives 2 moles of acetic acid for each mole of acetic anhydride. The acetic acid liberated is titrated with standard sodium hydroxide.

(1) $ROH + (CH_3CO)_2O \rightarrow CH_3COOR + CH_3COOH$

(2) $H_2O + (CH_3CO)_2O \rightarrow 2CH_3COOH$

The difference in milliequivalents between the sodium hydroxide required to titrate the acetic acid from the alcohol determination and the amount required by the acetic acid from an aliquot of acetic anhydride reagent treated with water represents the milliequivalents of alcohol present.

Although the time required for complete reaction varies, most primary and secondary alcohols can be acetylated completely in 45 minutes.[1] Pyridine is present during the reaction, its function being to increase the reaction rate and, perhaps, to shift the equilibrium in the desired direction by partial neutralization of the acetic acid formed. Acetyl chloride has also been used in quantitative acetylation methods.[2]

Phthalic anhydride in pyridine may also be used as a reagent for the determination of alcoholic hydroxyl groups.[3] Phthalation proceeds more slowly than acetylation and is not as widely applicable in that many glycols cannot be determined by phthalation. Advantages of the phthalic anhydride method are that phenols, saturated and unsaturated aldehydes, and ketones do not interfere as they do in the acetylation method. Greater accuracy is also claimed in the determination of alcohols in dilute aqueous solutions. Some amines react quantitatively with phthalic anhydride; others (aniline and ethylenediamine, for example) consume too much reagent, possibly because of phthalimide formation.

One limitation of both acetylation and phthalation procedures is that tertiary alcohols cannot be determined quantitatively because of dehydration by the anhydride.

$$\text{(3)} \qquad \underset{\underset{OH}{|}}{R\!-\!CH_2\!-\!\overset{\overset{R}{|}}{C}\!-\!R} + Ac_2O \rightarrow R\!-\!CH\!=\!\overset{\overset{R}{|}}{C}\!-\!R + 2AcOH$$

Reaction with acid anhydrides is easily the most important method available for the determination of alcohols (see also Chapter 6 for active hydrogen methods). Although the determination of primary and most secondary amines is also quantitative, acidimetric titration of amines in nonaqueous solution is a more convenient and selective method. In mixtures it is possible to determine the sum of alcohol

[1] S. Siggia and I. R. Kervenski, *Anal. Chem.*, **23**, 117 (1951).

[2] D. M. Smith and W. M. D. Bryant, *J. Am. Chem. Soc.*, **57**, 61 (1935).

[3] P. J. Elving and B. Warshowsky, *Anal. Chem.*, **19**, 1006 (1947).

and amine by acetylation. The amount of alcohol present is obtained by subtracting the amine titer as determined by a nonaqueous acidimetric titration (Chapter 3).

DETERMINATION OF CARBONYL GROUPS

The determination of carbonyl by oximation was thoroughly discussed in Chapter 2. The reaction of bisulfite with aldehydes is also useful analytically, and the extent of reaction, as indicated in equation 4, is often measured by indirect acid-base methods. The dissociation

$$(4) \qquad \text{RCHO} + \text{HSO}_3^- \rightleftharpoons \text{RCH} \overset{\text{OH}}{\underset{\text{SO}_3^-}{<}}$$

constants of the bisulfite addition products (see equation 5) of a

$$(5) \qquad K = \frac{[\text{RCHO}][\text{HSO}_3^-]}{[\text{RCH(OH)SO}_3^-]}$$

number of aldehydes and ketones have been measured.[4] The negative log (pK) of these constants is tabulated in Table 12. For most alde-

TABLE 12

Dissociation Constants of Some Bisulfite Addition Compounds

Bisulfite Compound of	pK
HCHO	6.9
CH$_3$CHO	5.6
C$_6$H$_5$CH=CHCHO	5.4
C$_6$H$_5$CHO	4.0
⟨ ⟩—CHO (O)	3.9
CH$_3$COCH$_3$	2.4
CCl$_3$CHO	1.5

hydes the equilibrium is favorable, but acetone and most other ketones form rather unstable addition products.

Several titrimetric methods have been proposed for the determination of aldehydes, using the bisulfite addition reaction. In the iodo-

[4] W. Kerp and E. Bauer, *Arb. kaiser. Gesundh.*, **21**, 180 (1904); **26**, 231, 269 (1907); W. Kerp and P. Wohler, *ibid.*, **32**, 88, 120 (1907). See also *Chem. Abstr.*, **4**, 442–443 (1910).

metric method an excess of standard bisulfite solution is added to the sample, and, after allowing sufficient time for complete reaction, the excess bisulfite is titrated with standard iodine. One difficulty with this method is that the bisulfite solutions are unstable and must be standardized each day. Another difficulty is that as the excess bisulfite is removed by the oxidation with iodine, the equilibrium is shifted, and some of the product decomposes.

In another procedure, an excess of sodium sulfite (not a standard solution) is added, and the sodium hydroxide formed in the reaction is titrated with standard acid.

$$
(6) \qquad \mathrm{RCHO} + \mathrm{SO_3^=} + \mathrm{H_2O} \rightleftharpoons \mathrm{RCH} \overset{\displaystyle OH}{\underset{\displaystyle SO_3^-}{\Big\langle}} + \mathrm{OH^-}
$$

Again equilibrium difficulties are encountered because the hydroxyl ion tends to reverse the reaction.

The method of Siggia and Maxcy[5] is probably the best of the bi-sulfite procedures. A measured amount of $1\,N$ sulfuric acid is added to a large excess of $1\,M$ sodium sulfite. A quantity of bisulfite equivalent to the sulfuric acid added is generated *in situ*. The bisulfite produced then reacts directly with the aldehyde. When the reaction is complete (2 to 5 minutes), the excess bisulfite is titrated to sulfite with $1\,N$ sodium hydroxide. The only standard solutions used in this method are sulfuric acid and sodium hydroxide. A large excess of sulfite or bisulfite is present at all times to prevent the product from decomposing. The end point is sharp for most aldehydes, reasonably sharp for benzaldehyde, and quite indistinct for most ketones.

Stewart and Donally[6] have made a careful study of the bisulfite addition compound of benzaldehyde. They have measured the equilibrium constant for the dissociation of the addition compound, shown in equation 7, where Σ in each case denotes the summation of

$$
(7) \qquad K = \frac{[\Sigma \mathrm{C_6H_5CHO}][\Sigma \mathrm{H_2SO_3}]}{[\Sigma \mathrm{C_6H_5CH(OH)SO_3H}]}
$$

all the ionic species (for example, $\Sigma \mathrm{H_2SO_3}$ includes $\mathrm{H_2SO_3}$, $\mathrm{HSO_3^-}$, and $\mathrm{SO_3^=}$). Table 13 lists values of this constant for benzaldehyde-

[5] S. Siggia and W. Maxcy, *Anal. Chem.*, **19**, 1023 (1947).

[6] T. D. Stewart and L. H. Donally, *J. Am. Chem. Soc.*, **54**, 3555, 3559 (1932).

TABLE 13

Dissociation Constants for Benzaldehyde-Bisulfite at 21° C.

pH	pK	pH	pK
0.0	2.3	7.0	3.7
1.0	3.3	8.0	3.0
2.0	3.9	9.0	2.2
3.0	4.0	10.0	1.9
4.0	4.0	11.0	1.8
5.0	4.0	12.0	1.7
6.0	4.0	13.0	1.0

bisulfite as a function of pH. From these data it will be seen that the optimum pH range for this reaction is approximately 3 to 6. In the method of Siggia and Maxcy, the pH of the reaction mixture is 7.5 to 8.0.

Kolthoff and Stenger [7] have devised a method for calculating the titration error due to dissociation of an aldehyde-bisulfite addition compound (see Chapter 2 for related discussion). The expression derived is:

$$(8) \qquad \% \text{ Error} = 100K \frac{(a + b)}{(bm - an)} = \frac{(a + b)}{\text{meq. excess bisulfite}}$$

where K = decomposition constant,
$\quad a$ = milliliters of aldehyde solution,
$\quad b$ = milliliters of bisulfite solution,
$\quad m$ = molarity of bisulfite solution,
$\quad n$ = molarity of aldehyde solution.

Using this formula and the value of K reported by Stewart and Donally, the error in determining benzaldehyde by the procedure of Siggia and Maxcy is:

$$100(1.07 \times 10^{-3})\tfrac{300}{220} = 0.15\%$$

This is the per cent error at pH 8.0, which is the approximate pH of the reaction mixture just before the final titration with sodium hydroxide. At pH 9.0, the pH at the end point of this titration, the error is:

$$100(6.2 \times 10^{-3})\tfrac{325}{220} = 0.85\%$$

[7] I. M. Kolthoff and V. A. Stenger, *Volumetric Analysis*, New York, Interscience, 1942, Vol. I, p. 218.

If the titration is carried out rapidly, the mixture probably would not come to equilibrium at pH 9.0 and the titration error would be somewhere between 0.15 and 0.85%. In actual practice the determination of benzaldehyde by the bisulfite method does give slightly low results. Because a decrease in temperature increases the stability of benzaldehyde-bisulfite and also decreases the rate of both the formation and decomposition reactions, it might be advantageous to cool the reaction mixture before the final titration in order to minimize decomposition of the product as the pH is raised.

ION EXCHANGE METHODS

It is not within the scope of this book to present more than a brief discussion of the principles of ion exchange resins. Further details in the theory and use of ion exchange techniques in analytical chemistry are available in books by Samuelson [8] and Kunin and Myers,[9] and in a review article by Rieman.[10]

Ion exchange resins are of two general types. Those that are able to take up positively charged ions are called cation exchange resins; those that take up anions are known as anion exchange resins. The cation exchange resins most widely used in analytical work are sulfonated styrene-divinylbenzene copolymers. Styrene polymerizes in a linear fashion, but divinylbenzene causes cross-linking because of its bifunctional character. Resins are commercially available with various degrees of cross-linking from 2% to 16% or more. (The per cent of cross-linking is taken to be equal to the per cent of divinylbenzene in the original polymerization mixture). A moderate amount of cross-linking is desirable in that it prevents excessive swelling and shrinking as different ions are taken up by the resin.

Cation exchange resins are generally used in the hydrogen, sodium, or ammonium form. The affinity of resins for different cations varies with the charge on the ion and follows the general order $+4 > +3 > +2 > +1$. Suppose that a given amount of cation exchange resin in the sodium form is shaken with an aqueous solution of a calcium salt. An equilibrium is rather quickly attained which can be expressed by the following equation:

$$(9) \qquad 2R_S{}^-Na^+ + Ca^{++} \rightleftharpoons (R_S{}^-)_2Ca^{++} + 2Na^+$$

[8] O. Samuelson, *Ion Exchangers in Analytical Chemistry*, Wiley, New York, 1953.

[9] R. Kunin and R. J. Myers, *Ion Exchange Resins*, Wiley, New York, 1950.

[10] W. Rieman III, *Record Chem. Progress*, **15**, 85 (1954).

The equilibrium constant for equation 9 may be determined and is found to be greater than 1. In batchwise ion exchange operations such as this, the equilibrium is seldom such that an ion in solution will be quantitatively taken up by the resin unless a prohibitively large weight of the resin is used.

If a solution containing a cation such as calcium is passed through a tube packed with resin in the sodium form, the calcium ion will be quantitatively taken up by the resin, and an equivalent amount of sodium ion from the resin will go into solution. Ion exchange column operation is similar to a multiple-stage extraction or distillation. The entering calcium solution comes to equilibrium with the resin in the topmost portion of the column. A certain per cent, p, of the calcium is taken up by this portion of the resin, and the solution that comes into contact with the resin in the next lower part of the column thus contains a lower concentration of calcium. The resin in this second portion of the column also removes approximately p per cent of the calcium present at this stage, and a still more dilute calcium solution passes into the third portion of the column. It is evident that only a few such stages are necessary to effect essentially quantitative removal of the calcium.

Using a cation exchange column in the hydrogen form, it is possible to determine most cations quickly and accurately. The cation is taken up quantitatively by the resin, and an equivalent amount of hydrogen ion goes into solution and can be titrated. The anion present passes through the column unchanged but will affect the strength of the acid formed. For example, a sample of sodium benzoate may be analyzed by washing a measured portion through the hydrogen-form ion exchange column and titrating the benzoic acid formed with standard base. The solution must, of course, be kept fairly dilute to avoid precipitation of benzoic acid. Sodium tartrate, magnesium lactate, ammonium adipate, and many other salts of organic acids have been successfully determined by this method.[11]

Ion exchange determination of sulfonic acid salts is useful. It is possible to differentiate sulfonic acid and carboxylic acid salts by taking advantage of the fact that the sulfonic acid liberated can be titrated in the presence of the weaker carboxylic acid. Sulfonic acid salts cannot be differentiated from salts of strong inorganic acids such as hydrochloric and sulfuric. An illustration of the practical value of the ion exchange method was found in a scheme used in checking

[11] C. H. Van Etten and M. B. Wiele, *Anal. Chem.*, **25**, 1109 (1953).

a purified sample of sodium alizarin sulfonate, I.[12]   The technical
material was known to contain appreciable quantities of sodium chlo-

I

ride and sodium sulfate, and possibly some disulfonated alizarin.
Passage of a sample of purified sodium alizarin sulfonate through a
hydrogen-form cation exchange column, followed by potentiometric
titration with sodium hydroxide gave a curve with two breaks. The
first break corresponds to titration of the sulfonic acid group and the
second to the titration of one acidic phenol group (the pK_a of this
group is 5.5). The fact that the buret reading at the first end point
is exactly half that at the second end point showed that all inorganic
salts had been removed in the purification process and that no disulfonated material was present. Although the alkali metal salts of
sulfonic acids are soluble in water, the calcium and barium salts are
likely to be insoluble. Even insoluble salts can usually be analyzed
by shaking a suspension of the salt with ion exchange resin in the
hydrogen form until solution is complete and then passing the aqueous
extract through an ion exchange column to convert the last traces of
the salt to the acid form.[13]

SAPONIFICATION

The term saponification originally applied to the hydrolysis of fats
(glycerol esters of the higher carboxylic acids). As the term is now
used saponification applies to the alkaline hydrolysis of all types of
esters and amides.

(10) $$RCOOR' + KOH \rightarrow RCOOK + R'OH$$

To be useful analytically, this reaction must be quantitative in a
reasonable length of time. One condition that favors a rapid and
quantitative reaction is the use of as strong a base as possible.

The saponification of many esters is rather slow, and various means
of accelerating the reaction have been used to increase its utility as

[12] J. J. Ford, M.S. Dissertation, Iowa State College, 1954.
[13] E. Brockmann-Hanssen, *J. Am. Pharm. Assoc., Sci. Ed.,* **43,** 307 (1954).

an analytical procedure. Organic solvents, such as alcohols and glycols, are ordinarily used to obtain one-phase reaction mixtures. If, as is likely to be true with fats, the ester is not soluble in any solvent that will also dissolve strong bases, a soap is often added to form an emulsion and thus provide a greater surface area. Elevated temperatures are commonly used to effect rapid conversions. For this reason glycols are often used as solvents because of their high boiling points. Although sodium hydroxide and potassium hydroxide become essentially equivalent as bases in water solution, the latter appears to be the stronger of the two in nonaqueous media. From the kinetic point of view it is desirable to use high concentrations of the base, although this can lead to some inconvenience in the final titration.

Two general analytical methods are available for measuring the amount of ester saponified. In one procedure, a measured volume of standard sodium or potassium hydroxide is added to the sample. After saponification, the solution is cooled, diluted, and the excess potassium hydroxide is titrated with standard acid. In glycol-alcohol two sharp end points are obtained when the saponification mixture is titrated with acid. The first end point corresponds to the neutralization of the excess potassium hydroxide, and the difference between the first and second end points is the volume of acid required to convert the RCO_2K formed to RCO_2H. In aqueous solution only the first end point is sharp. The second method does not require an accurately measured portion of potassium hydroxide. After saponification the excess potassium hydroxide is exactly neutralized with a strong solution of unstandardized hydrochloric acid; then the potassium salt of the carboxylic acid is neutralized with a weaker standard solution of hydrochloric acid. This is often referred to as the double-indicator method.

A widely applicable double-indicator method for the determination of difficultly saponifiable esters has been described by Shaefer and Balling.[14] This method is essentially nonaqueous throughout. The reagent employed is approximately $0.8\,N$ potassium hydroxide in 92% diethyleneglycol-8% phenetole. After refluxing gently at 175° C. for about 2 hours (a much shorter time would be needed for more easily saponifiable esters), the potassium hydroxide remainder is neutralized approximately to thymol blue with $1\,N$ alcoholic hydrochloric acid, then exactly to the thymol blue end point with $0.25\,N$ alcoholic sodium hydroxide. The RCO_2K is then titrated to RCO_2H with $0.25\,N$ alco-

14 W. E. Shaefer and W. J. Balling, *Anal. Chem.*, **23**, 1126 (1951).

holic hydrochloric acid, using a tetrabromphenol blue end point (greenish-yellow color). A blank (which should require less than 1 ml. of 0.25 N HCl) is run in a similar manner to correct for carbonate in the potassium hydroxide used.

This procedure avoids many of the common difficulties of saponification. Incomplete reaction is avoided by use of a moderately large excess of a strong base, an adequate digestion period, and a solvent that permits a one-phase reaction and a moderately high reflux temperature. Reaction of alkali with the glass during the long reflux is prevented by the use of special alkali-resistant glass which is essentially boron free. Atmospheric oxygen is largely excluded during the refluxing step by phenetole, which keeps a protective vapor over the solution. When the reaction is complete, the flask is detached and alcohol is added to remove most of the air from the flask and prevent absorption of carbon dioxide from the atmosphere. Because RCOOK is the only substance actually titrated, it is not necessary to standardize or measure accurately the rather viscous potassium hydroxide solution used. The blank to correct for carbonate in the potassium hydroxide needs to be checked only occasionally.

Ion exchange may also be usefully employed in conjunction with the saponification of esters.[15,16] After the saponification step the sample is diluted with water and passed through a cation exchange column in the hydrogen form. The excess potassium or sodium hydroxide is neutralized, and the carboxylate ion is converted to the free carboxylic acid. The carboxylic acid is titrated directly with standard

$$(11) \quad \left. \begin{array}{l} KOH \\ RCOOK \\ R'OH \\ K_2CO_3 \end{array} \right\} \xrightarrow[\text{catex}]{\text{H-form}} \left[\begin{array}{l} HOH \\ RCOOH \\ R'OH \\ H_2O + CO_2 \end{array} \right.$$

sodium hydroxide. Interference from any carbonate picked up during the saponification is avoided by boiling off the carbon dioxide before the titration.

This method possesses several definite advantages. It permits a higher ratio of caustic to sample, thus speeding the saponification. In the microdetermination of esters, Wiesenberger was able to increase the sodium hydroxide concentration used during saponification from 0.02 N to 0.5 N and thus reduce the digestion time from 1 hour to

[15] E. Wiesenberger, *Mikrochemie ver. Mikrochim. Acta*, **30**, 241 (1942).
[16] H. Tani and A. Nara, *J. Pharm. Soc. Japan*, **74**, 1399 (1954).

10 minutes.[15] It is not necessary to protect the solution from carbon dioxide during either the saponification or titration steps. Because only one direct titration is required, there is less chance for error than when the ester is determined by difference or where two neutralizations are required, as in the double-indicator method. It is also unnecessary to pipet accurately a viscous potassium hydroxide solution.

Although the ion exchange-saponification method has thus far been applied only to the microdetermination of esters, it should be equally applicable to the micro- and macrodetermination of amides and nitriles. Saponification of amides gives ammonia or amines, either of which are quantitatively removed by a cation exchange column in the hydrogen form. Nitriles give the same products as unsubstituted amides.

DETERMINATION OF OXIRANES (EPOXIDES)

In anhydrous media, hydrochloric acid will quantitatively convert compounds containing an oxirane ring to the corresponding chlorohydrin.

(12)
$$-\overset{|}{\underset{}{C}}\overset{}{\underset{\diagdown\!\diagup}{}}\overset{|}{\underset{}{C}}- + HCl \rightarrow -\overset{|}{\underset{|}{C}}\overset{}{}\overset{|}{\underset{|}{C}}-$$
$$OOH\quad Cl$$

In the method proposed by Nicolet and Poulter [17] and modified by Swern et al.,[18] a measured excess of 0.2 N anhydrous hydrogen chloride in ethyl ether is added to the sample in a glass-stoppered flask. When the reaction is complete (3 hours at room temperature), the mixture is diluted with ethanol and the excess hydrochloric acid is titrated with 0.1 N aqueous sodium hydroxide. The amount of oxirane is calculated by difference from this titration and from two blank determinations, which should agree to within 0.1 ml. of sodium hydroxide. It is also necessary to correct for any free acid in the sample.

This method is accurate to 1 or 2% and is selective. Analysis of a variety of compounds containing various functional groups indicates that no interference is caused by the following: primary and secondary alcohol, carbonyl, carboxyl, conjugated double bonds, isolated double bond, ester, glycol, organic peroxides and hydroperoxides, and epoxy compounds other than oxirane. The method seems to be especially useful for air oxidation mixtures where peroxide may also be present.

[17] B. H. Nicolet and T. C. Poulter, J. Am. Chem. Soc., 52, 1186 (1930).

[18] D. Swern, T. W. Findley, G. N. Billen, and J. T. Scanlan, Anal. Chem., 19, 414 (1947).

DIELS-ALDER REACTION

Anthracene will react quantitatively with maleic anhydride to form an addition product typical of the Diels-Alder reaction.

(13)

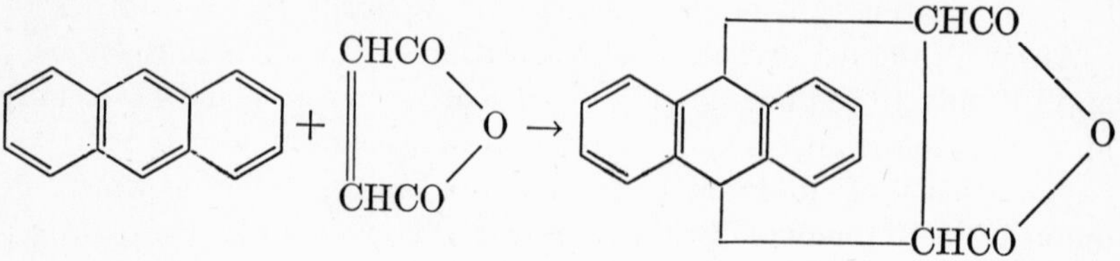

Ubaldini, Crespi, and Guerrieri [19] used this reaction in the quantitative determination of anthracene. A weighed amount of maleic anhydride is added to an approximately 1-gram sample of anthracene in 5 ml. of chlorobenzene. The solution is boiled for 20 to 25 minutes; then the excess maleic anhydride is extracted with several portions of hot water. The addition product is practically insoluble in water and is not extracted. The excess maleic anhydride is finally titrated with 0.2 N sodium hydroxide. This method gives good results for technical anthracene paste as well as for essentially pure samples of anthracene.

A very attractive general diene method has been suggested.[20] Chloromaleic anhydride is used as the reagent, and advantage is taken of the great ease of β-elimination from the product. The halogen in the reagent is eliminated only with difficulty.

(14)

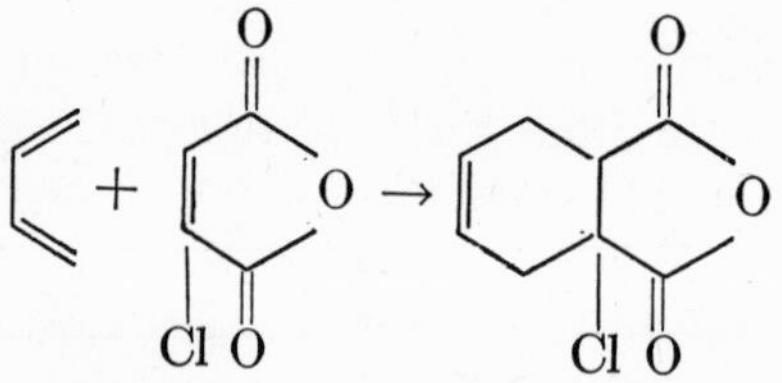

(15)

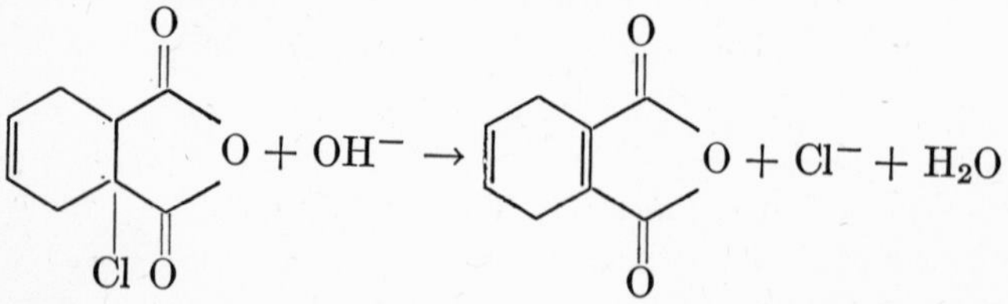

[19] I. Ubaldini, V. Crespi, and F. Guerrieri, *Ann. chim. appl.*, **39**, 77 (1949).

[20] S. T. Putnam, M. L. Moss, and R. T. Hall, *Ind. Eng. Chem., Anal. Ed.*, **18**, 628 (1946).

PERIODATE OXIDATIONS

The periodate oxidation method for vicinal diols discussed in Chapter 5 is selective and stoichiometric. When the extent of reaction is measured iodometrically, however, the amount of the substance oxidized is calculated from the rather small difference of two titrations (iodate plus excess periodate and titration of an aliquot of the original periodate). The acidimetric method of Dal Nogare and Oemler [21] for determination of vicinal hydroxyl groups with periodate largely avoids this difficulty.

In this method aqueous sodium periodate (pH 5) is used to oxidize vicinal glycols. Twenty minutes' reaction time is required for most compounds; ethylene glycol requires only 10 minutes. Sterically hindered substances react more slowly, and a preliminary trial is needed to check the time required for complete reaction. When oxidation is complete the temperature is brought to less than $1°$ C. with crushed ice, and the excess periodate is titrated with $0.1 N$ sodium hydroxide to the thymolphthalein end point. The reactions involved are as follows:

$$
(16) \quad
\begin{array}{c}
| \\
-C-OH \\
| \\
-C-OH \\
|
\end{array}
+ NaIO_4 \rightarrow 2 \rangle C{=}O + NaIO_3 + H_2O
$$

$$
(17) \quad NaIO_4 + 2H_2O \rightleftharpoons NaH_4IO_6
$$

$$
(18) \quad NaH_4IO_6 + NaOH \rightarrow Na_2H_3IO_6 + H_2O
$$

The end point is sharper at low temperature because the metaperiodate-paraperiodate equilibrium (equation 17) is shifted to the right by low temperatures.

Some compounds form acidic oxidation products which must be taken into account. Glycerol is oxidized by periodate to 2 moles of formaldehyde and 1 mole of formic acid. This formic acid may be titrated after adding excess pure ethylene glycol to reduce the periodate remaining after the original oxidation. The formic acid may be subtracted from the total acid found in the periodate titration, or the amount of glycerol can be based only on the formic acid titration.

This method gives excellent results for ethylene glycol, 1,2-propylene glycol, 2,3-butylene glycol, and glycerol, both for pure samples and

[21] S. Dal Nogare and A. N. Oemler, *Anal. Chem.*, **24**, 902 (1952).

for various combinations. The mean deviation obtained was ±0.3%.
Organic acids in the original sample can be compensated for in the
same manner as for formic acid formed during the oxidation. Weak
organic bases interfere.

UNSATURATION BY MERCURIC ACETATE ADDITION

Styrene and certain other types of unsaturated compounds will add
mercuric acetate quantitatively to the double bond. On the basis of
this reaction an analytical method applicable to the determination of
styrene and its derivatives was developed.[22] Das [23] has proposed a
somewhat simplified procedure which is also based on this reaction.
In his method, the sample is mixed with a measured aliquot of 0.25 N
mercuric acetate in methanol and allowed to react for 5 to 30 minutes
at room temperature. Then a propylene glycol-chloroform solvent mixture is added, and the excess mercuric acetate is titrated with standard
hydrochloric acid in propylene glycol. The mercury that is added to
the double bond also reacts with the hydrochloric acid. The unsatura-

(19) $-\overset{|}{C}=\overset{|}{C}- + (CH_3CO_2)_2Hg + CH_3OH \rightarrow$

$$-\overset{|}{\underset{OCH_3}{C}}-\overset{|}{\underset{HgOCOCH_3}{C}}- \quad + CH_3CO_2H$$

(20) $-\overset{|}{\underset{OCH_3}{C}}-\overset{|}{\underset{HgOCOCH_3}{C}}- \quad + HCl \rightarrow$

$$-\overset{|}{\underset{OCH_3}{C}}-\overset{|}{\underset{HgCl}{C}}- \quad + CH_3CO_2H$$

(21) $(CH_3CO_2)_2Hg + 2HCl \rightarrow HgCl_2 + 2CH_3CO_2H$

tion present may be calculated from the difference of the amount of
hydrochloric acid required to titrate a reagent blank (reaction 21)
and that required to titrate the sum of the mercuric acetate addition
compound (reaction 20) and the excess reagent (reaction 21). This
method gives excellent results for styrene, cyclohexene, allyl alcohol,
allyl acetate, and vinyl acetate, but fails for α-methylstyrene, cinnamic
acid, and diisobutylene because of the instability of the addition prod-

---

[22] R. P. Marquardt and E. N. Luce, *Anal. Chem.*, **20**, 751 (1948); **21**, 1194 (1949).
[23] M. N. Das, *Anal. Chem.*, **26**, 1086 (1954).

ucts. The reaction provides a useful supplement to bromination (Chapter 5) and hydrogenation (Chapter 6) as a method for unsaturation.

DECARBOXYLATION

A simple method for the titrimetric assay of sodium trichloroacetate, trichloroacetic acid, and esters of trichloroacetic acid employs an indirect acid-base titration.[24] The method is based on the decarboxylation of trichloroacetic acid. In the presence of dilute sulfuric acid this reaction is complete in 1 hour.

$$(22) \qquad CCl_3CO_2^- + H_3O^+ \xrightarrow[H_2O]{100° C.} CHCl_3 + CO_2 + H_2O$$

A dioxane-water solution of the sample is first neutralized with sulfuric acid or sodium hydroxide to pH 5.3 to 5.5. A measured excess of sulfuric acid is then added to sodium trichloroacetate to provide the acidic conditions necessary for the decarboxylation. When the reaction is complete, the excess sulfuric acid is titrated with a standard base. In this method sodium dichloroacetate and sodium monochloroacetate can be tolerated in amounts up to 32% and 9.5%, respectively. Small amounts of sodium bicarbonate or phosphate may also be present without causing interference.

The same principle used in the trichloroacetic acid determination should be applicable for the determination of many β-keto acids and other unstable carboxylic acids. For example, a frequently used assay for acetone dicarboxylic acid takes advantage of the decarboxylation of that compound under mild conditions.

$$(23) \qquad HO_2C—CH_2COCH_2—CO_2H \rightarrow CH_3COCH_3 + 2CO_2$$

The acetone dicarboxylic acid content of the sample is calculated from the difference of alkalimetric titration of aliquots before and after decarboxylation.

DETERMINATION OF CARBOXYLIC ACID ANHYDRIDES

Reaction of a carboxylic acid anhydride with a primary or secondary amine serves as the basis of a method for determining anhydrides in the presence of carboxylic acids. In one procedure the anhydride is reacted with a standard solution of morpholine in methanol,[25] as shown in reaction 24. In most cases this reaction requires only 5 minutes at room temperature. The excess morpholine is then titrated with hydro-

[24] W. A. Schneider, Jr., and L. E. Streeter, *Anal. Chem.*, **27**, 1774 (1955).
[25] J. B. Johnson and G. L. Funk, *Anal. Chem.*, **27**, 1464 (1955).

(24) $(RC)_2O$ + H—N⟨ ⟩O ⟶ RC—N⟨ ⟩O + RC—OH

chloric acid in methanol. Morpholine is a moderately strong base and can be titrated sharply even in the presence of carboxylic acids.

DETERMINATION OF ISOCYANATES AND ISOTHIOCYANATES

Isocyanates and isothiocyanates will react with aliphatic amines, forming substituted ureas or thioureas.

(25) $RN{=}C{=}O + R'NH_2 \rightarrow RNHCONHR'$

(26) $RN{=}C{=}S + R'NH_2 \rightarrow RNHCSNHR'$

In the method of Siggia and Hanna [26] a measured excess of standard butylamine in dioxane is added to the sample of isocyanate or iso-thiocyanate to be analyzed. Alkyl derivatives of isocyanates require 45 minutes at room temperature for complete reaction, but the aromatic isocyanates react almost immediately. After the reaction is complete, water is added and the excess butylamine is titrated with standard acid.

OTHER METHODS

Many organic halides will react with bases. The reaction undergone is usually dehydrohalogenation, displacement, or a combination of the two, as shown in reactions 27 and 28. The fact that a reaction

(27) $-\overset{|}{\underset{\underset{H}{|}}{C}}-\overset{|}{\underset{|}{C}}-X \xrightarrow{OCH_3^-} -\overset{|}{C}{=}\overset{|}{C} + X^- + CH_3OH$

(28) $-\overset{|}{\underset{\underset{H}{|}}{C}}-\overset{|}{\underset{\underset{H}{|}}{C}}-X \xrightarrow{OCH_3^-} -\overset{|}{\underset{\underset{H}{|}}{C}}-\overset{|}{\underset{|}{C}}-OCH_3 + X^-$

may proceed partly by reaction 27 and partly by reaction 28 may be frustrating to the preparative organic chemist, but this need not concern the analytical chemist since the same amount of base is consumed in either case. By proper choice of experimental conditions it is possible to achieve considerable selectivity in the determination of organic halides by this scheme. This subject is discussed in some detail in Chapter 9.

[26] S. Siggia and J. G. Hanna, *Anal. Chem.*, **20**, 1084 (1948).

Some organic compounds that react with metal ions are measured by indirect acid-base methods. These methods are considered in Chapter 7.

PROBLEMS

1. Compound A contains only C, H, and O and is a high-boiling (179°) liquid. A sample weighing 0.900 gram is treated with 10 ml. of 2.00 M acetic anhydride in pyridine. After 1 hour on the steam bath the solution is titrated with 1.000 N NaOH requiring 30.0 ml. A second sample of A weighing 0.200 gram is treated with excess LiAlH$_4$ in dibutyl ether (see active hydrogen determination in Chapter 6). A total of 51.5 ml. of hydrogen was evolved at 25° C. and 740 mm.

What do you consider to be the probable structure of the compound? Can you suggest another determination that might serve to confirm your hypothesis?

2. How would you determine the composition of a mixture of n-butylamines known to contain R$_3$N, R$_2$NH, and RNH$_2$? Consider first a general method, and then consider the special case in which it is especially desirable to determine directly a small amount of the tertiary amine in the mixture.

3. Why does diethyl ketone interfere with the determination of an aldehyde by the bisulfite method despite the fact that the former cannot itself be determined by the procedure?

4. By consultation of the original literature describing the preparation of phthalides by the reaction:

evaluate this reaction as a possible means of determining primary amines in the presence of secondary amines.

5. Devise a procedure for determining the amounts of cyclohexene and 1,3-cyclohexadiene present in a benzene solution.

6. In determining the saponification equivalent of C$_6$H$_5$CH(Cl)CO$_2$Et, different results are obtained by the single-indicator and double-indicator methods. Explain.

5.

OXIDATIVE

AND

REDUCTIVE METHODS

INTRODUCTION

Redox reactions do not occupy the same unique position in organic analysis as they do in inorganic. Most oxidations and reductions of organic compounds are irreversible in the electrochemical sense. This means that mixtures of the oxidized and reduced forms do not give interpretable electrode readings and that most oxidations and reductions of organic materials are measurably slow reactions. As a consequence, the definition of terms occasionally becomes somewhat arbitrary. A familiar example is demonstrated by the following sequence of transformations:

(1) $$RCH{=}NOH \xrightarrow{-H_2O} RC{\equiv}N$$

(2) $$RC{\equiv}N \xrightarrow{+2H_2O} RCO_2H + NH_3$$

(3) $$RCH{=}NOH \xrightarrow{+H_2O} RCHO + NH_2OH$$

Each of the individual reactions would probably be referred to as a dehydration or a hydrolysis. However, comparison of the products of reactions 2 and 3 reveals that nitrogen and carbon are in different oxidation states in the products of the two reactions. Reaction

1 could be defined as a redox reaction in which the nitrogen atom is reduced and the carbon oxidized. It is of no great import that we do this as long as we do not maintain that it is necessary to use a completely rigorous terminology. In the ensuing discussion we shall adopt the pragmatic view that reactions that consume easily recognizable inorganic oxidants or reductants are respectively oxidations or reductions of the organic substrate.

REVERSIBLE SYSTEMS

Quinone-hydroquinone couples constitute the best-known and most common class of electrochemically reversible, organic redox systems.

The oxidation of a hydroquinone occurs in steps, and in alkaline solution the intermediate semiquinone may be stable enough to accumulate in solution.[1] This leads to the appearance of two inflection points in the potentiometric titration curves for some quinones (or the corresponding hydroquinones) but presents no serious complication in their

[1] L. Michaelis, *Chem. Revs.*, **16**, 242 (1935).

determination. Neglecting the semiquinone, the over-all oxidation is represented by equation 7.

(7) $$H_2Q \rightleftharpoons Q + 2H^+ + 2e$$

Since hydrogen ions are produced in the electrode reaction, it is necessary to control the pH of the media in which quinones or hydroquinones are to be titrated in order to obtain reproducible end-point behavior. Unless the system contains other sensitive functional groups, the choice of a titrant may be made on the basis of the standard potential for the particular couple that is to be determined. Many values for the oxidation potentials of representative quinones have been reported in the literature.[2] Since semiquinones and quinhydrones (1:1 molecular complexes of a quinone and a hydroquinone) often impart deep colors to partially titrated solutions, the determinations are often most conveniently carried out by potentiometric titration.

Other closely related compounds show similar reversible redox behavior and may be considered essentially equivalent to quinone-hydroquinone couples. The nitrogen analogues of hydroquinones, ortho and para aminophenols, and ortho and para arylenediamines are oxidized rapidly and reversibly. However, the ready hydrolysis of the quinonimine oxidation products makes solutions of the oxidized form unstable toward conversion of the corresponding quinones. This does not affect the stoichiometry of the oxidation step. These compounds, as are certain hydroquinones, are usually rather susceptible to air oxidation, which may constitute a serious interference in the determination of micro amounts unless proper precautions are taken.

Some dye stuffs such as methylene blue (I) can be reversibly reduced to their corresponding leuco bases. The same is true of some of

(8)

I

[2] G. E. K. Branch and M. Calvin, *Theoretical Organic Chemistry*, Prentice-Hall Co., New York, 1941, p. 303.

the related triphenylmethane dyes. This behavior constitutes a valuable method for the determination of either the dyes or the leuco bases.

THE HALOGENS

The halogens and certain of their close relatives have found frequent use in organic analysis. Bromine is a particularly satisfactory reagent, since it is sufficiently active to react rapidly with a rather large number of unsaturated compounds but reacts only slowly with most saturated centers unless they are adjacent to various unsaturated functional groups. Furthermore, catalysis by Lewis acids speeds up many reactions of bromine, which permits the achievement of both versatility and selectivity. In addition, standard bromide-bromate solutions, which release bromine upon addition of acid, are indefinitely stable; and the determination of excess bromine by iodometric assay is both easy and accurate if proper procedures are used.

Difficulty frequently arises in the use of starch-iodine end points in solutions that contain large amounts of organic materials. The end-point color is brown instead of the familiar blue, and the end-point change becomes very gradual. This problem can usually be solved by diluting the titration mixture with a considerable excess of water as the end point is approached. Another problem arises from the presence of a second organic phase in the titration mixture. Iodine is much more soluble in many organic solvents than it is in water, and errors can arise either because of slow extraction or because an appreciable amount of iodine remains in the oil phase after an end point, as indicated by disappearance of the starch-iodine color in the aqueous phase, has been reached. This problem can usually be circumvented by adding a large amount of iodide to the aqueous phase. The formation of I_3^- effects a much more favorable distribution of iodine between the two phases.

Olefins

Most olefins add bromine stoichiometrically according to equation 9. The addition of chlorine takes place similarly but is frequently ac-

$$(9) \qquad \text{>C=C< + Br}_2 \rightarrow \begin{array}{c} | \quad | \\ -C-C- \\ | \quad | \\ Br \ Br \end{array}$$

companied by some substitution. The addition of iodine also occurs but the equilibrium constants for iodine addition are small enough to render the reaction analytically incomplete. Interhalogen compounds, such as

ICl, add satisfactorily and have been used for the determination of unsaturation. However, the operational convenience in the use of bromine is such as to make it the reagent of choice for nearly all determinations.

The reactivity of olefins in bromine addition varies widely.[3] Alkenes, dienes, vinyl esters, and aryl ethylenes (such as styrene) all react very rapidly. On the other hand, the reactions of double bonds which are conjugated with unsaturated, electron-withdrawing groups such as

$$\rangle C{=}O, \quad -C\overset{\displaystyle O}{\underset{\displaystyle OH}{\diagup}}, \quad -C\overset{\displaystyle O}{\underset{\displaystyle OR}{\diagup}}, \quad -C{\equiv}N, \quad -NO_2, \quad \text{and} \quad \rangle SO_2 \quad \text{react}$$

much more slowly. Addition to the latter group can be accelerated by Lewis acids such as aluminum bromide, mercuric ion, and silver ion as catalysts. Excellent procedures [4,5] have been developed utilizing mercuric sulfate as a catalyst. Superficially, the catalytic effect can be explained by the following equations:

$$(10) \qquad\qquad Br_2 + Hg^{++} \rightleftharpoons [Hg{-}Br{-}Br]^{++}$$

$$(11) \quad [Hg{-}Br{-}Br]^{++} + \rangle C{=}C\langle \rightarrow HgBr^+ + Br{-}\overset{|}{C}{-}\overset{+}{\underset{|}{C}}{-}$$

Reaction 11 is much more rapid than the corresponding reaction 12,

$$(12) \qquad\qquad Br_2 + \rangle C{=}C\langle \rightarrow Br^- + Br{-}\overset{|}{C}{-}\overset{+}{\underset{|}{C}}{-}$$

of free bromine. However, mercuric ion can also form complexes with other basic species including olefins. The most stable complexes are formed from the olefins that are most reactive toward halogens. As a consequence, the rate of halogen addition to such compounds may actually be *slowed down* in the presence of the mercuric ion. A dramatic example of these effects has been reported by Bartlett and Nozaki.[6] They found that it was possible to determine allyl acetate and maleic anhydride individually in mixtures of the two olefins. Bromination in the absence of mercuric ion gave stoichiometric recov-

[3] C. K. Ingold, *Structure and Mechanism in Organic Chemistry*, Cornell University Press, Ithaca, N. Y., 1953, Chapter 12.

[4] S. Siggia, *Quantitative Organic Analysis via Functional Groups*, Wiley, New York, 1954, p. 68.

[5] H. J. Lucas and D. Pressman, *Ind. Eng. Chem., Anal. Ed.*, **10**, 140 (1938).

[6] P. D. Bartlett and K. Nozaki, *J. Am. Chem. Soc.*, **68**, 1495 (1946).

ery of the allyl acetate. In order to determine maleic anhydride, it was necessary to add mercuric ion after the complete bromination of allyl acetate. The maleic anhydride was then brominated quantitatively. If mercuric ion was added initially, low results were obtained because of the incomplete bromination of allyl acetate.

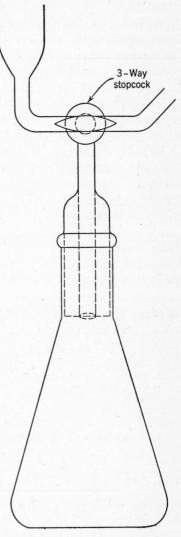

Since the determinations were carried out in acetic anhydride as a solvent, allyl acetate may have been partially converted to the acetoxy mercuric derivative, $CH_3CO_2HgCH_2$-$CH(O_2CCH_3)CH_2O_2CCH_3$. This is another factor, in addition to complexing, that can lead to low results in the mercuric catalyzed reaction in some solvents.

If the nature of the olefinic material is known, best results will generally be obtained if mercuric ion is used only in the determination of olefins whose reactions are too slow to permit their estimation by the uncatalyzed reaction. If total unsaturation is to be determined in a sample of unknown composition, the catalyzed reaction will generally be chosen. However, it is worth noting that the application of both procedures will often supply additional information which may be helpful in characterization problems.

Since photobromination of the solvent at saturated centers or of the olefin itself, especially at allylic positions, may become fast enough to introduce errors, bromine additions

Figure 11. Bromination flask.

are usually carried out in the dark. This is easily done by using a painted flask or by wrapping a dark cloth about an ordinary flask. Another useful precaution is the use of a brominating flask such as that shown in Fig. 11. The flask is partially evacuated before the addition of the bromide-bromate mixture which can then be sucked into the flask. The reaction is carried out in a closed system which prohibits loss of excess bromine by volatilization.

In the choice of solvent, care must be taken to avoid materials that react readily with bromine. Carbon tetrachloride, acetic acid, acetic anhydride, benzene, and pyridine have all been used successfully. Alcohols and ketones are not recommended as solvents.

Interference is to be expected from any of the materials whose determination by bromination is discussed below. Determinations can be carried out in the presence of small amounts of ketones and alcohols if the olefin reacts rapidly so that the reaction time can be kept brief.

Iodine and interhalogen compounds have also been used traditionally for the determination of unsaturation, and the iodine number of fats is defined as the centigrams of iodine equivalent to 1 gram of sample. Iodine additions are not really very satisfactory because of the reversibility of the reaction, and the determination of a specific compound requires calibration and strict adherence to specified reaction conditions. Occasionally, advantages over bromination can be realized because the lower reactivity of iodine allows one to avoid interference from side reactions.

Iodine solutions can be used either in carbon tetrachloride or in aqueous potassium iodide.[7] The Hanus method[8] employs a solution of iodine monobromide in acetic acid. Wijs solution contains iodine chloride and is used in much the same way.

Aromatic Amines and Phenols

Compounds of this type substitute rapidly in the positions ortho and para to the amino or hydroxyl group. The reaction is exceedingly

(13)

rapid and is of great value, particularly in characterization studies as it counts the open, activated positions. Occasionally groups other

[7] W. W. Scott, *Standard Methods of Chemical Analysis*, 5th ed., N. H. Furman, Editor, Van Nostrand Co., New York, 1939, p. 1767.

[8] S. Siggia, *Quantitative Analysis via Functional Groups*, p. 72.

than hydrogen are displaced. Carboxyl groups are lost with particular ease, and the sulfonic acid function may also be displaced. The presence of strongly deactivating groups is not sufficient to prevent reaction as is evidenced by the fact that p-nitrophenol consumes two equivalents of bromine rapidly and cleanly. The substitution of electron-accepting functions on the nitrogen does, however, decrease the reactivity. As an example of this behavior, we can cite the use of bromination to follow the rate of reaction 14. Aniline can be bromi-

(14)

nated quantitatively in the presence of the reaction product.[9] Similarly, the attachment of an acyl group to the oxygen or nitrogen, as in aryl esters or anilides, renders the compounds sufficiently unreactive to ruin the analytical accuracy of the reaction. Such compounds can be determined if they are hydrolyzed before bromination.[10]

Enols

One of the best-known applications of analytical bromination is the Kurt Meyer determination of the enol content of β-diketones and β-keto esters.[11] The determination cannot be carried out in the usual manner because the keto $\rightleftharpoons$ enol interconversion is rather rapid and is catalyzed by the acid produced in bromination. The best procedure involves quenching the reaction by adding an excess of β-naphthol, which will react with all excess bromine. The amount of bromoketone that has been formed is then determined by virtue of the fact that such compounds are reduced by hydrogen iodide. The equations for the reactions involved when the reaction is applied to acetoacetic ester are as follows:

(15) $CH_3COCH_2CO_2C_2H_5 \rightleftharpoons$

[9] N. B. Chapman and R. E. Parker, *J. Chem. Soc.*, **1951**, 33-1.
[10] G. Hammond and D. Thornburg, unpublished observations.
[11] K. H. Meyer, *Ber.*, **45**, 2843 (1912).

(16)

$$\rightarrow CH_3\overset{O}{\underset{\|}{C}}CHBrCO_2C_2H_5 + HBr$$

(with structure: chelate ring structure with H, O, O, C, C, CH₃, CH, OC₂H₅ + Br₂)

(17) $CH_3COCHBrCO_2C_2H_5 + 2HI \rightarrow$

$$CH_3COCH_2CO_2C_2H_5 + 2I_2 + HBr$$

(18) (naphthol structure) $+ Br_2 \rightarrow$ (bromonaphthol structure) $OH + HBr$

In careful work a correction is made for overestimation due to the enolization of the keto form during the reaction. This is done by taking several points at different bromination times and extrapolating the values to zero contact time. In a determination of the sum of the enol and keto forms, longer contact times are used and the determination is ordinarily not very satisfactory because of the slow formation of dibromoketones. The total analysis is, therefore, much easier to carry out by the formation of a metal chelate (see Chapter 7) or titration as an acid in a nonaqueous solvent.

Sulfur Compounds

Most sulfur compounds, except sulfonic acids and their esters, sulfonamides, and sulfones, which are already in the highest state of oxidation that can be achieved without breaking carbon-sulfur bonds, are oxidized rapidly by the halogens. Bromine and chlorine convert most other compounds more or less rapidly to the highest possible oxidation state. Iodine, on the other hand, oxidizes mercaptans smoothly and rapidly to disulfides (equation 19) but does not affect most other sulfur species. Iodometric titration is, therefore, an excellent procedure for the determination of mercaptans.[12]

(19) $2RSH + 2I_2 \rightarrow RSSR + 2HI$

The other halogens may be used satisfactorily in other determina-

[12] S. Siggia, *Quantitative Analysis via Functional Groups*, p. 131.

tions involving either partial or complete oxidation. Thus, dialkyl sulfides may be estimated either by partial oxidation to sulfoxides [13] or by exhaustive oxidation to sulfones with bromine as the oxidant. The second stage of the oxidation is much slower than the first, a fact that accounts for there being a choice as to procedure. With reasonably reactive compounds, the best precision is probably attainable in complete oxidation if the analyst deems the longer time involved to be justified by the problem. Interferences from other compounds or other functional groups in the same compound are, of course, more serious if complete oxidation is attempted. The equations for the transformations are as follows:

$$(20) \qquad R_2S + Br_2 + H_2O \rightarrow R_2S{\rightarrow}O + 2HBr$$

$$(21) \qquad R_2S{\rightarrow}O + Br_2 + H_2O \rightarrow R_2S\underset{\searrow O}{\overset{\nearrow O}{}} + 2HBr$$

Diaryl sulfides and heterocyclic compounds such as thiophene do not give good results because of the unreactive nature of the sulfur atoms and the competition from substitution in the activated aromatic nuclei. These two properties are related, as the activation of the nuclei is attributable to the interaction of the nonbonding sulfur electrons with the unsaturated systems as indicated by resonance structures such as IV.

Disulfides may be determined by oxidative bromination. They are cleaved to the sulfonyl bromides in the presence of strong mineral acids.[14] The reaction is carried out in water or in an acetic acid-water solvent. The bromine is liberated from a standard bromide-bromate

$$(22) \qquad RSSR + 5Br_2 + 4H_2O \xrightarrow{H^+} 2RSO_2Br + 8HBr$$

mixture by the technique described previously.

[13] S. Siggia, *Quantitative Analysis via Functional Groups*, p. 138.
[14] S. Siggia, *Quantitative Analysis via Functional Groups*, p. 141.

Since this procedure does not discriminate between disulfides and other sulfur compounds, it is sometimes convenient to determine the former by reduction to mercaptans followed by titration of the mercaptan by iodine (p. 84) or by silver ion (p. 91). If mercaptans are also present in the sample, they must be determined by a blank analysis. The reduction step has been carried out by passing a solution of the disulfide in acidic ethanol through zinc amalgam (0.02% with respect to mercury) in a Jones reductor.[15]

It is to be expected that additional oxidative procedures for other sulfur compounds will be developed in the future. It would be particularly useful to have available specific methods for the determination of the aromatic sulfur heterocycles.

Iodoform Reaction

The determination of ketones by halogenation does not seem to be generally practical. Polybromination occurs without satisfactory decreases in the reaction rates occurring between the successive steps of the reactions. By kinetic methods (see Chapter 9) it might be possible to determine the bromine requirement for monobromination. With a variety of excellent methods available, there seems to be little point in an attempt to develop such a procedure for any but very specialized applications. The situation is different with methyl ketones, which undergo the haloform reaction. The conversion of these compounds to iodoform by alkaline solutions of iodine shows reliable stoichiometry according to equation 23.

$$(23) \quad RCOCH_3 + 3I_2 + 4OH^- \rightarrow RCO_2^- + HCI_3 + 3I^- + 3H_2O$$

The reaction can be monitored by colorimetric determination[16] of the iodoform produced or by back titration of excess iodine after acidification of the reaction mixtures.[17] The method is also applicable to the determination of acetaldehyde and alcohols such as ethanol and isopropanol which are oxidized to give acetaldehyde or methyl ketones.

Aldehydes

Glucose has been determined by oxidation with iodine to gluconic acid.[18]

[15] I. M. Kolthoff, et al., Ind. Eng. Chem., Anal. Ed., **18**, 442 (1946).

[16] S. Dal Nogare, T. O. Norris, and J. Mitchell, Anal. Chem., **23**, 1473 (1951).

[17] J. Messinger, Ber., **21**, 3366 (1888).

[18] O. Spengler, F. Todt, and R. Ismer, Z. Wirtshaftsgruppe Zuckerind., **87**, Tech. Tl., 559 (1937).

$$(24) \quad \begin{matrix} \text{CHO} \\ | \\ \text{(CHOH)}_4 \\ | \\ \text{CH}_2\text{OH} \end{matrix} + \text{I}_2 + 2\text{OH}^- \rightarrow \begin{matrix} \text{CO}_2^- \\ | \\ \text{(CHOH)}_4 \\ | \\ \text{CH}_2\text{OH} \end{matrix} + 2\text{I}^- + \text{H}_2\text{O}$$

Similar procedures have not been developed for aldehydes in general, but it is likely that the method could be applied to compounds such as trimethylacetaldehyde and benzaldehyde which do not have active α-hydrogens.

PERACIDS AND HYDROGEN PEROXIDE

The organic peracids have been found to be versatile oxidizing agents in organic synthesis, and it is probable that they will find a similar wide application in analytical work. At the present time very few successful applications have been developed. For the most part, the oxidations that have been studied are inconveniently slow, and the peracids undergo decomposition at such a rate as to necessitate the determination and use of fairly large blank corrections. However, Emmons and his co-workers [19] have reported a new reagent, peroxytrifluoroacetic acid, which carries out many oxidations very rapidly and in high yield. The epoxidation of even α,β-unsaturated acids is very rapid, as is the oxidation of ketones. Even unreactive aromatic amines can be converted smoothly to nitro compounds. It might be anticipated that such a versatile reagent would not be selective enough for analytical use. However, the reactivity of the reagent mixture can be controlled by the amount of water present. The reagent is formed by the addition of trifluoroacetic acid (or its anhydride) to hydrogen peroxide.

$$(25) \quad \text{CF}_3\text{CO}_2\text{H} + \text{H}_2\text{O}_2 \rightleftharpoons \text{CF}_3\text{CO}_3\text{H} + \text{H}_2\text{O}$$

A definite deficiency in the reagent for analytical purposes arises from its high volatility. This can perhaps be remedied by the use of the higher perfluoroperacids or by conducting analyses in closed systems.

In view of the potential development in the general field, it is worth while to consider previous analytical work even though results are not impressive at the present time.

Two reactions of perbenzoic acid have been studied by kinetic methods. They are the epoxidation of olefins, equation 26, and the

[19] W. D. Emmons, A. S. Pagano, and J. P. Freeman, *J. Am. Chem. Soc.*, **76**, 3472 (1954).

oxidation of ketones to esters, equation 27. The epoxides formed in

(26) $C_6H_5CO_3H + \,\rangle C{=}C\langle \rightarrow C_6H_5CO_2H + \,\rangle C\underset{O}{\overbrace{}}C\langle$

(27) $C_6H_5CO_3H + RCOR' \rightarrow C_6H_5CO_2H + RCO_2R'$

the olefin reaction do not always survive as such but may undergo ring opening in hydroxylic solvents. This has no effect upon the stoichiometry of the consumption of the peracid. The reaction is catalyzed by acids and with polyalkyl substituted olefins becomes quite rapid.[20] However, those olefins that can be determined easily with perbenzoic acid are those that give best results in the uncatalyzed reaction with bromine (see p. 79). Electron-withdrawing substituents decrease the rates of reaction of the olefinic linkage.

As a potential method for ketones, peracid oxidation is more promising than bromination. The first product of the reaction is inert toward the reagent, and the specific rates of oxidation of typical ketones are similar to those of moderately reactive olefins. The reactions are acid catalyzed.[21] In verification of the analytical expectation, Hawthorne has found that aliphatic ketones are easily determined with peroxytrifluoroacetic acid.[22]

Reactive aromatic nuclei are hydroxylated by perbenzoic acid,[23] and even benzene is attacked by peroxytrifluoroacetic acid.[24] Polyhydroxylation occurs because of the increase in reactivity caused by the introduction of a phenolic hydroxyl. As a result, it is doubtful that aromatic hydroxylation will be of any analytical importance. Aromatic compounds may, however, give interference in the determination of other compounds.[22]

Hydrogen peroxide oxidizes many organic compounds and is reactive under both acidic and alkaline conditions. None of the common reactions show much analytical promise. The oxidation of alcohols with Fenton's reagent, ferrous ion, and hydrogen peroxide has been studied rather thoroughly.[25] Stoichiometric relationships are not very definite, but some use might be made of the method in analysis for

[20] D. Swern, *J. Am. Chem. Soc.*, **69**, 1692 (1947).

[21] Y. Yukawa and T. Yokayama, *J. Chem. Soc. Japan, Pure Chem. Sect.*, **73**, 371 (1952).

[22] M. F. Hawthorne, *Anal. Chem.*, **28**, 540 (1956).

[23] S. L. Fries and A. Miller, *J. Am. Chem. Soc.*, **72**, 2611 (1950).

[24] W. D. Emmons, private communication.

[25] I. M. Kolthoff and A. I. Medalia, *Anal. Chem.*, **23**, 595 (1951).

special applications since the results of the kinetic studies could be utilized in setting up an empirical method.

Hydrogen peroxide has been used in the determination of formaldehyde.[26] Hydrogen is produced in a rather remarkable reaction.

(28) $2HCHO + 2OH^- + H_2O_2 \rightarrow 2HCO_2^- + 2H_2O + H_2$

The reaction has been followed by titration of the strong base consumed and by volumetric measurement of the hydrogen produced.[27] Other aldehydes undergo similar reactions and, therefore, constitute an interference in the determination of formaldehyde.

A general restriction in operation is worth keeping in mind in any attempts to work out methods based upon peroxide oxidations. All peroxidic compounds undergo thermal decomposition to give free radicals.[28] The reactions of these fragments are quite different from those of the parent compounds. For this reason, no more than gentle heating should be used in attempting to accelerate analytical reactions.

All determinations with peroxidic compounds are conveniently completed by iodometric analysis. The assay solution is added to an excess of potassium iodide in either aqueous acid or glacial acetic acid solution, and the iodine released is titrated with standard thiosulfate.

SPECIFIC GLYCOL REAGENTS

Three reagents are known that show specific action in oxidizing glycols to carbonyl compounds. They are metaperiodic acid, lead tetraacetate, and cerium[IV] reagents. Their action is represented by equations 29, 30, and 31.

(29) $H_5IO_6 + \underset{\underset{OH}{|}}{-C}\underset{\underset{OH}{|}}{-C-} \rightarrow HIO_3 + 2\rangle C{=}O + 3H_2O$

(30) $Pb(OAc)_4 + \underset{\underset{OH}{|}}{-C}\underset{\underset{OH}{|}}{-C-} \rightarrow Pb(OAc)_2 + 2\rangle C{=}O + 2HOAc$

(31) $2Ce^{IV} + \underset{\underset{OH}{|}}{-C}\underset{\underset{OH}{|}}{-C-} \rightarrow 2Ce^{III} + 2H^+ + 2\rangle C{=}O$

[26] O. Blank and H. Finkenbeiner, *Ber.*, **31**, 2974 (1898); **32**, 81 (1899).
[27] G. B. Frankforter and R. West, *J. Am. Chem. Soc.*, **27**, 714 (1905).
[28] J. E. Leffler, *Chem. Revs.*, **45**, 385 (1949).

Metaperiodic acid has been used very frequently for the determination of water-soluble glycols, especially in the carbohydrate field. The reactions are usually rapid, although Duke and Bulgrin [29] have found that pinacol is much slower than most of its analogues. Generally satisfactory results are obtained by allowing the glycol and the reagent to stand in aqueous solution for 10 to 15 minutes. Iodide is then added, and the periodate and iodate are both reduced to iodine. The difference between the observed titer and that calculated for the

(32) $8H^+ + IO_4^- + 7I^- \rightarrow 4I_2 + 4H_2O$

(33) $6H^+ + IO_3^- + 5I^- \rightarrow 3I_2 + 3H_2O$

original charge gives the amount consumed by the glycol. Alternatively, the excess periodate may be determined by titration as an acid at low temperature (Chapter 4). Lead tetraacetate has received little attention as an analytical reagent but should complement metaperiodic acid uniquely since it is applicable to the determination of water-insoluble glycols. A considerable amount of kinetic work [30] has been devoted to the study of the mechanism of the cleavage, and the results assure us that most glycols can be oxidized reasonably rapidly at ordinary temperatures. The rate-controlling step of the reaction is probably decomposition of a cyclic ester of the glycol.

(34)
$$\begin{array}{ccc} >C & --- & C< \\ | & & | \\ O & & O \\ & \diagdown \diagup & \\ & Pb & \\ \diagup & & \diagdown \\ OAc & & OAc \end{array} \rightarrow\; >C{=}O + O{=}C< + Pb(OAc)_2$$

Acetic acid is the medium of choice for the determination, and the reagent can be prepared and kept for some time in this solvent. However, slow, spontaneous decomposition occurs, and the solution must be restandardized frequently. The oxidation usually requires a period of several hours for complete reaction, and it is advisable to run a blank simultaneously in order to correct for the small amount of decomposition of the reagent during the reaction period. The solutions should not be heated because increasing temperature accelerates the decomposition rather strongly. An application to the determination of benzpinacol is discussed in Chapter 13.

[29] F. R. Duke and V. Bulgrin, *J. Am. Chem. Soc.*, **76**, 3803 (1954).
[30] R. Criegee and E. Büchner, *Ber.*, **738**, 563 (1940); R. Criegee, E. Büchner, and W. Walther, *Ibid.*, 571 (1940).

A third reagent that is capable of cleaving 1,2-diols is cerium^{IV} in perchloric or sulfuric acid solution.[31] Other compounds such as α- and β-diketones, malonic ester, and malic acid are also oxidized smoothly. The end products are formic acid and ketones, with the latter being produced when there is no hydrogen attached to one or both of the hydroxylated carbon atoms. The following are examples of the stoichiometric relationships that are obtained:

(35)
$$\begin{array}{c} CH_2OH \\ | \\ CHOH \\ | \\ CH_2OH \end{array} + 8Ce^{+4} + 3H_2O \rightarrow 3HCO_2H + 8Ce^{+3} + 8H^+$$

(36)
$$\begin{array}{c} CH_3 \quad OH \\ \diagdown \quad | \\ C-CH_2OH + 4Ce^{+4} + H_2O \rightarrow \\ \diagup \\ CH_3 \end{array}$$

$$(CH_3)_2CO + HCO_2H + 4Ce^{+3} + 4H^+$$

OTHER INORGANIC OXIDANTS

Although periodic acid and lead tetraacetate, as was discussed above, are highly specific in their action as oxidants, most inorganic reagents are less discriminating in their action. For this reason, the powerful inorganic oxidants have not found wide application in organic analysis. A limited number of useful methods based upon their use have been developed.

Ammoniacal Silver (Tollen's Reagent)

Ammoniacal silver has been used successfully for the quantitative determination of aldehydes. The reaction is the same as that involved in the familiar qualitative test for aldehydes. Aliphatic aldehydes give good results, but the method is unsuited for aromatic aldehydes

(37) $RCHO + 2Ag(NH_3)_2{}^+ + 3OH^- \rightarrow$

$$RCO_2{}^- + 2Ag^0 + 2NH_3 + 2H_2O$$

in general although furfural gives satisfactory results.[32]

The standard solution must be made up freshly by dissolving silver

[31] G. F. Smith and F. R. Duke, *Ind. Eng. Chem., Anal. Ed.*, **13**, 558 (1941); G. F. Smith and F. R. Duke, *Ibid.*, **15**, 120 (1943).

[32] S. Siggia, *Quantitative Analysis via Functional Groups*, p. 32.

oxide in ammonium hydroxide. A known amount is added to the assay sample, and after 10 to 20 minutes at room temperature the excess silver ion is titrated potentiometrically with potassium iodide, using a silver indicator electrode. A calomel electrode is used as a reference.

Cupric Copper

Fehling's solution, which is a solution of cupric copper in alkaline tartrate, and other soluble cupric complex ions are familiar from their use in characterization work and have been applied to the quantitative determination of aldehydes, especially the reducing sugars. As is indicated by equation 38, the aldehyde (or potential aldehyde) is oxidized to the corresponding carboxylic acid, and the copper is

$$(38) \quad RCHO + 2Cu^{II} + 5OH^- \rightarrow RCO_2^- + Cu_2O + 3H_2O$$

reduced to cuprous oxide.

The analysis can be completed by conventional iodometric determination [33] of the excess cupric ion or by weighing the cuprous oxide. Good results have also been reported in the determination of glucose by potentiometric titration with Fehling's solution.[34]

Chromic Acid

Chromic acid is too powerful an oxidant to be generally useful as a specific reagent in organic analysis but may find limited use in the determination of primary and secondary alcohols, which it oxidizes rapidly to acids and ketones.[35]

$$(39) \quad 5RCH_2OH + 4Cr_2O_7^= + 36H^+ \rightarrow 5RCO_2H + 8Cr^{+3} + 23H_2O$$

$$(40) \quad 5R_2CHOH + 2Cr_2O_7^= + 18H^+ \rightarrow 5R_2CO + 4Cr^{+3} + 14H_2O$$

A drastic oxidation by chromic acid has been used for many years in the determination of terminal methyl groups.[36] It is known as the Kuhn-Roth analysis and consists of the digestion of organic material with chromic acid at a temperature that is high enough to distill acetic acid from the reaction mixture. The acetic acid in the distillate is then titrated with a standard base. The results usually fall in the range from 75 to 90% of the theoretical value. Nonetheless, the pro-

[33] H. S. Isbell, W. W. Pigman, and H. L. Frush, *J. Research Natl. Bur. Standards,* **24,** 241 (1940).

[34] H. T. S. Britton, *Analyst,* **65,** 18 (1940).

[35] For a pertinent study of kinetics and stoichiometry, see F. H. Westheimer and A. Novik, *J. Chem. Phys.,* **11,** 506 (1943).

[36] Lemieux and Poirves, *Can. J. Research,* **25B,** 485 (1947).

cedure is quite useful as a diagnostic tool in establishing the structures of natural products.

Other Drastic Oxidations

The exhaustive oxidation of specific organic compounds to carbon dioxide can sometimes be used for their determination in aqueous solution if it is known that they are the only such oxidizable species present. Examples of such procedures are the determination of oxalic and formic acid by oxidation with permanganate and the determination of glucose by oxidation with ferricyanide.[37] These procedures, which amount to wet combustions, have only limited application. An interesting variant on this type of analysis is found in the determination of compounds such as acetic and succinic acids, which are particularly resistant to oxidation, as the organic residuum after the drastic oxidation of all other organic compounds in a sample. For example, succinic acid in extracts from plant tissues has been estimated by conversion to the p-toluide derivative after other compounds have been destroyed by successive treatments with permanganate and nitric acid.[38] The results of such assays must, however, be interpreted with caution since the resistant compounds may be formed as artifacts in the degradation of more complex materials.

Nitrous Acid

Nitrous acid has been employed for the determination of primary amines. The reaction with aliphatic amines constitutes the basis of the well-known Van Slyke determination, which is discussed in Chapter 6. With aromatic amines, stable diazonium salts are produced in many cases. The reaction has been adapted to quantitative work by colori-

$$(41) \qquad ArNH_2 + HNO_2 + H^+ \rightarrow ArN_2^+ + 2H_2O$$

metric determination of the diazonium ion by coupling with a phenol or an aromatic amine [39] and by titration with a standard solution of nitrous acid, using a starch-iodide paper as an external indicator.[40]

REDUCTIVE METHODS

A number of very satisfactory organic analyses can be carried out through the use of reducing agents. The reagents range from the

[37] D. T. Englis and H. C. Becker, *Ind. Eng. Chem., Anal. Ed.*, **15**, 262 (1943).
[38] G. W. Pucher and H. B. Vickery, *Ind. Eng. Chem., Anal. Ed.*, **13**, 412 (1941).
[39] M. B. Shin, *Ind. Eng. Chem., Anal. Ed.*, **13**, 33 (1941).
[40] A. V. Pamfilov, *Z. Anal. Chem.*, **69**, 283 (1926).

iodide ion to the very powerful metal hydrides. On the whole, it seems that selectivity is rather easier to accomplish with reducing agents than with oxidants. Among the useful procedures are several that effect the removal of halogen or sulfur from organic molecules; they are discussed in Chapter 8. Reductions with hydrogen are almost always followed manometrically and are included in Chapter 6.

IODIDE

Iodometric analyses are always operationally convenient and several classes of organic oxidizing agents, some of which are themselves useful analytical reagents, are reduced cleanly by potassium or sodium iodides or hydriodic acid. These include peroxides, positive halogen compounds such as N-halo amides, and quinones that have sufficiently high oxidation potentials. The unique feature of the alkali iodides as reagents is their remarkably high solubility in many organic solvents. Potassium iodide has been employed in acetic acid, acetic anhydride, and isopropanol.

A rather large number of procedures for the determination of peroxides have been reported.[41, 42, 43] Diacyl peroxides, such as benzoyl peroxide, can be determined with ease by reduction in acetic acid, and alkyl hydroperoxides usually react cleanly under the same conditions. Various procedures have been recommended and strong preferences

(42)

$$RC(=O)-O-O-C(=O)R + 2I^- + AcOH \rightarrow 2RCO_2H + I_2 + 2AcO^-$$

(43) $$RO_2H + 2I^- + AcOH \rightarrow ROH + H_2O + I_2 + 2AcO^-$$

have been expressed as to the choice of solvent. The authors have found that acetic acid gives excellent results if air is excluded by addition of Dry Ice to the reaction vessel. Most compounds react rapidly with a near saturated iodide solution at room temperature. Small amounts of water can be tolerated unless they cause the precipitation of organic material, as may occur in the determination of residual peroxidic initiator in polymer samples. Heating periods have been recommended but should not be used routinely but only when ex-

[41] S. Siggia, *Quantitative Analysis via Functional Groups*, p. 148.
[42] C. D. Wagner, R. H. Smith, and E. D. Peters, *Anal. Chem.*, **19**, 976 (1947).
[43] K. Nozaki, *Ind. Eng. Chem., Anal. Ed.*, **18**, 583 (1946).

periments have shown that oxidation at room temperature is inconveniently slow. If this procedure is used, care must be taken to assure the presence of high concentrations of iodide, which binds iodine as the triodide ion and prevents its loss by volatilization. Analyses can be completed conveniently by titration with standard thiosulfate. The procedure adopted at this juncture depends somewhat on the physical characteristics of the sample constituents. In order to utilize the starch-iodine end point, it is necessary to dilute the acetic acid with several volumes of water. This frequently leads to either the separation of solid organic material or a second liquid phase. The second phase may contain iodine which is extracted only slowly. This is true if the second phase is a precipitated polymer or a relatively large volume of a solvent such as carbon tetrachloride or benzene. Difficulty can frequently be avoided by delaying the dilution of the acetic acid with water until the end point, as indicated by the fading of the iodine color, has been approached very closely. It is interesting that at least one worker, after use of this procedure for some time, decided that the color of iodine in acetic acid was itself a sufficiently precise end point and dispensed with the water and starch completely. However, this method requires a practiced eye and is, of course, valueless if there are any colored materials in the sample. Good end points are also obtained by observation of the purple iodine color in a small amount of a solvent such as carbon tetrachloride or benzene when it is present as a second phase. If a large amount of a second phase is present, it is preferable to add a large amount of iodide to the aqueous phase, to extract the iodine as triiodide, and to utilize the starch end point.

Peracids and alkyl hydroperoxides can be determined by substantially the same procedure as has been described for diacyl peroxides.[43] Dialkyl peroxides react much more slowly with iodide ion but can usually be reduced if the reaction mixture is heated.[44]

Interference can be encountered in the presence of major amounts of aldehydes and ketones or readily substituted aromatic compounds such as phenols and aryl amines. The oxidation of primary and secondary alcohols is not ordinarily serious but could conceivably be a problem if the peroxide reduction is slow.

Iodide is also oxidized quantitatively by N-halo amines and amides such as chloramine-T (V) and N-bromosuccinimide (VI). Depending

44 F. H. Dickey, F. F. Rustand, and W. E. Vaughan, *J. Am. Chem. Soc.*, **71**, 1432 (1949).

$$\left[CH_3-\!\!\left\langle\!\!\bigcirc\!\!\right\rangle\!\!-SO_2NCl \right]^- Na^+$$

V

VI

on the solubility of the compound to be determined, the assays can be carried out in water or in acetic acid as solvents. The oxidations are very rapid and can be carried out without any particular danger of side reactions.

TITANOUS REDUCTIONS

The titanous ion is a very powerful reductant and has been used for the determination of a number of organic oxidizing functions, the most extensive application having been made with nitro compounds. Titanous reductions are inhibited by strong acid, and the most rapid reactions can be accomplished in media that are just acidic enough to prevent the precipitation of basic titanous compounds such as the hydroxide.[45] The determination can be carried out in solvent mixtures of water with acetic acid, alcohol, or other solvents that are not easily reduced. It is necessary to store stock solutions of titanous salts under nitrogen, and the titration vessel must be protected from the atmosphere during the determination as the air oxidation of the reagent to titanic ion is quite rapid. As is shown by equation 44, the reduction of a nitro group requires six equivalents of reductant.

$$(44) \quad 6Ti^{+++} + RNO_2 + 6H^+ \rightarrow RNH_2 + 6Ti^{+4} + 2H_2O$$

It has been found that at low hydrogen ion concentrations nitrobenzene is converted in part to azoxybenzene rather than to aniline.[46] The azoxybenzene can be reduced further to aniline, but the rate of reduction is much slower than the reduction of the nitro compound or other partially reduced intermediates. If the reaction mixture is allowed to stand for 15 to 20 minutes before the determination of excess reagent, satisfactory results can be obtained for any but the most dilute solutions. Excellent results have been reported with both

[45] W. W. Becker and W. E. Shaefer, *Organic Analysis,* Interscience Publishers, New York, 1954, Vol. 2, p. 94.

[46] S. A. Newton, F. J. Stubbs, and C. N. Hinshelwood, *J. Chem. Soc.,* **1953,** 3384.

aromatic nitro compounds and nitroalkanes. Polynitro alkanes sometimes give poor results.[47]

The reduction of nitrate esters by titanous ion has also been employed for the determination of the former. The stoichiometry is as shown in equation 45. The nitrogen compounds which are involved

$$(45) \quad RONO_2 + 8Ti^{+++} + 8H^+ \rightarrow ROH + NH_3 + 8Ti^{+4} + 2H_2O$$

in the reduction of nitro groups to amines are themselves reduced very rapidly and may, therefore, be determined in the same way as the parent substances. The sequence of reduction is shown in equation 46.

$$(46) \qquad RNO_2 \xrightarrow{2e} RNO \xrightarrow{2e} RNHOH \xrightarrow{2e} RNH_2$$

Peroxides have been assayed by titanometry[48] but the method seems to have little to recommend it in preference to the iodometric method and suffers from the inconvenience inherent in the use of an oxygensensitive titrant.

Determinations with titanous chloride or sulfate solutions are carried out by adding an excess of standard reagent solution to the unknown sample. The rate of reduction can be increased by adding a buffer such as sodium acetate to the acidic mixture. If a solid separates as a consequence of this addition, more sulfuric acid should be added to make the solution homogeneous. Heating periods have been recommended, but the authors know of no evidence that they are generally necessary, and a few minutes at room temperature is sufficient for the complete reduction of the above-mentioned classes of compounds. Heating is, therefore, to be discouraged in keeping with the principle of avoiding overly drastic conditions in all functional group determinations in order to minimize side reactions.

FERROUS ION

Ferrous ion has been utilized widely for the determination of nitrate esters and because of the importance of nitroglycerine, nitrocellulose, and their relatives, much study has been made of the procedure.[49] The reduction reaction is shown in equation 47.

$$(47) \quad RONO_2 + 3Fe^{++} + 3H^+ \rightarrow ROH + NO + 3Fe^{+++} + H_2O$$

In the preferred procedure, the analytical sample is dissolved in alcohol and an excess of standard ferrous ion in an aqueous solution is added.

[47] K. McCallum, private communication.
[48] R. Strohecker, R. Vaubel, and A. Tenner, *Fette u. Seifen,* **44,** 246 (1937).
[49] W. W. Becker and W. E. Shaefer, *Organic Analysis,* Vol. 2, p. 98.

The solution is warmed briefly, and the ferric ion produced is titrated with standard titanous chloride, using thiocyanate as an indicator.

TIN AND STANNOUS CHLORIDE

Both stannous chloride and metallic tin have been used for the assay of nitro compounds. The former gives good results with most but not all aromatic compounds. Reports concerning nitro alkanes are scattered, but there is an indication that definable stoichiometric relationships are not obtained with this class of compounds. The reductions are slower than those involving titanium[III], and heating periods are necessary. Since both reagents must be protected from air oxidation, it seems that there is little reason for choosing the stannous reduction in preference to the more versatile titanous assays.

Metallic tin was suggested for the determination of aromatic nitro compounds by Vanderzee and Edgell.[50] Their procedure has certain unique features that make the method worthy of careful consideration. The method depends upon the fact that, in the presence of excess metallic tin, oxidation by nitro compounds produces only stannous chloride in hydrochloric acid solution.

$$(48) \qquad 3Sn^0 + ArNO_2 + 6H^+ \rightarrow 3Sn^{++} + ArNH_2 + 2H_2O$$

If the solution is not stirred, the nitro compound—once adsorbed on the surface of the metal—is completely reduced with the production of stannous tin. The rate of reduction of the nitro compound by stannous ion is slow enough to be neglected. With rapid stirring, the rate of diffusion of intermediate nitroso compounds and aryl hydroxylamines away from the surface becomes appreciable. These species are rapidly reduced by stannous ion in solution. This results in the introduction of an error since the disproportionation of tin and stannic chloride is rather slow. However, in unstirred reaction mixtures the oxidation of some of the stannous ion produced by air does not introduce serious error if the analysis is completed by weighing the unreacted tin. Alternatively, the reaction mixture may be protected during the reduction by the addition of small pieces of Dry Ice. In this case the excess tin can be removed by filtration, and the stannous ion may be determined by the usual volumetric method. The method has not been tested for applicability to the analysis of aliphatic nitro compounds.

[50] C. E. Vanderzee and W. F. Edgell, *Anal. Chem.*, **22**, 572 (1950).

METAL HYDRIDES

The complex metal hydrides, especially lithium aluminum hydride and sodium borohydride, have found many applications as reducing agents in synthetic organic chemistry; and it is not surprising to find that they hold great promise as analytical reagents. Higuchi [51] has reviewed the analytical applications that have been developed to date. There is some question as to whether the metal hydrides should be classified as reducing agents or as bases since some of their reactions seem to fit in one class and others appear to belong in the other. Consider the following, for example. Reaction 49 could be easily classified

$$(49) \qquad LiAlH_4 + 4ROH \rightarrow LiAl(OR)_4 + 4H_2$$

$$(50) \qquad LiAlH_4 + 4 \quad \overset{R}{\underset{R}{\diagup}} C{=}O \rightarrow LiAl(OCHR_2)_4$$

as an acid-base reaction as has been done by Higuchi. Since the hydrolysis of the product of reaction 50 gives a secondary alcohol, it is similarly convenient to classify the reaction of a ketone with the hydride as a reduction. However, one could also maintain that the production of hydrogen is the consequence of the reduction of a positive hydrogen of the alcohol by the hydride or that reaction 50 is an acid-base reaction in which the ketone functions as a secondary Lewis acid. Because of this ambiguity in terminology, no attempt has been made to classify metal hydride reactions and to divide their discussion between this chapter and Chapter 4. Similarly, applicable manometric procedures are discussed here although the techniques involved are considered in Chapter 6.

All classes of carbonyl compounds, even carboxylic acids, can be reduced to alcoholates by lithium aluminum hydride if excess reagent is used. In addition, other functional groups react approximately according to the following equations:

$$(51) \qquad RX + LiAlH_4 \rightarrow RH + LiX + AlH_3$$

$$(52) \qquad 2ArNO_2 + 2LiAlH_4 \rightarrow ArN{=}NAr + 2LiAlO_2 + 4H_2$$

$$(53) \qquad 2RCN + LiAlH_4 \rightarrow LiAl(NCH_2R)_2$$

$$(54) \qquad 2RCONR'_2 + 2LiAlH_4 \rightarrow 2RCH_2NR'_2 + LiAlO_2$$

$$\rightarrow LiAl(OCH_2R)_4 + LiAl(NR'_2)_4$$

[51] T. Higuchi, *Organic Analysis*, Interscience, New York, 1954, Vol. 2, p. 123 *ff.*

Although there is considerable variation in rates of these reactions, there is little prospect that suitable conditions can be developed for the use of the compound as a selective reagent. Assay for active hydrogen can be carried out in the presence of other compounds that react with the hydride if excess reagent is used and if the reaction is monitored by the manometric determination of the hydrogen produced.

Higuchi and his co-workers have developed an ingenious method for carrying out potentiometric titrations of lithium aluminum hydride solutions. They found that solutions of the hydride in tetrahydrofuran effect a characteristic response from silver and platinum indicator electrodes. An external reference electrode is connected to the solution by a salt bridge. As a solution of the hydride is titrated with a solution of an alcohol in benzene or other inert solvent, the potential changes and breaks sharply at the stoichiometric point. Aldehydes and ketones may be determined by adding the unknown sample to a known excess of the hydride in tetrahydrofuran. After a reaction period of several minutes, the excess hydride is titrated with the standard alcohol solution. The rates of reactions of aldehydes and ketones, especially the latter, vary a great deal, and it is recommended that the assay of sterically hindered compounds be studied specifically to insure that the reaction time is sufficient for complete reduction.

Aromatic nitro compounds have been determined by measurement of the hydrogen produced (reaction 52).[52] In the particular report the hydrogen produced was determined by combustion analysis. It is likely that the determination could also be carried out by the less precise but more rapid manometric method. It is also reasonable to expect that the determination can be adapted to the potentiometric titration. It should be carefully noted that not all aromatic nitro compounds are reduced according to the stoichiometry indicated in equation 52.[53] Little is known about the applicability of the method to nitroalkanes but stoichiometric complications are to be expected.

It is quite possible that lithium aluminum hydride methods can be developed for other functional groups such as esters, amides, and nitriles. An example of an interesting possibility is the reduction of nitriles followed by hydrolysis and extraction of the amine from a strongly alkaline solution (to dissolve aluminum hydroxide) with an organic solvent such as benzene. The amine could then be conveniently determined by a nonaqueous titration (Chapter 3). Such procedures, which depend upon the independent determination of a reduction prod-

[52] K. McCallum and A. Kennedy, private communication.

[53] H. Gilman and T. N. Goreau, *J. Am. Chem. Soc.*, **73**, 2939 (1951).

uct, will permit specific determinations to be carried out in the presence of other types of compounds which react with the hydride.

Sodium borohydride is much more selective in its action than is lithium aluminum hydride. It can be used in methanol solution, and its action is restricted almost exclusively to the reduction of aldehydes and ketones.[54] Little work has been done with analytical applications, but there is good prospect that useful and selective methods can be developed.

MISCELLANEOUS REDUCING AGENTS

Arsenious Oxide

As_2O_3 has been recommended by Siggia [55] for the determination of a limited number of peroxides. The oxidation product, arsenic pentoxide, does not react with most organic compounds, whereas iodine formed in the iodometric procedure (page 94) reacts with many compounds. Only the most reactive peroxides, such as benzoyl peroxide, will oxidize arsenious acid, and so the method is not general.

$$(55) \quad 2(C_6H_5CO_2)_2 + As_2O_3 + 5H_2O \rightarrow 4C_6H_5CO_2H + 2H_3AsO_4$$

The determination is carried out by heating the unknown sample with a standard solution of arsenious oxide in aqueous bicarbonate. Ethanol may be added to obtain a homogeneous solution. Excess reagent is determined by titration with a standard solution of iodine in water.

Sodium hydrosulfite has been recommended for use in the selective determination of polynitro compounds in the presence of mononitro compounds.[56]

Mercaptans

Mercaptans have been used quite successfully in the determination of α,β-unsaturated carbonyl compounds and acrylonitrile. The mercaptans add readily to such compounds in the presence of catalytic

$$(56) \qquad RSH + CH_2{=}CHCN \rightarrow RSCH_2CH_2CN$$

amounts of base. The reaction can be carried out in aqueous or alcoholic solution and the excess mercaptan is readily determined by either iodometric assay (page 94) or by titration with silver nitrate.

[54] S. W. Chaikin and W. G. Brown, *J. Am. Chem. Soc.* **71**, 122 (1949).
[55] S. Siggia, *Ind. Eng. Chem., Anal. Ed.*, **19**, 827 (1927).
[56] W. E. Shaefer and W. W. Becker, *Anal. Chem.*, **19**, 307 (1947).

This reaction should be general for all compounds having a strongly electron-attracting group in conjugation with an olefinic linkage. It should, therefore, give good analytical results with α,β-unsaturated sulfones and 1-nitroalkenes although we know of no attempts to use the method for these types of compounds. Both aliphatic mercaptans and thiophenol have been used as reagents.[57]

KARL FISCHER REAGENT

The determination of water in organic solvents is an important procedure in its own right and, in addition, is a useful adjunct to other analyses since water is produced or consumed quantitatively in many organic reactions. The classification of the method is somewhat arbitrary, but it is included in this chapter since the reaction involves the oxidation of sulfur dioxide by iodine.

$$(57) \qquad I_2 + SO_2 + H_2O \rightarrow 2HI + SO_3$$

The Karl Fischer reagent is a standard solution of iodine and excess sulfur dioxide in a mixed solvent consisting of pyridine and methanol. The unknown sample is titrated with the reagent solution with the persistence of the brown iodine color being taken as the end point. The reagent solution must be standardized frequently, and it is, of course, necessary to protect the system from atmospheric moisture during the titration. Compounds that react very rapidly with iodine interfere with the determination, although moderately reactive compounds such as acetone can be tolerated since the concentration of iodine in the assay mixture is very small at all times.

Although it would not be prudent to attempt a survey of methods that utilize the Karl Fischer titration, it is worth while to consider a few representative examples at this time. Others are mentioned in various other places in this book, and applications of the method have been reviewed.[58,59]

An interesting procedure for the determination of hydroxyl groups involves the reaction of the hydroxylic compound with a large excess of acetic acid followed by titration of the water produced. This method, unlike other acylation procedures (Chapter 4), does not discriminate tertiary alcohols from primary and secondary. The former

[57] D. W. Beesing, W. P. Tyler, D. M. Kurtz, and S. A. Harrison, *Anal. Chem.*, **21**, 1073 (1949).

[58] J. Mitchell, *Anal. Chem.*, **23**, 1069 (1951).

[59] J. Mitchell and D. M. Smith, *Aquametry*, Interscience, New York, 1948, Part II.

are dehydrated rather than acylated. Conversely, a procedure for the determination of carboxylic acids can be based upon the titration of

(58) $\qquad RCH_2OH + CH_3CO_2H \xrightarrow{BF_3} RCH_2OCOCH_3 + H_2O$

(59) $\qquad RCH_2C(OH)R'_2 \xrightarrow{BF_3} RCH{=}CR'_2 + H_2O$

the water liberated in the esterification of the acid with a large excess of methanol. Nitriles which are not readily determined by ordinary hydrolytic procedures are hydrated rather rapidly by even small amounts of water in the presence of boron trifluoride. The excess water can be titrated to complete the analysis.

(60) $\qquad RCN + H_2O \xrightarrow{BF_3,\ CH_3CO_2H} RCONH_2$

6.

MANOMETRIC METHODS

INTRODUCTION

A number of very useful procedures involve the measurement of the amount of gas evolved or absorbed during a chemical reaction. These are classed as manometric procedures although the common method of measurement is to adjust the volume of the gas in such a way as to maintain the pressure constant. With a suitable apparatus the technique of measurement is rather easily mastered. The initial expense involved in the construction of a versatile apparatus is not large, but is sufficient to place a premium on careful design.

TECHNIQUE OF MEASUREMENT

Fundamentally, the manometric procedures involve the change in either the pressure or the volume of gas in a closed system as the consequence of the production or consumption of a gaseous substance in a chemical reaction. Most methods are based upon reactions that take place in solution or, occasionally, in a solid phase. Conventional gas analysis of hydrocarbons and other volatile organic compounds is based upon reaction in the vapor phase between a combustible organic compound and oxygen.

A typical apparatus is shown in Fig. 12. This is more elaborate than

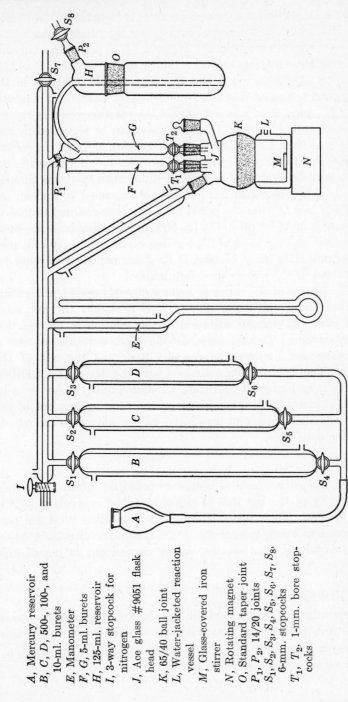

A, Mercury reservoir
B, C, D, 500-, 100-, and
   10-ml. burets
E, Manometer
F, G, 5-ml. burets
H, 125-ml. reservoir
I, 3-way stopcock for
   nitrogen
J, Ace glass #9051 flask
   head
K, 65/40 ball joint
L, Water-jacketed reaction
   vessel
M, Glass-covered iron
   stirrer
N, Rotating magnet
O, Standard taper joint
P_1, P_2, 14/20 joints
S_1, S_2, S_3, S_4, S_5, S_6, S_7, S_8,
   6-mm. stopcocks
T_1, T_2, 1-mm. bore stop-
   cocks

Figure 12. Manometric apparatus. (The design is essentially that of Hochstein, Reference 2.)

is needed for all manometric procedures since it includes reservoirs and burets for the addition of reagents, such as metal hydrides, which must be protected from the atmosphere. However, it is perfectly adaptable for use in simpler operations such as catalytic hydrogenation. Reagents are stored in the reservoirs, F and H. The sample is placed in the reaction vessel L, and stirring is accomplished by means of a magnetic stirrer. The inclusion of a jacket around the reaction vessel is recommended since this will permit the temperature to be regulated by circulating water from a constant temperature bath through the jacket. If it is desirable to carry out the reaction under reduced pressure, the apparatus may be evacuated and then refilled with inert gas through stopcock I. The volume of gas evolved or consumed is read on the gas buret B, C, or D, after the liquid level has been restored to that in the reference column by raising or lowering the leveling bulb A. Mercury is most commonly used as the leveling liquid but heavy oils, such as dibutyl phthalate, may be used if they are not good solvents for gases involved in the particular determination.

Since the success of the entire procedure depends upon equilibration between the liquid and vapor phases, it is necessary to have some means of effecting vigorous agitation of the solution in the reaction vessel. Mechanical shaking may also be used, but this requires a flexible connection between the reaction flask and the rest of the apparatus. This is not easily combined with the devices for addition of reagents from protected reservoirs. If the reaction vessel is to be heated, it is wise to add a condenser on the tube leading out of the reduction chamber to prevent distillation of the solvent to the remote parts of the apparatus.

METHODS

We shall discuss methods of actual or potential interest according to the identity of the gas that is either absorbed or evolved by the reacting system. There are relatively few substances that are permanent gases at room temperature.[1] Therefore, a discussion based upon individual chemical species can be carried out in manageable form.

Active Hydrogen Methods

Organometallic compounds and lithium aluminum hydride have been used very frequently in the determination of weakly acidic hydrogen

[1] High solubility in most organic solvents makes the gaseous hydrocarbons unsuitable for use in most manometric procedures.

in organic compounds. Alcohols, amines, and amides, as well as more highly acidic compounds, yield hydrogen with lithium aluminum hydride [2] or methane with methyl magnesium iodide.[3, 4, 5, 6] In principle all the hydrogens of lithium aluminum hydride are available for reaction according to equation 1.

$$(1) \qquad 4AH + LiAlH_4 \rightarrow 4H_2 + LiAlA_4$$

In practice it is wise to use a liberal excess of the reagent in quantitative work. With methyl lithium and methyl Grignard reagents similar reactions occur.

$$(2) \qquad AH + CH_3Li \rightarrow CH_4 + LiA$$

$$(3) \qquad AH + CH_3MgX \rightarrow CH_4 + MgAX$$

The procedure using the Grignard reagent has been referred to as the Zerewitinoff determination. Solvents that have been recommended include dibutyl ether, tetrahydrofuran, and N-ethyl morpholine. It is necessary to protect the system from atmospheric moisture in any of these determinations. The general apparatus shown in Fig. 12 is de-

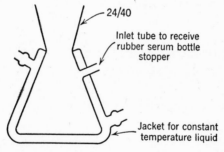

Figure 13. Reaction flask for active hydrogen determination.

signed for use with these sensitive reagents. However, an apparatus that lacks the protected reservoirs can be used. Transfers of the solutions of reagents are made by means of volumetric syringes. The reaction vessel may be simply a small Erlenmeyer flask with a standard taper ground joint and a side arm of appropriate diameter to receive a rubber serum bottle stopper. Figure 13 indicates such a flask.

[2] F. A. Hochstein, *J. Am. Chem. Soc.*, **71**, 305 (1949).

[3] T. Zerewitinoff, *Ber.*, **40**, 2023 (1907).

[4] A. Soltys, *Michrochemie*, **20**, 107 (1937).

[5] P. M. Maginnity and J. B. Cloke, *Anal. Chem.*, **20**, 978 (1948).

[6] G. F. Wright, *Organic Analysis*, Interscience, New York, 1953, Vol. I.

The principal inaccuracy introduced by such a method arises from the inadequacy of a syringe as a volumetric pipet.

An indirect application of the active hydrogen procedure can be made to the determination of aldehydes, ketones, and esters. All these substances undergo addition reactions with either the methyl Grignard reagent or lithium aluminum hydride (Chapter 5). The reduction of esters, shown in equation 4, is typical.

(4) $2RCO_2R' + LiAlH_4 \rightarrow (RCH_2O)_2Al^-(OR')_2Li^+$

In the determination an excess of the reagent is added to the sample in one of the solvents mentioned above. After a suitable period, 15 to 20 minutes for most carbonyl compounds, an excess of alcohol is then added and the volume of hydrogen or methane produced from the excess reagent is measured. The difference between the hydrogen equivalent of a standard aliquot of the reagent solution and that after reaction with the analytical sample gives the amount consumed by addition reactions.

Nitro compounds constitute an interfering group of substances in all active hydrogen determinations. They are usually reduced in accordance with equations 5 and 6.

(5) $2ArNO_2 + 2LiAlH_4 \rightarrow Ar—N{=}N—Ar + 2LiAlO_2 + 4H_2$

(6) $2RNO_2 + 3LiAlH_4 \rightarrow (RN)_2Al^-Li^+ + 2LiAlO_2 + 6H_2$

These stoichiometric relationships hold reasonably well for aromatic and aliphatic nitro groups, but exceptions have been observed.[7] Nitriles, amides, carboxylic acids, alkyl halides, and epoxides are all reduced more or less rapidly by lithium aluminum hydride[8] and also react with the Grignard reagent to give displacement or addition reactions. Most of these classes of substances can, in principle, be determined with these reagents. However, many of them react slowly, and reaction conditions would have to be studied in individual cases before the method as described for carbonyl compounds could be generalized.

Hydrogenation

Quantitative catalytic hydrogenation has been reported many times as a means of estimating olefinic and acetylenic unsaturation. Most simple olefins take up hydrogen reasonably easily at room temperature in the presence of finely divided platinum, paladium, or nickel. Quan-

---

[7] H. Gilman and T. N. Goreau, *J. Am. Chem. Soc.*, **73**, 2939 (1951).

[8] R. F. Nystrom and W. G. Brown, *J. Am. Chem. Soc.*, **70**, 3738 (1948).

titative procedures are most commonly based upon platinum since it is easily prepared in a finely divided state by the *in situ* reduction of platinic oxide (Adams' Catalyst).

(7) $$PtO_2 + 2H_2 \rightarrow Pt + 2H_2O$$

Nickel catalysts of very high activity can be prepared.[9] Their use in quantitative work may be limited by the fact that the catalyst preparations contain a large and variable amount of hydrogen adsorbed on the metal surface. Hydrogenation on micro scale may therefore involve the adsorption of appreciably less than a stoichiometric amount of hydrogen from the gas phase. The error introduced in this way is minimized by replacement of the surface hydrogen by adsorption of more from the vapor phase and may become negligible in many instances. When platinum oxide is used it is necessary to correct for the amount of hydrogen consumed in reduction to the metal. Since the composition of oxide samples is somewhat uncertain, the correction is based upon experimental values obtained by hydrogenating weighed samples. If the calibration is carried out under the solvent used in the analytical procedure, the correction will include any hydrogen uptake due to the presence of unsaturates in the solvent. Alternatively, the catalyst may be prereduced before introduction of the analytical sample.

In addition to simple olefins, the conjugated dienes and polyenes and arylethylenes are usually hydrogenated readily on platinum. Conjugated, unsaturated acids and their derivatives are much slower in hydrogenation than their unconjugated relatives.

Hydrogen Evolution

There is at least one example of a reaction in which the evolution of hydrogen is recommended as an analytical method. The remarkable reaction of equation 8 has been said to occur quantitatively with formaldehyde and other simple aldehydes.[10]

(8) $$2RCHO + H_2O_2 + 2NaOH \rightarrow 2RCO_2Na + H_2 + 2H_2O$$

Since there are so many other excellent procedures for aldehydes (Chapters 2 and 5), the method has received little attention, although the reported good stoichiometric relationship commends it for a study of the mechanism of a seemingly bizarre reaction if for no other reason.

[9] A. A. Pavlic and H. Adkins, *J. Am. Chem. Soc.*, **68**, 1471 (1946).
[10] G. B. Frankforter and R. West, *J. Am. Chem. Soc.*, **27**, 714 (1905).

A reaction that is, perhaps, related is the thermal decomposition of primary hydroperoxides.

$$(9) \qquad RCH_2OOH \rightarrow RCO_2H + H_2$$

The reaction was reported in 1955,[11] but the evolution of hydrogen was not stoichiometric so that the method is not immediately adaptable for analytical work. We have considerable doubt that the reaction will be developed for that purpose because of the relative ease of the iodometric assay for these compounds (Chapter 5).

Nitrogen Evolution

A number of methods have as a basis reactions in which nitrogen is evolved. The most familiar is the determination of primary amines by the Van Slyke procedure.[12] Although the chemistry of the reaction varies greatly with respect to the fate of the carbon skeleton, the reaction is usually very clean with respect to evolution of nitrogen and may be represented by the following equations.

$$(10) \qquad RNH_2 + H^+ + HNO_2 \rightarrow RN_2^+ \rightarrow N_2 + \underset{\underset{\text{products}}{\text{various}}}{R^+} + 2H_2O$$

The behavior of aromatic amines is modified by the stability of the derived diazonium ions and the fact that they couple readily with the parent amines in the familiar diazo coupling reaction.

$$(11) \quad ArNH_2 + ArN_2^+ \rightarrow ArNHN{=}NAr \rightarrow ArN{=}N{-}ArNH_2$$

As a consequence, the Van Slyke determination of an aromatic primary amine requires individual attention to experimental conditions such as concentration and temperature. Since there are a wealth of other procedures that can be used, the method is seldom applied to this class of substances. One of the alternatives is, of course, diazotization in cold, dilute solution followed by coupling of the diazonium ion with a reactive substance such as β-naphthol to give an azo dye which can be determined spectrophotometrically (Chapter 10).

Another reaction in which quantitative evolution of nitrogen is accompanied by a variety of chemical changes in the residual organic fragment is the acid-catalyzed decomposition of azides.

---

[11] H. S. Mosher and C. F. Wurster, *J. Am. Chem. Soc.*, **77**, 5451 (1955).
[12] D. D. Van Slyke *et al.*, *J. Biol. Chem.*, **102**, 489, 651 (1933).

$$(12) \qquad R\!\!-\!\!\overset{+}{N}\!\!=\!\!\overset{-}{N}\!\!=\!\!\overset{+}{N} + H^+ \rightarrow R\overset{+}{N}H + N_2$$
$$\downarrow$$
various
products

The evolution of nitrogen from nearly all azides is quantitative and rapid if the compounds are treated with concentrated sulfuric acid.[13]

A number of aliphatic azonitriles and azoesters decompose at temperatures well below 100°. Since free radicals are produced in the process, these compounds have found wide use as initiators of vinyl polymerization. Typical examples are azo-bis-isobutyronitrile, I, and azo-bis-ethylisobutyrate, II. The compounds of interest are decom-

$$(CH_3)_2CCN$$
$$|$$
$$N$$
$$||$$
$$N$$
$$|$$
$$(CH_3)_2CCN$$
$$I$$

$$(CH_3)_2CCO_2C_2H_5$$
$$|$$
$$N$$
$$||$$
$$N$$
$$|$$
$$(CH_3)_2CCO_2C_2H_5$$
$$II$$

posed at brisk rates in the temperature region, 80 to 100°. The rates of decomposition have frequently been measured by following the evolution of nitrogen, and the total volume of nitrogen evolved in total decomposition serves as a good assay method. It is necessary to carry out the decomposition under a nitrogen atmosphere since the radicals produced react readily with oxygen. The latter reaction will, of course, consume gas and ruin the analysis.

Diazomethane and other aliphatic diazo compounds are decomposed quantitatively by treatment with mineral acids.

$$(13) \qquad HX + CH_2N_2 \rightarrow CH_3X + N_2$$

The relatively high vapor pressure of diazomethane over its solutions limits the use of the method for the determination of that compound, but other diazo compounds may be assayed by nitrogen evolution.

Carbon Dioxide Evolution

The unique behavior of malonic acids, β-keto acids, and related compounds in undergoing facile decarboxylation at rather low temperatures is of interest as a highly selective analytical tool for such substances. Temperatures in the vicinity of 100° C. are usually required to effect

[13] P. A. S. Smith and B. B. Brown, *J. Am. Chem. Soc.*, **73**, 2439 (1951); and P. A. S. Smith, private communication.

decomposition at a reasonable rate, and tertiary amines are often effective as catalysts for the reaction. Pyridine and quinoline are commonly used as solvents since they also serve as basic catalysts for the decomposition. Typical discussions of the problems involved are to be found in the reports of kinetic data on the decomposition of malonic acids [14] and alkylidene malonic acids.[15]

In addition to diacids and keto acids a number of other acids which are heavily substituted with electron-attracting substituents are readily decarboxylated. Examples are cyanoacetic, nitroacetic, and trichloroacetic acids. The last-named compound requires rather concentrated, hot alkali for decomposition, and so analysis must be carried out in two steps. Decomposition is accomplished by heating with alkali with the careful exclusion of atmospheric carbon dioxide. After the heating period the reaction mixture is cooled and then acidified to release the carbon dioxide.

Carbon Monoxide Evolution

The number of examples of compounds that are decomposed to yield carbon monoxide is not large. Alpha keto esters are known to undergo such decomposition on being heated under strongly alkaline conditions, but there is some doubt as to whether this procedure can be adapted to constitute a suitable analytical procedure. However, the ready decomposition of formic and oxalic acids in the presence of concentrated sulfuric acid constitutes a selective procedure for the determination of these compounds in the presence of other carboxylic acids. This method, as shown in equations 14 and 15, will not often represent the procedure of choice unless the mixture to be analyzed contains

$$(14) \qquad HCO_2H \xrightarrow{\text{conc. } H_2SO_4} CO + H_2O$$

$$(15) \qquad (CO_2H)_2 \xrightarrow{\text{conc. } H_2SO_4} CO_2 + CO + H_2O$$

other reducing materials that will interfere with the oxidative methods for formic and oxalic acids (Chapter 5).

Evolution of Oxides of Nitrogen

The nitrometer method is the most general procedure for the determination of either organic or inorganic nitrates. The volume of nitric oxide produced in reaction 16 is measured after the sample has been

[14] J. Hine, *Physical Organic Chemistry*, McGraw-Hill Book Co., New York, 1956; Chapter 13 provides an excellent discussion with leading references.

[15] E. J. Corey, *J. Am. Chem. Soc.*, **74**, 5897 (1952).

decomposed by reaction with 89% sulfuric acid and metallic mercury.

(16) $2NO_3^- + 8H^+ + 3Hg^0 \rightarrow 3Hg^{++} + 4H_2O + 2NO$

Because of the importance of nitrate determination in the explosives field, specialized instruments known as nitrometers [16,17] have been developed. However, the analysis could also be carried out in the more elaborate apparatus shown in Fig. 12 if the latter is available in the laboratory for general purposes. It would be necessary to add metallic mercury to the reaction vessel, whereas in a nitrometer the mercury is supplied by the gas leveling device.

Primary nitramines are quantitatively decomposed by treatment with strong acids.[18] For example, methyl nitramine reacts to produce nitrous oxide in stoichiometric amount when treated with concentrated nitric acid at 0° C.[19] The reaction has every aspect of being an excellent method for the selective determination of a particu-

(17) $CH_3NHNO_2 + HNO_3 \rightarrow CH_3ONO_2 + N_2O + H_2O$

lar class of nitro compounds. Curiously enough it has been found that secondary nitramines (R_2NNO_2) are unaffected by 40% sulfuric acid at room temperature and often resist the action of acids even at 100° C.[20] The reactivity of the primary compounds is probably related to the fact that they can be equilibrated with small amounts of tautomeric N-nitronic acids.

(18)
$$RNHNO_2 \underset{}{\overset{H^+}{\rightleftharpoons}} RN{=}\overset{+}{N}\begin{array}{l} {\diagup} OH \\ {\diagdown} O^- \end{array}$$

It is consistent with this view that O-alkyl isomers of the secondary nitramines may be estimated by their facile decomposition.[20]

(19)
$$RN{=}\overset{+}{N}\begin{array}{l} {\diagup} O^- \\ {\diagdown} OR' \end{array} + H_2O \xrightarrow[H_2SO_4]{40\%} ROH + R'OH + N_2O$$

[16] W. Furman, *Scott's Standard Methods of Analysis,* 5th ed., D. Van Nostrand Co., New York, 1939, p. 650.

[17] W. W. Becker and W. E. Shaefer, *Organic Analysis,* Interscience, New York, 1954, Vol. II, p. 97.

[18] H. van Erp, *Rec. trav. chim.,* **14** (1895).

[19] A. P. N. Franchimont, *Rec. trav. chim.,* **29**, 296 (1910).

[20] A. P. N. Franchimont, *Rec. trav. chim.,* **17**, 287 (1898).

Oxygen Absorption

The Warburg procedure [21] for measuring oxygen uptake by living cell tissue in the course of normal metabolism is adaptable for use in the determination of some physiologically active compounds but defies definition as a regular chemical analysis.

Many hydrocarbons undergo oxidation by atmospheric oxygen but the reaction cannot be recommended for analytical work because of the poor definition of the stoichiometry. Free radicals, such as triphenylmethyl, have been assayed by oxygen uptake. If oxygen is admitted to the system *slowly*, the radicals are converted to peroxides.

$$(20) \qquad 2(C_6H_5)_3C \cdot + O_2 \rightarrow (C_6H_5)_3C-O-O-C(C_6H_5)_3$$

The method is probably as accurate as any for the determination of the total concentration of triarylmethyl and hexaarylethane in solution.

PROBLEMS

(*Note:* Do not restrict consideration to the methods of this chapter.)

1. The decomposition of the following, unsymmetrical, dialkyl peroxide in toluene is complex.

$$\phi-\underset{\underset{CH_3}{|}}{\overset{\overset{CH_3}{|}}{C}}-O-O-\underset{\underset{CH_3}{|}}{\overset{\overset{CH_3}{|}}{C}}-CH_3 + \phi CH_3$$

$$\rightarrow \phi\overset{O}{\overset{\|}{C}}CH_3 + CH_3-\underset{\underset{CH_3}{|}}{\overset{\overset{CH_3}{|}}{C}}-OH + CH_4 + \phi CH_2CH_2\phi$$

$$\rightarrow CH_3\overset{O}{\overset{\|}{C}}CH_3 + \phi-\underset{\underset{CH_3}{|}}{\overset{\overset{CH_3}{|}}{C}}-OH + CH_4 + \phi CH_2CH_2\phi$$

[21] F. M. Huennekens, *Technique of Organic Chemistry*, A. Wiessberger, editor, Interscience, 1953, Vol. VIII, Chapter IX.

$$\rightarrow \phi\overset{\overset{\text{O}}{\|}}{\text{C}}\text{CH}_3 + \text{CH}_3\overset{\overset{\text{O}}{\|}}{\text{C}}\text{CH}_3 + 2\text{CH}_4 + \phi\text{CH}_2\text{CH}_2\phi$$

$$\rightarrow \phi\overset{\overset{\text{CH}_3}{|}}{\underset{\underset{\text{CH}_3}{|}}{\text{C}}}\text{—OH} + \text{CH}_3\text{—}\overset{\overset{\text{CH}_3}{|}}{\underset{\underset{\text{CH}_3}{|}}{\text{C}}}\text{—OH} + \phi\text{CH}_2\text{CH}_2\phi$$

How would you determine the fractions of each of the alkoxy groups which are converted to ketone and alcohol?

2. Devise five methods for the determination of the purity of aspirin made by the acetylation of salicylic acid with acetic anhydride.

3. After consultation of the general chemical literature concerning quaternary ammonium compounds, evaluate the possibility of developing a method for the determination of a quaternary such as I by an active hydrogen method.

$$\underset{\text{CH}_3 \quad \quad \text{CH}_3 \quad \text{X}^-}{\overset{+}{\text{N}}}$$

I

4. Would it be possible to estimate II by an indirect active hydrogen procedure?

$$\text{ClCH}\!=\!\text{CHCH}_2\text{Cl}$$
II

5. A sample is known to contain approximately equal amounts of *sec*-butanol and methyl ethyl ketone. Assume that both constituents are to be determined by reaction with a 0.200 M solution of LiAlH_4, using a 50-ml. gas buret. What range of sample weights and how much of the hydride solution should be taken to obtain maximum accuracy in the results?

7.

METAL ION COMPLEXES

INTRODUCTION

Most analytical work involving formation of metal-organic salts or chelates has been in connection with the determination of metal ions. There are an extremely large number of organic reagents described in the literature for the determination of inorganic ions by gravimetric, colorimetric, and titrimetric methods. In some cases it is possible to reverse this operation and use the reaction of organic compounds with metal ions as the basis for determining the organic compound. Methods for measuring the reacting organic compound include titration of the acid liberated in chelate formation, direct titration with a metal ion employing a visual or electrometric end point, spectrophotometric measurement of the color formed, and gravimetric determination of the metal-organic precipitate.

One definite advantage of this approach is that very similar organic compounds can often be distinguished quantitatively. For example, o-aminobenzoic acid (anthranilic acid) can be precipitated quantitatively by zinc ions in the presence of m- and p-aminobenzoic acid.[1] The precipitate has a somewhat uncertain composition but it can be washed, redissolved, and analyzed specifically for the anthranilic acid

[1] K. J. Douglas, Ph.D. Dissertation, Iowa State College, 1955.

116

content by bromination. Except for its chelating ability due to the position of the functional groups, o-aminobenzoic acid is very similar to the meta and para isomers in its chemical and physical properties.

Unfortunately many organic compounds cannot be easily determined on the basis of their metal chelating ability. The reason for this is that a great many chelates are formed by stepwise reactions. The ferrous-1,10-phenanthroline system provides such an example. Small amounts of iron are often determined by measuring the intensity of the red color produced when an excess of 1,10-phenanthroline, I, is added to a solution containing the ferrous ion. The color is due to the $Fe(phen)_3^{++}$ complex.

I

If an excess of 1,10-phenanthroline is not present, however, appreciable amounts of $Fe(phen)^{++}$ and $Fe(phen)_2^{++}$ will be formed. These species have molar absorptivities and wavelengths of maximum absorption which are different from the $Fe(phen)_3^{++}$. In attempting to determine 1,10-phenanthroline with iron, it is obvious that enough ferrous iron would have to be added to combine with all the 1,10-phenanthroline in some well-defined manner. The spectrophotometric measurements would then have to be made on a mixture of colored species of different molar absorptivity and of unknown relative concentrations. This is not an attractive analytical situation.

PRINCIPLES OF CHELATE FORMATION

Metal cations can react with organic compounds in several ways. One of these is by simple salt formation. Examples of this are the reaction of silver ions with thiols or with acetylenic hydrogen.

(1) $$RSH + Ag^+ \rightarrow RSAg + H^+$$

(2) $$RC{\equiv}CH + Ag^+ \rightarrow RC{\equiv}CAg + H^+$$

Another mode of metal-organic complex formation is through the formation of chelate rings. An example of this is the formation of cupric ethylenediamine chelate, II, as shown in equation 3. Here the

$$
(3) \quad 2 \quad
\begin{array}{c}
NH_2 \\
/ \\
CH_2 \\
| \\
CH_2 \\
\backslash \\
NH_2
\end{array}
\quad + Cu^{++} \rightarrow \quad
\left[
\begin{array}{c}
\overset{H_2}{N} \qquad\qquad \overset{H_2}{N} \\
/ \qquad\backslash\quad/\qquad \backslash \\
CH_2 \qquad Cu \qquad CH_2 \\
| \qquad\nearrow\quad\nwarrow\qquad | \\
CH_2 \qquad\qquad CH_2 \\
\backslash \qquad\qquad / \\
\underset{H_2}{N} \qquad\qquad \underset{H_2}{N}
\end{array}
\right]^{++}
$$

coordination positions of the cupric ion are satisfied by four coordinate bonds from the nitrogen atoms in the two ethylenediamine molecules. In this type of chelation there is no neutralization of the charge on the metal ion. Metal chelates usually have substantially larger formation constants than complexes in which the location of coordinating groups is such that chelate ring formation cannot take place. Thus the cupric ethylenediamine ion is more stable than the cupric ammino ion or other coordination complexes between copper(II) and simple mono-amines.

Chelate formation often effects the neutralization of the charge of the metal ion. One way in which this is done is by replacing two hydrogen atoms of the organic reagent for each chelate ring formed.

$$
(4) \quad
\begin{array}{c}
O \\
\parallel \\
C-OH \\
| \\
C-OH \\
\parallel \\
O
\end{array}
\quad + Pb^{++} \rightarrow \quad
\begin{array}{c}
O \\
\parallel \\
C-O \\
\backslash \\
\qquad Pb \\
/ \\
C-O \\
\parallel \\
O
\end{array}
\quad + 2H^+
$$

$$
(5) \quad
\begin{array}{c}
\text{SH} \\
\\
\text{SH}
\end{array}
\quad + Sn^{++} \rightarrow \quad
\begin{array}{c}
\text{S} \\
\backslash \\
\qquad Sn \\
/ \\
\text{S}
\end{array}
\quad + 2H^+
$$

Another type of chelation with charge neutralization involves the binding of twice as many singly charged ligands.

$$
(6) \quad 2 \quad
\begin{array}{c}
C=N \\
| \qquad \backslash OH \\
C=N \\
\qquad \backslash OH
\end{array}
\quad + Ni^{++} \longrightarrow \quad
\begin{array}{c}
O\text{--}H\text{--}O \\
C=N \qquad N=C \\
\qquad Ni \\
C=N \qquad N=C \\
O\text{--}H\text{--}O
\end{array}
\quad + 2H^+
$$

(7) 2 [structure: benzene ring with CHO and OH substituents] + Cu^{++} ⟶ [copper chelate structure] + $2H^+$

(8) 3 [structure: benzene ring with N=O group] + Fe^{+++} ⟶ [iron chelate structure]$_3$

In order to form the latter type of chelate, the organic molecule must contain one acidic group and one basic, or electron-donating group. Typical acidic groups which may participate in chelate formation are: $-CO_2H$, $-OH$, $-SH$, $=NOH$, $=NH$, $-As(OH)_2$ and $-AsO(OH)_2$. Common basic groups are: $C=O$, $C=S$, $-N=O$, $-NH_2$, $-RNH$, $-R_2N$, and $=N-$.

In order for any type of chelation to occur the participating functional groups must be properly located in the organic molecule. A general rule is that chelation will occur only if it is possible to form a 5- or 6-membered chelate ring. This means that aromatic compounds with ortho substituents frequently are capable of forming metal chelates whereas those with only meta and para substituents are not. An excellent discussion of the types of organic structures that will form metal chelates is given by Welcher.[2]

A successful gravimetric determination of an organic chelating compound demands an appreciable solubility difference between the metal chelate and the other substances with which the metal ion might react. Where stepwise chelate formation can occur, it is also necessary that one metal chelate of definite composition be sufficiently stable and insoluble to be the only complex precipitated. The pH for the precipitation should be such that the excess metal ion will not form insoluble hydroxides or basic metal salts. In determining 1,3-diketones by precipitation with copper(II), for example, the pH must be kept within rather narrow limits.[3] For acetylacetone the pH range is 5.2 to 6.0; for ethyl acetyl pyruvate it is 4.8 to 6.5. Above these ranges, basic copper salts are precipitated; at lower pH values precipitation of the copper 1,3-dicarbonyl compound is incomplete.

[2] F. J. Welcher, *Organic Analytical Reagents*, Van Nostrand, New York, 1947, Vol. I, Chapter IV.

[3] W. Seaman, J. T. Woods, and E. A. Massad, *Anal. Chem.*, **19**, 250 (1947).

The success of titrimetric methods (and to some extent of colorimetric methods) can be predicted from the titration curve in which the pM (− log of metal ion concentration) of the solution is plotted against the volume of titrant added. In general an accurate measurement can only be obtained when there is a reasonably sharp break in the titration curve.

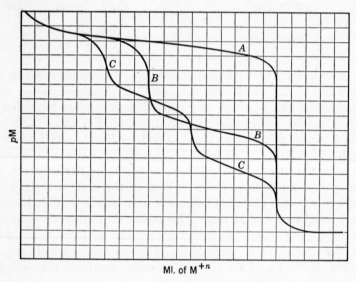

Ml. of M^{+n}

Figure 14. Theoretical curves for titration of various chelating agents with a metal ion.

In Fig. 14 the effect of stepwise formation of complexes on the titration curve is shown. Curve A represents the case where only a 1:1 complex is formed. If this is a reasonably stable complex there will be a large change in pM at the end point.

Curve B in Fig. 14 shows a typical curve for the case where both mono- (MA^+) and di-chelates (MA_2) can form. At the start of the titration the organic compound is in excess and the 2:1 complex is formed. In the example chosen the strength of this complex is such that the pM is essentially the same as in the 1:1 complex in curve A. When 1 mole of metal has been added for each 2 moles of organic compound, each further addition of titrant results in the formation of an equivalent amount of the 1:1 chelate.

(9) $$MA_2 + M^{++} \rightarrow 2MA^+$$

Often, as shown in this example, this 1:1 chelate is somewhat weaker than the 2:1, and the pM drops as shown by the first end point in this curve. When reaction (9) is complete, a second drop in pM is observed. Conditions in curve B are less favorable for titration because the magnitude of the break observed in curve A is now split between two end points.

Curve C in Fig. 14 is for the case where 3:1, 2:1, or 1:1 organic-metal complexes can form, depending on the relative amounts of or-

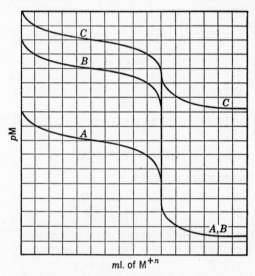

Figure 15. Effect of pH on the titration of a typical chelating agent with a metal ion. The order of decreasing pH values is $A < B < C$.

ganic compound and metal ion mixed together. Although the pM in the first third of the titration is as high as in curve A, no sharp change of pM with volume of titrant added is obtained. This is because the pM drop is divided among three end points instead of being concentrated in one single end point as in curve A.

The effect of acidity on the stability of organic-metal chelates is important. In general the strength of all chelates decreases with increasing acidity. This is reflected in the titration curve as shown by curves A and B in Fig. 15. The pH chosen for a chelate-formation titration should be sufficiently high so that the metal chelate will be strong enough to give a sharp change in pM at the end point. If the pH is too high, however, the end point will become less sharp owing to reaction of the metal ions and monochelate with the added base according to equations 10 and 11. This effect is shown by curve C in Fig. 15.

$$(10) \qquad\qquad M^{+n} + OH^- \rightarrow M(OH)^{+(n-1)}$$

$$(11) \qquad\qquad MA^{+(n-1)} + OH^- \rightarrow MA(OH)^{+(n-2)}$$

Titration curves like those in Fig. 15 can be calculated using the known concentration of sample and titrant. The pH at which the titration is carried out, as well as the formation constant of the organic-metal chelate and the acid dissociation constants of the free organic compound, must also be known. The reaction of a divalent metal to form a 1:1 complex with EDTA, III (ethylenediaminetetraacetic acid, also abbreviated as H_4Y), may be used for illustration.

$$^-O_2C-CH_2 \quad H \qquad\qquad H \quad CH_2CO_2^-$$
$$\searrow | \qquad\qquad\qquad | \nearrow$$
$$N-CH_2CH_2-N$$
$$\nearrow + \qquad\qquad + \searrow$$
$$HO_2C-CH_2 \qquad\qquad\qquad CH_2CO_2H$$
$$\text{III}$$

The metal ion is considered to react only with the tetravalent anion of EDTA (Y^{-4}).

$$(12) \qquad\qquad M^{++} + Y^{-4} \rightarrow MY^{-2}$$

The formation constant expression is

$$(13) \qquad\qquad K = \frac{(MY^{-2})}{(M^{++})(Y^{-4})}$$

Because at most pH values only part of the uncomplexed EDTA is present as Y^{-4}, it is convenient to write the above expression as

$$(14) \qquad\qquad K = \frac{(MY^{-2})}{(M^{++})(Y_u)\beta}$$

where Y_u is the total uncomplexed EDTA and β the ratio of Y^{-4} to Y_u. With the aid of the following expression, β can be readily evaluated at the pH used in the titration.

$$(15) \qquad \frac{1}{\beta} = \frac{(H^+)^4}{k_1k_2k_3k_4} + \frac{(H^+)^3}{k_2k_3k_4} + \frac{(H^+)^2}{k_3k_4} + \frac{(H^+)}{k_4} + 1$$

(Here k_1, k_2, k_3, and k_4 are the acid dissociation constants of H_4Y.)

ANALYTICAL METHODS FOR COMPLEXING AGENTS

A number of analytical methods are available for determining organic compounds on the basis of their reaction with a metal ion. Some of these have found rather extensive use in actual practice. Others have thus far been used only to a very limited extent, but are mentioned here because they appear to be potentially very useful.

One rather general method is to titrate the acid liberated in complex formation. This method is usually limited to complexes that are stable in acid solution, because titration of the liberated acid to an alkaline end point would in most cases cause the excess metal ion to react with the basic titrant. The determination of acetylenic hydrogen is an important practical example. The determination is based on the reaction of silver nitrate or perchlorate with alkynes having a replaceable hydrogen.

(16) $RC\!\equiv\!CH + Ag^+ \rightarrow RC\!\equiv\!CAg + H^+$

In most procedures the silver acetylide separates as an insoluble precipitate. By adding a concentrated solution (2.0 to 3.5 M) of silver nitrate or silver perchlorate to the organic sample, precipitation can be avoided.[4] An approximately measured portion of the silver reagent is neutralized with base to the methyl purple end point (approximately pH 5). The sample is added and the liberated acid is titrated with 0.1 N base to the same end point. Any acidic or basic functional groups present in the sample may be determined separately, and appropriate corrections must be applied. Halides and aldehydes cause no difficulty in this procedure.

Some chelating agents can be titrated with a metal ion, using a substance which forms a weaker, colored complex with the metal ion as the indicator. Ethylenediaminetetraacetic acid (EDTA), N-hydroxyethylethylenediaminetriacetic acid, and related compounds can be determined in this manner. A common procedure is to buffer the solution at pH 10 and titrate with a standard zinc or magnesium solution, using Eriochromeblack T, IV, as the indicator. The free indicator is blue at this pH, but the first excess of metal ion produces a red color due

IV

to formation of the corresponding metal complex of Eriochromeblack T. This usually determines only the free chelating agent. If some or all is already present as a metal chelate, it is usually possible to deter-

[4] L. Barnes and L. J. Molinini, *Anal. Chem.*, **27**, 1025 (1955).

mine the *total* organic reagent present by titrating with a metal ion with which it forms an even stronger chelate. For example the total EDTA content of a sample containing the divalent metal complexes may be determined by titration at pH 1.5 to 2.0 with standard bismuth nitrate, using thiourea as the indicator.[5]

(17) $$MY^{-2} + Bi^{+++} \rightarrow BiY^- + M^{++}$$

(18) $$\text{Thiourea} + Bi^{+++} \rightarrow \text{Yellow color}$$

Potentiometric titration of organic chelating agents is sometimes possible. In one method the chelating agent is titrated in pyridine-water with a suitable metal ion, using a mercury-coated platinum indicator electrode. This is probably a secondary electrode, the potential of which is determined by the concentration of mercuric ions at the electrode surface, which in turn is determined by the affinity of the chelating agents in solution for mercury (II). Copper (II), zinc (II), iron (III), and other metal ions can be used for the titration. Using zinc (II) as the titrant, two separate end points can be obtained in the titration of mixtures of EDTA and ammonia triacetic acid.[6]

Complexation of polarographically reducible metal ions shifts the half-wave potential toward more negative values. The magnitude of this shift becomes greater as the strength of the metal complex increases. For reasonably stable complexes it is therefore often possible to obtain two polarographic waves—one for the excess metal ion and one for the chelated metal ion. A practical example of this is in the polarographic determination of propylenediamine.[7] In this method low concentrations of propylenediamine are determined polarographically after the addition of excess cupric chloride. Although propylenediamine also forms a very stable 2:1 complex with copper (II), only the 1:1 complex will form in the presence of excess copper (II). The polarogram obtained has an excess copper wave with a half-wave potential of about -0.2 volt and a propylenediamine-copper complex wave at -0.4 to -0.6 volt, depending on the propylenediamine concentration of the sample. The propylenediamine concentration is read from a calibration curve after measuring the ratio of the diffusion current of the complex wave to that of the excess copper wave. This method should be generally useful for organic substances that form

[5] J. S. Fritz, *Anal. Chem.*, **26**, 1978 (1954).

[6] S. Siggia, D. W. Eichlin, and R. C. Rheinhardt, *Anal. Chem.*, **27**, 1745 (1955).

[7] A. D. Horton, P. F. Thomason, and M. T. Kelley, *Anal. Chem.*, **27**, 269 (1955).

copper chelates that are sufficiently strong to shift the half-wave potential for copper(II) at least 0.2 volt.

Use of an amperometric end point in the titration of organic compounds with metal ions appears to be very promising. In this method the titrant is a polarographically reducible metal ion which will form a precipitate or soluble complex of definite composition with the organic compound. The concentration of free metal ion is monitored polarographically (Chapter 12) during the titration. The polarograph is set at an applied potential sufficiently negative to obtain the limiting current for the free metal ion but less negative than the decomposition potential of the metal complex. The diffusion current will remain essentially constant and very small during the early part of the titration when most of the metal is consumed by complex formation. After the equivalence point the current will increase rapidly and should become essentially linear with the volume of titrant added. The end point of the titration is the point of intersection of the two straight lines that can be drawn through the points on the graph.

The titration of thiols with a silver salt is one of the most simple and widely used applications of this method.[8,9] The chemical reaction is precipitation of the silver thiol.

$$\text{(19)} \qquad \text{RSH} + \text{Ag}^+ + \text{NH}_3 \rightarrow \text{RSAg} + \text{NH}_4^+$$

A small, mechanically rotated platinum electrode is used as the indicator electrode. A large $\text{Hg}^0 - \text{HgI}_4^=$ electrode connected to the system by means of a salt bridge serves as the reference electrode. It also provides sufficient potential to reduce the silver ion, thus obviating the necessity for an electrically controlled applied potential. It is not necessary to purge dissolved oxygen from the system because oxygen is not reduced at the applied potential used in this titration. This method is especially useful for determining small amounts of thiols, such as are found in petroleum products.

Amperometric titration with metal ions should be widely applicable for the determination of organic compounds. Many metal ions are polarographically reducible at potentials lower than those required for the reduction of most organic groups. By making careful choices of applied potentials one should be able to develop reasonably selective procedures based upon differences in the aptitudes of related organic compounds for complex formation with metal ions.

[8] I. M. Kolthoff and W. E. Harris, *Ind. Eng. Chem., Anal. Ed.*, **18**, 161 (1946).
[9] M. D. Grimes, J. E. Puckett, B. J. Newby, and B. J. Heinrich, *Anal. Chem.*, **27**, 152 (1955).

In some instances precipitation of organic substances as metal salts of chelates proves to be the most convenient approach to an analytical problem. The determination of anthranilic acid by precipitation with zinc, and 1,3-diketones by precipitation with copper(II) have already been mentioned. Most thiols are quantitatively precipitated by silver and can thus be determined gravimetrically as an alternate to the titrimetric methods. Many alkaloids and synthetic drugs form insoluble precipitates of definite composition with cadmium(II) or mercury(II) and thiocyanate. A typical example is the precipitation of dimethylaminophenyldimethylpyrazalone as $Cd(Py)(SCN)_4$, with the subsequent measurement of the quantity of precipitate formed by titrating the cadmium (II) with EDTA.[10]

Compounds that form highly colored metal chelates or even non-chelated complexes can often be determined spectrophotometrically. Small amounts of o-phenylphenol and certain other phenols can be determined by measurement of the yellow color formed with titanium(IV) in concentrated sulfuric acid solution.[11] A method for macro quantities of glycerol is based on spectrophotometric measurement of the blue cupric complex formed in strongly alkaline aqueous solution.[12] The excess copper(II) is precipitated as cupric hydroxide and is separated by centrifugation. Ethylene glycol and 1,2-propylene glycol also form colored complexes but pentaerythritol, diethylene glycol, dipropylene glycol, and other nonvicinal glycols do not interfere.

An important general method for carboxylic acid esters and lactones is based on metal chelate formation.[13] The ester is first converted to the hydroxamic acid by reaction with alkaline hydroxyl amine.

$$\text{(20)} \qquad \underset{\displaystyle \|}{\overset{\displaystyle O}{R C}}\!-\!OR' + NH_2OH \xrightarrow{\ OH^-\ } \underset{\displaystyle \|}{\overset{\displaystyle O}{R C}}\!-\!NHOH + R'OH$$

Addition of ferric perchlorate and acid then converts the hydroxamic acid to a highly colored ferric chelate. This red color is measured spectrophotometrically. Carboxylic acid anhydrides also form hydroxamic acids, but amides do not react under the conditions used. Ketones and aldehydes consume the hydroxylamine reagent but do not otherwise interfere.

Small amounts of dithiocarbamates are frequently determined by

[10] W. Groebel and E. Schneider, *Zeit. anal. Chem.*, **146**, 191 (1955).
[11] P. H. Caufield and R. J. Robinson, *Anal. Chem.*, **25**, 982 (1953).
[12] F. Spagnolo, *Anal. Chem.*, **25**, 1566 (1953).
[13] R. F. Goddu, N. F. LeBlanc, and C. M. Wright, *Anal. Chem.*, **27**, 1251 (1955).

measurement of the intense yellow copper complex. Analysis of benzene for traces of carbon disulfide has been accomplished in a similar manner.[14] Addition of diethylamine to the sample quickly converts the carbon disulfide to the diethyldithiocarbamate. Addition

$$(21) \quad (C_2H_5)_2NH + CS_2 \rightarrow \left[(C_2H_5)_2N-C\begin{matrix} \nearrow S \\ \searrow S \end{matrix} \right]^- (C_2H_5)_2NH_2{}^+$$

of cupric acetate then converts the dithiocarbamate to the yellow copper complex.

PROBLEMS

1. Devise several possible procedures for the determination of the composition of a mixture of cis- and trans-1,2-cyclohexanediol. Consult the literature concerning these compounds to see if you can find an indication as to whether or not your methods might be successful.

2. Anthranilamide, I, does not form very stable chelates. Can you devise a method for the determination of this compound in a mixture with its meta and para isomers?

$$\underset{\text{I}}{\overset{\overset{\displaystyle NH_2}{|} \quad CONH_2}{\bigcirc}}$$

3. A chelating agent, A, is useful in the specific determination of a metal ion, B. Discuss the proposition that it follows that B will be a good reagent for the determination of A.

4. Will CH_3COCH_2CN form stable chelates similar to those derived from $CH_3COCH_2CO_2C_2H_5$?

5. 1-Hexanethiol and 1-butanethiol are present in approximately equal proportions in an alcoholic solution. Suggest a method for determining the amount of each.

[14] T. A. Dick, J. Soc. Chem. Ind., 66, 253 (1947).

8.

ELEMENTAL ANALYSIS

Elemental analysis may be defined as analysis for the total amount of each element present without regard to how the elements may be arranged in the molecule. Formerly elemental analysis was almost the only type of quantitative organic analysis commonly carried out. Analysis for carbon, hydrogen, nitrogen, etc., is still used by virtually all organic research chemists to determine or verify the empirical formulae of pure organic compounds. Analysis of pure compounds by quantitative functional group methods often yields more detailed information, and because of this such methods are gaining in favor. It is sometimes possible to almost completely characterize an unknown compound by quantitative analysis for the various functional groups present. Also most functional group methods are simple titrimetric procedures, whereas many elemental analytical procedures are time-consuming and require very careful technique and controlled conditions. Indeed, many micro combustion procedures such as the carbon-hydrogen determination are almost more of an art than a science.

Despite the disadvantages mentioned, elemental analysis does have an important place in quantitative organic analysis. It is the only way to determine the empirical formula of pure compounds. Another use is to determine quantitatively a compound containing an element not present in any other constituent of a mixture. Many important analytical methods such as protein in food by total nitrogen, determination of insecticides by analysis for halogen, and analysis for certain medicinals by arsenic analysis employ this scheme. The quantitative determination of an element unique to one constituent of a mixture should always be considered when one is attacking a new analytical problem.

DETERMINATION OF CARBON AND HYDROGEN

This method is based on the complete conversion of the hydrogen in the sample to water and of the carbon to carbon dioxide. This is achieved by burning the sample in a stream of oxygen. Partial combustion is effected by heating the portion of the combustion tube containing the sample to dull red heat. The combustion is completed as the gases pass through a heated portion of the tube packed with copper oxide and lead chromate. The water vapor produced is quantitatively taken up by a weighed absorption tube containing anhydrous magnesium perchlorate. The carbon dioxide produced is not absorbed by magnesium perchlorate but is quantitatively taken up by a second weighed absorption tube containing Ascarite or Mikohbite, a preparation consisting of an inert substance of great surface area coated with sodium hydroxide.

In order to shorten the time required for complete combustion of the sample, the determination is carried out on a micro scale, using a 5- to 10-mg. sample. In the following section the salient features of the apparatus employed and the procedure followed are described. For instruction in weighing on a micro scale and for a detailed procedure, a reliable textbook on micro analysis should be consulted.[1]

Combustion Train

A typical combustion train for determination of carbon and hydrogen consists of the following parts, connected in the order listed:

1. Source of oxygen and compressed air.
2. Pressure regulators, one each for the oxygen supply and for the compressed air supply.
3. Bubble counter to measure the rate of oxygen flow.

[1] A. Steyermark, *Quantitative Organic Microanalysis*, Blakiston, Philadelphia, 1951; J. B. Niederl and V. Niederl, *Micromethods of Quantitative Organic Analysis*, 2nd. ed., Wiley, New York, 1948; F. Pregl and J. Grant, *Quantitative Organic Microanalysis*, 4th English edition, Blakiston, Philadelphia, 1946.

4. A "U" tube filled with Ascarite and anhydrous magnesium perchlorate. The function of this tube is to remove any traces of water or carbon dioxide from the oxygen or compressed air.

5. Combustion tube with electric furnaces or burners for heating.

6. Absorption tube for water.

7. Absorption tube for carbon dioxide.

8. Guard tube containing anhydrous magnesium perchlorate. This is to prevent moisture from entering the system from the Mariotte bottle.

9. The Mariotte bottle aids the passage of gas through the last part of the system by applying gentle suction. By collecting the water displaced from the Mariotte bottle in a graduate cylinder the volume of gas that has passed through the train can be measured.

Combustion Tube

Combustion tubes are packed in various manners depending on the type of compounds to be analyzed and on the personal preference of the analyst. A typical packing is shown in Fig. 16.

Condensed Procedure

1. The flow rate is adjusted and residual gases in the system are swept out.

2. With air flowing, the boat containing the sample is introduced as quickly as possible into the combustion tube.

3. After shifting from compressed air to oxygen the first combustion is started. The movable burner G is started at position 1 and slowly traveled to position 2 over a period of 15 to 20 minutes. An apparatus is commercially available that has a mechanical drive for the movable burner.

4. A second combustion is carried out in much the same manner as the first except that the burner G is moved at a faster rate.

5. The entire train is swept out with air and the absorption tubes are disconnected and weighed.

NITROGEN

Two general methods are available for the determination of total organic nitrogen. These are the Kjeldahl and Dumas methods. Each has its limitations but they tend to supplement each other so that almost any organic compound can be analyzed for nitrogen by one of the two methods.

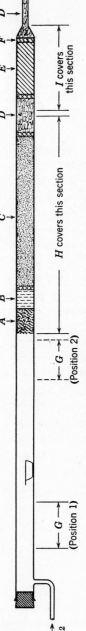

Figure 16. Carbon-hydrogen combustion tube filling.

A. Fine silver wire. This is to absorb halogens which would otherwise interfere with the determination.

B. Platinum gauze or platinized asbestos. This is to aid in the combustion of condensed ring systems.

C. Mixed cupric oxide and lead chromate. The cupric oxide catalyzes oxidation of carbon to carbon dioxide and hydrogen to water while the lead chromate removes any sulfur.

D. Silver wire. This is to conduct enough heat to these parts of the combustion tube to prevent condensation of water vapor.

E. Lead dioxide. This is to remove oxides of nitrogen from the gas stream.

F. Asbestos "choke plug." This consists of asbestos packed tightly enough to offer sufficient resistance for proper rate of gas flow through the system.

G. Movable gas burner or electric heater.

H. Electric furnace (or long gas burner) maintained at approximately 680° C.

I. Electric heating mortar maintained at a constant temperature in the range 175°–190° C.

Kjeldahl Method

The reactions involved in this method may be summarized as follows:

(1) $\text{Organic N} \xrightarrow[\text{catalyst}]{\text{H}_2\text{SO}_4} \text{NH}_4{}^+ \xrightarrow{\text{NaOH}} \text{NH}_3$

The sample is digested with concentrated sulfuric acid to destroy the organic matter and to convert the nitrogen to ammonium hydrogen sulfate. The solution is then made alkaline with sodium hydroxide, and the ammonia is distilled into a measured quantity of hydrochloric acid. The excess hydrochloric acid is then titrated with standard sodium hydroxide. The amount of nitrogen in the original sample is equivalent to the hydrochloric acid neutralized by the ammonia.

The digestion is carried out in a flask of a special type called a Kjeldahl flask. It is common practice to carry out a number of determinations simultaneously, using digestion racks with fume eradicators. Potassium hydrogen sulfate is added to the sulfuric acid to raise the boiling point of the solution and permit a higher digestion temperature. A small amount of mercury, copper, selenium, or cupric selenite is also added to catalyze the reaction. The time for digestion varies greatly according to the nature of the sample. The solution becomes homogeneous and lightens in color as the reaction nears completion.

A typical set-up for the distillation step is shown in Fig. 17. When digestion is complete, the solution is cooled and diluted somewhat. Sodium hydroxide is added carefully so that two layers form, and the Kjeldahl flask is quickly connected to the distillation apparatus. Some types of apparatus have a stopcock arrangement for adding the sodium hydroxide after the flask has been connected to the distillation set-up, thus avoiding possible loss of ammonia. When a Kjeldahl determination is carried out on a micro basis, steam distillation is usually employed.

A widely used modification employs boric acid instead of hydrochloric acid in the receiver for the distillate. The ammonium borate formed is then titrated directly with standard hydrochloric acid.

(2) $\text{NH}_3 + \text{H}_3\text{BO}_3 \rightarrow \text{NH}_4{}^+ + \text{H}_2\text{BO}_3{}^-$

(3) $\text{H}_2\text{BO}_3{}^- + \text{H}^+ \rightarrow \text{H}_3\text{BO}_3$

The advantage of this method is that only one titration and one standard solution (hydrochloric acid) is required. Boric acid is sufficiently acidic to react with ammonia and prevent loss by volatilization but is too weak to interfere with the titration of ammonium borate with hydrochloric acid.

Amines and substances that yield amines on hydrolysis (such as amides, nitriles, proteins, ureas, and thioureas) can be analyzed readily

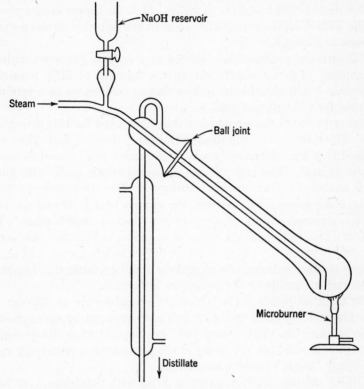

Figure 17. Apparatus for micro Kjeldahl distillation.

by the Kjeldahl method. By a preliminary reduction step many nitro and nitroso compounds, oximes, azo, and diazo compounds can also be successfully determined. Aromatic heterocycles, such as pyridine, are very resistant to oxidation and thus are likely to give very low results for nitrogen. Nevertheless numerous reports of the successful determination of this type of compound by the Kjeldahl method are in the literature.

Dumas Method

This is a combustion procedure in which all the chemically combined nitrogen is converted into gaseous nitrogen. The combustion is carried out in an atmosphere of carbon dioxide, but cupric oxide is present in the combustion tube to catalyze the conversion of carbon to carbon dioxide and hydrogen to water. Metallic copper is also present in one section of the combustion tube to convert any nitrogen oxides present to nitrogen.

The nitrogen produced is collected in a special gas buret called a nitrometer. The nitrometer contains a solution of 50% potassium hydroxide which absorbs the carbon dioxide and serves as a confining solution for the nitrogen gas.

Figure 18 shows the combustion train employed for this determination. The source of carbon dioxide is a large thermos flask filled with crushed Dry Ice. Alternately a Kipp generator can be used to supply carbon dioxide. The two sections of coarse cupric oxide wire and a single section of reduced copper turnings represent the permanent filling of the combustion tube. Around the sample boat is placed an additional temporary filling of fine, loosely packed cupric oxide. The nitrometer contains mercury to the level shown in Fig. 18. This serves as a seal between the nitrometer and the combustion tube and makes the gas bubbles entering the nitrometer small to facilitate absorption of the carbon dioxide by the potassium hydroxide.

The essential points of the laboratory procedure are as follows:

1. The residual gases in the system are swept out by rapid passage of carbon dioxide. The "sweep out" is complete when absorption of the carbon dioxide bubbles rising in the nitrometer is essentially complete, only "micro" bubbles remaining.

2. With the nitrometer completely filled with potassium hydroxide, the first combustion is begun, starting with the movable burner at the position shown in Fig. 18 and gradually moving it to the long burner over a period of about 20 minutes. The sample must be heated very cautiously during the first part of the combustion.

3. A second combustion is carried out in a similar manner to the first but at a faster rate (about 10 minutes is required). The flow rate is then increased to flush the remaining nitrogen into the nitrometer. When micro bubbles are attained the flow of carbon dioxide is stopped.

4. The volume of gas in the nitrometer is read and corrected to standard conditions of temperature and pressure.

The Dumas method gives good results with almost all types of organic nitrogen compounds. Pyrimidines, sulfonamides, and semicar-

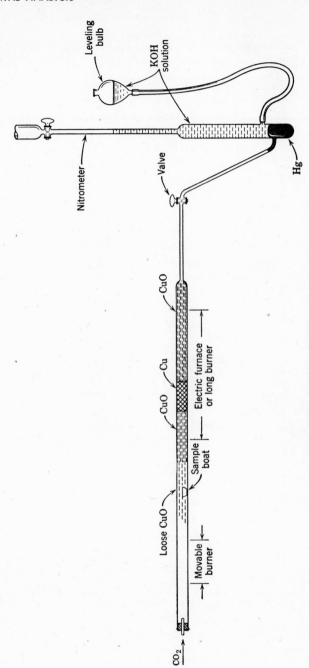

Figure 18. Apparatus for Dumas nitrogen determination.

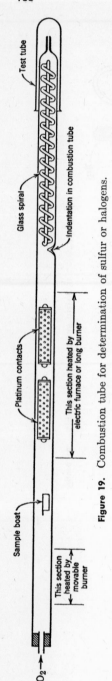

Figure 19. Combustion tube for determination of sulfur or halogens.

bazides often give low results but this can usually be corrected by adding cupric acetate, potassium chloride, or potassium dichromate to aid combustion of the sample.[2] Compounds having long aliphatic chains may be incompletely combusted, forming some methane. This is measured along with the nitrogen, giving high results. Cupric acetate and potassium chlorate are useful in correcting this condition.

A single Dumas nitrogen determination can usually be carried out in less time than is required for a single Kjeldahl determination. However, multiple determinations can be more readily carried out by the Kjeldahl method, making it generally superior to the Dumas procedure for routine analyses which place a premium on speed of manipulation. On the other hand, the Dumas method gives satisfactory results with a wider variety of compounds.

SULFUR

A large number of methods have been proposed for determining sulfur in organic matter. Virtually all these methods consist of two general parts: destruction of the organic matter and determination of the isolated sulfur which has been converted to the sulfate form.

Pregl Combustion Method

The combustion to be employed in this determination is shown in Fig. 19. A small, weighed sample is burned in a stream of oxygen in the presence of platinum contacts. The carbon and hydrogen in the sample is converted to carbon dioxide and water, respectively, and the sulfur is oxidized to a mixture of sulfur dioxide and sulfur trioxide. The sulfur gases are absorbed by a hydrogen peroxide solution which has been used to moisten the surface of the glass spiral. The

[2] A. Steyermark, *Quantitative Organic Microanalysis*, Blakiston, Philadelphia, 1951, p. 56.

function of the hydrogen peroxide solution is to oxidize sulfur dioxide to sulfuric acid. Sulfur trioxide, of course, combines with water alone to form sulfuric acid.

(4) $$SO_2 + H_2O_2 \rightarrow H_2SO_4$$

(5) $$SO_3 + H_2O \rightarrow H_2SO_4$$

The peroxide solution on the surface of the glass spiral is washed into a beaker, and the sulfate is determined as described in a later section.

Carius Method

This is another widely used, general method for the micro determination of sulfur in organic compounds. Destruction of the organic matter is accomplished by heating with fuming nitric acid in a sealed tube. An alkali salt is also present so that the sulfur will be converted to an alkali hydrogen sulfate instead of volatile sulfur dioxide or sulfur trioxide.

(6) $$\text{Organic S} \xrightarrow[\text{NaX}]{\text{HNO}_3} NaHSO_4 + (CO_2, H_2O, X_2, \text{etc.})$$

The sample size and the amount of fuming nitric acid must be controlled within rather narrow limits; otherwise the reaction either will be incomplete or will become too violent and blow out the sealed tube. Some glass-blowing technique is required in order to seal the reaction tube properly. The sealed tube is placed in a special furnace maintained at 250° C. After heating for about 8 hours in the furnace, the tube is cooled and carefully opened. The contents of the tube are carefully washed into a small beaker and evaporated to dryness on a steam bath to remove nitric acid. The residue is dissolved in distilled water, and the sulfate content is determined.

Sodium Peroxide Bomb

The sample is thoroughly mixed with sodium peroxide and with smaller amounts of potassium nitrate and sucrose. The mixture is then placed in a Parr bomb (Fig. 20) and ignited by applying a sharply pointed flame to the bottom of the bomb. Once the reaction begins, the flame is removed, and after a minute or two the bomb can be cooled and opened. The organic matter is completely destroyed, and the sulfur present is converted to sodium sulfate.

An obvious advantage of the sodium peroxide bomb is its speed and the comparatively small amount of manipulation required. A serious

Figure 20. Sodium peroxide bomb. (Courtesy Parr Instrument Co.)

disadvantage, however, is that the large excess of alkali salts used makes the final determination of the sulfate more difficult.

Other Methods

Substances such as coal are often analyzed for sulfur by burning the finely powdered sample in an oxygen bomb. In the Ter Meulen method [3] the sample is decomposed by destructive catalytic hydrogenation, the sulfur being converted to hydrogen sulfide. Sulfur in coal,[4] rubber,[5] and some pure organic compounds [6] has been determined by first destroying the organic matter by heating with mixed nitric and perchloric acids. This method is simple and accurate, but seems to work best on compounds that are difficult to oxidize completely. In samples of other types results are often low, some sulfur being lost presumably as sulfur dioxide.

Completing the Determination

The procedure used to complete the sulfur determination depends on the amount of sulfur present and on the method used to destroy the organic matter. Very small amounts of sulfur are often determined

[3] H. Ter Meulen, *Rec. trav. chim.*, **41**, 112 (1922); N. H. Furman and W. W. Scott, *Standard Methods of Chemical Analysis*, Van Nostrand, New York, 1939, Vol. II.

[4] G. F. Smith and A. G. Deem, *Ind. Eng. Chem., Anal. Ed.*, **4**, 227 (1932).

[5] E. Kahane, *Caoutchouc et gutta-percha*, **24**, 13549 (1927); *C.A.*, **21**, 2817 (1927); E. Wolesensky, *Ind. Eng. Chem.*, **20**, 1234 (1928).

[6] J. H. Jones, *J.A.O.A.C.*, **26**, 182 (1943).

by precipitation of sulfate with barium and measurement of the turbidity produced. This is a rapid but rather inaccurate procedure. Larger amounts of sulfate are usually determined by precipitation of barium sulfate followed by filtration, washing, ignition, and weighing of the precipitate. This operation may be either on a macro or micro scale.

Following the Pregl micro combustion, the sulfuric acid produced can be titrated with standard sodium hydroxide, provided that the sample does not contain nitrogen or halogen which would also form acids.

Determination of sulfate by titration with standard barium solution is another possibility. One method employs tetrahydroxyquinone (T.H.Q.) to provide an end point in the titration by forming a red violet complex with the first excess barium.[7] Unfortunately this end point is not sharp and matching the color of the titration with a standard (preferably by means of a photometer) is required to determine the end point accurately.

A new titrimetric method [8] has been developed which could undoubtedly be used to determine sulfate after decomposition of the sample by either the Carius or Pregl combustion method. This involves titration of sulfate in 80% alcohol with 0.01 M barium perchlorate. Thorin [2-(2-hydroxy-3,6-disulfo-1-naphthylazo)-benzenearsonic acid] serves as the indicator, forming a pink complex on the surface of the precipitate when the first excess barium ion has been added. The end point is reversible and quite easily detectable. Metal cations cause a significant error due to coprecipitation, but this difficulty may be avoided by passing the solution through a small cation exchange column before the titration.

If large amounts of foreign ions are present, as in the solution from the sodium peroxide bomb, titration of sulfate by this method is impossible. This difficulty may be avoided, however, by decomposing the sample in a peroxide bomb and separating the sulfate from most of the other salts by preferential adsorption onto a column of activated alumina.[9] The sulfate is eluted from the alumina column with dilute ammonia and passed through a cation exchanger in the hydrogen form.

[7] J. F. Alicino, *Anal. Chem.*, **20**, 85 (1948); C. L. Ogg, C. O. Willits, and F. J. Cooper, *Anal. Chem.*, **20**, 83 (1948); A. Steyermark, E. Bass, and B. Littman, *Anal. Chem.*, **20**, 587 (1948).

[8] J. S. Fritz and S. S. Yamamura, *Anal. Chem.*, **27**, 1461 (1955); J. S. Fritz and M. Q. Freeland, *Anal. Chem.*, **26**, 1593 (1954).

[9] J. S. Fritz, S. S. Yamamura, and M. J. Richard, *Anal. Chem.*, **29**, 158 (1957).

The sulfate is then titrated in 80% alcohol with 0.01 M barium perchlorate as described above.

CHLORINE, BROMINE, AND IODINE

A large number of methods have been proposed for the quantitative determination of halogens in organic compounds. All these methods require first the conversion of organic halogen to the halide ion, and second the quantitative determination of the halide ion produced. It is convenient to discuss the analysis of organic fluoro compounds separately from the other halogen compounds, because organic compounds containing fluorine are often difficult to decompose and require more drastic treatment. Another reason is that the method for completing the analysis is different because fluoride, unlike the other halide ions, cannot be determined by precipitation with silver.

The Carius, Pregl combustion, and sodium peroxide bomb procedures used for organic sulfur can with slight modification also be used to decompose samples for halogen determination. The apparatus used in the Pregl combustion method is the same as for the sulfur determination, but the glass spiral is moistened with a solution of sodium bicarbonate and a reducing agent such as sodium bisulfite or hydrazine to convert free halogen to the halide ion. The halide ion can be determined

$$(7) \qquad \text{Organic X} \xrightarrow[\text{Pt}]{\text{O}_2} \text{X}_2 \xrightarrow[\text{HCO}_3^-]{\text{NH}_2\text{NH}_2} 2\text{X}^-$$

gravimetrically or by titration with silver.

The Carius method for halogens involves heating the sample with fuming nitric acid and silver nitrate in a sealed tube.

$$(8) \qquad \text{Organic X} \xrightarrow[\text{HNO}_3]{\text{fuming}} \text{X}_2 \xrightarrow{\text{Ag}^+} 2\text{AgX}$$

In the sodium peroxide bomb method the halogen is converted to the sodium halide, which can be determined either gravimetrically or titrimetrically.

$$(9) \qquad \text{Organic X} \xrightarrow{\text{Na}_2\text{O}_2} \text{NaX}$$

The methods described above involve total destruction of the organic compound and for this reason are usually carried out on a micro basis. Several methods are available for converting organic halogens to the halide ion without destroying all the organic matter. One of these is the Stepanow method.[10] In this procedure, the sample is dissolved

[10] A. Stepanow, *Ber.*, **39**, 4056 (1906).

in alcohol and metallic sodium is added to convert the halogen to the halide ion. This method is convenient and rapid but is limited in application to compounds with moderately reactive halogens.

A modification by Rauscher [11] has been proposed in which the sample is dissolved in ethanolamine and dioxane and then treated with sodium metal. Heat is applied during the reaction, and a cold finger condenser is used to prevent excessive loss of solvent.

A still more vigorous treatment involves the use of sodium and liquid ammonia.[12] The sample is dissolved in liquid ammonia or in a mixture of liquid ammonia and absolute ether. Small pieces of metallic sodium are added until a blue color (sodium metal dissolved in ammonia is blue) persists for a few minutes. Ammonium nitrate is then added to remove the excess sodium.

$$(10) \qquad Na^0_{\text{m}} + NH_4NO_3 \rightarrow NaNO_3 + NH_3 + H^0$$

The ammonia is then removed by evaporation, and the sodium halide is determined by conventional means.

Sodium biphenyl [13] and sodium naphthalene [14] have been shown to be excellent for converting halogens in organic compounds to an ionizable form. The reagent is prepared by adding biphenyl (or naphthalene) to finely dispersed sodium in toluene, then diluting with ethylene glycol dimethyl ether. The analysis is carried out by adding a portion of the sodium biphenyl reagent to the sample (dissolved in dry toluene in a separatory funnel) and shaking for about 30 seconds. After standing for an additional 5 minutes, the sodium halide produced is extracted once with distilled water and twice with dilute nitric acid. The halide in the combined extracts is then titrated by the Volhard procedure.

This procedure has given excellent results with a wide variety of compounds. No chloro or bromo compounds have yet been found for which the biphenyl reagent is ineffective. Small concentrations of halogen compounds, such as ethylene chloride and ethylene bromide in gasoline, can be conveniently determined by this method.

[11] W. H. Rauscher, Ind. Eng. Chem., Anal. Ed., 9, 296 (1937).

[12] T. H. Vaughn and J. A. Nieuwland, Ind. Eng. Chem., Anal. Ed., 3, 274 (1931); R. L. Shriner, Quantitative Analysis of Organic Compounds, Edwards Bros., Ann Arbor, 1944, 3rd ed., p. 71.

[13] L. M. Liggett, Anal. Chem., 26, 748 (1954); B. Pecherer, C. M. Gambrill, and G. W. Wilcox, Anal. Chem., 22, 311 (1950).

[14] F. L. Benton and W. H. Hamill, Anal. Chem., 20, 269 (1948).

Fluorine

Many organic compounds containing fluorine are especially resistant to heat and oxidation. Such properties make fluorine compounds useful commercially but complicate the task of the analyst. Compounds with more than one fluorine on the same carbon atom are especially difficult to decompose analytically. The Carius method, which is widely used for other halogen compounds, cannot be used because fluorine attacks the glass of the reaction tube.

Elving and Ligett [15] found that fusion with metallic potassium in an evacuated, sealed tube will successfully decompose practically all types of samples for determination of fluorine or other halogens. Thirty minutes' heating at 400° C. is sufficient to convert the sample to the alkali halide and pyrolysis products (mostly carbon). Fusion with metallic potassium or sodium in a nickel bomb has also found extensive use in the decomposition of organic fluorine compounds.

Miller, Hunt, and McBee [16] have described a convenient procedure for converting organic fluorine to ionizable form. The sample is weighed into a tube similar to a Carius tube and dissolved in ether. The tube is cooled in Dry Ice-alcohol, and liquid ammonia is distilled into the tube. The reaction tube is then sealed and shaken for 5 hours at room temperature.

The methods for determining fluoride after decomposition of organic samples are not completely satisfactory. A number of metals form insoluble fluorides but most of these are very gelatinous and difficult to handle. Lead chlorofluoride is one of the few insoluble, crystalline fluorides and has therefore been widely used for the gravimetric determination of fluoride. The conditions for precipitation must be carefully controlled in order to obtain a precipitate of the proper composition. Care must also be taken to avoid error due to solubility loss. Thorium fluoride is gelatinous but a determination of fluoride by titration with standard thorium solution has nevertheless found some use.[17] Sodium alizarin sulfonate serves as the indicator in this titration by forming a red complex with the first slight excess of thorium.

Halogens As Functional Groups

The reactivity of halogens in organic compounds varies according to the configuration of the group to which the halogen is attached. By

[15] P. J. Elving and W. B. Ligett, Ind. Eng. Chem., Anal. Ed., 14, 449 (1942).
[16] J. F. Miller, H. Hunt, and E. T. McBee, Anal. Chem., 19, 148 (1947).
[17] R. J. Rowley and H. V. Churchill, Ind. Eng. Chem., Anal. Ed., 9, 551 (1937).

taking advantage of differences in reactivity of the various halogens it is often possible to determine one halogen compound in the presence of another, or to distinguish between halogens in the same compound. The problem of finding conditions for the selective conversion of organic halogens to the halide ion is considered in Chapter 9 (pp. 151–158).

METALS

Metallic salts of organic compounds are usually determined by combustion. The sample is weighed into a porcelain or platinum boat, moistened with sulfuric acid, and burned in a stream of air to the

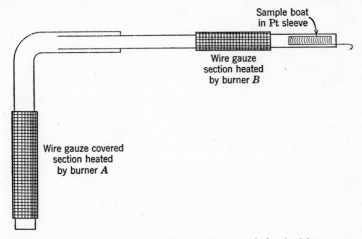

Figure 21. Apparatus for determining metals by ignition.

metal sulfate. The sulfuric acid is omitted for the determination of certain metals that are better weighed as the free metal (for example, silver) or as the metal oxide (for example, titanium and aluminum). The apparatus used for this determination is shown in Fig. 21. The vertical portion of the tube heated by burner A acts as a chimney and keeps a current of air constantly sweeping past the sample. Burner B is at the position shown in Fig. 21 at the start of the determination and is slowly moved toward the sample during the combustion.

The destruction of organic matter by oxidation in solution is widely used prior to the determination of metals. This technique is especially valuable when only trace amounts of metals are present such as in foods, drugs, biological fluids, etc. Various combinations of nitric acid, perchloric acid, sulfuric acid, and 30 to 90% hydrogen peroxide are suitable for this purpose. Of these, mixed nitric and perchloric acids are probably the most widely applicable. Using this reagent the organic matter in hay,[18] leather,[19] beer, wine,[20] rubber,[21] blood, oysters,[22] and many other substances can be quickly and completely destroyed. After the destruction of organic matter, the metals present can be determined by standard spectrophotometric, spectrographic, or titrimetric procedures.

The function of nitric acid is to destroy the more easily oxidized organic matter. Nitric acid must be present until this is accomplished because perchloric acid alone acting on easily oxidizable organic matter is likely to cause a serious explosion. When the action of the nitric acid is essentially complete, it is boiled off. At this point the temperature of the solution rises to about 200° C. and the perchloric acid completes the oxidation process. Oxidation of organic material is sometimes speeded by the addition of concentrated sulfuric acid, or by traces of catalysts such as vanadium and chromium salts.[22]

Destruction of organic matter with perchloric acid is completely safe if properly carried out. Necessary precautions include addition of nitric acid to the sample *before* any perchloric acid is added, avoiding too rapid removal of nitric acid during the oxidation, and the use of a good hood which does not expose any wood or organic tars to the action of perchloric acid fumes.

PROBLEMS

1. Analysis of a pure compound gave the following results: 16.5% nitrogen and 25.3% sulfur. Calculate the ratio of nitrogen atoms to sulfur atoms in the compound.

2. Analysis of a compound containing only carbon, hydrogen, and oxygen gave the following results: 46.8% carbon and 3.2% hydrogen. It was known that the compound contained fewer than 12 carbon atoms. Calculate the empirical formula.

3. Suggest a quantitative method for determining the composition of methyl methacrylate-acrylonitrile copolymers.

[18] J. F. Gieseking, H. J. Snider, and C. A. Goetz, *Ind. Eng. Chem., Anal. Ed.,* **7**, 185 (1935).

[19] G. F. Smith and J. S. Fritz, *J. Am. Leather Chem. Assoc.,* **42**, 195 (1947).

[20] L. G. Saywell and B. B. Cunningham, *Ind. Eng. Chem., Anal. Ed.,* **9**, 66 (1937).

[21] E. Kahane, *Ann. chim. anal.,* **9** II, 261 (1927).

[22] G. F. Smith, *Anal. Chim. Acta,* **8**, 397 (1953).

4. Outline a convenient method for determining each of the following:

(a) Magnesium in magnesium citrate.

(b) Benzyl chloride in the presence of benzyl alcohol.

(c) Chromium in chrome tanned leather (1 to 5% Cr).

5. Suggest a method for distinguishing quantitatively between pyridine- and pyrrole-type nitrogen in petroleum.

6. Nitrobenzene is brominated in the presence of iron at 140° C. Devise a method for the quantitative determination of the bromonitrobenzene formed that does not involve a separation from unreacted nitrobenzene.

9.

KINETICS

IN

ANALYSIS

INTRODUCTION

Many analytical procedures have been developed in the course of kinetic studies of organic reaction mechanisms, and the results of such investigations can be utilized in setting up still more methods. It is unfortunate that the large number of kinetic papers is not ordinarily considered a part of the literature of analytical chemistry. This probably arises from the awe which many an analyst feels for the apparent sophistication of kinetic discussions. Actually the complications usually arise in the interpretation of rate data in terms of reaction mechanism and the theories of relative reactivity. In many cases the rate data themselves are very straightforward and can be utilized for analytical purposes with a minimum of worry about their theoretical significance. It is true that an appreciation of the factors underlying the relative reactivities of organic compounds will sharpen the analyst's approach to devising new methods in general, but it is not directly pertinent to the examination of the numbers derived from a particular set of kinetic measurements. It is encouraging to note that interest in kinetics in analysis is on the upswing. An interesting chapter by Lee, entitled "Methods Based on Reaction Rates," appeared in the second volume of *Organic Analysis*.[1]

[1] T. S. Lee in *Organic Analysis*, Vol. II, Interscience, New York, 1954.

Basically, kinetic data state quantitatively how fast a reaction proceeds under a certain set of carefully specified conditions. Furthermore, the data ordinarily give the dependence of the reaction rate on the concentrations of the reactants and other constituents of the solution. If the solvent happens to be one of the reactants or is involved in some way as a catalyst, this does not appear explicitly in the statement of kinetic results. Data are usually summarized in terms of *rate constants* which have dimensions that depend upon the *order* of the reaction. Reaction order gives the dependence of rate on concentrations. Equation 2 is a generalized rate law which illustrates the terms for a reaction in which reactants A and B are converted, in the presence of other substances, C, to a set of products D and E.

$$(1) \qquad\qquad A + B \xrightarrow{C} D + E$$

$$(2) \qquad -\frac{d[A]}{dt} = -\frac{d[B]}{dt} = \frac{d[D]}{dt} = \frac{d[E]}{dt}$$

$$= k[A]^{n_1}[B]^{n_2}[C]^{n_3}$$

$$(3) \qquad n_1 + n_2 + n_3 = \text{over-all reaction order}$$

$$(4) \qquad n_1 = \text{order with respect to A}$$

For the first-order rate law,

$$(5) \qquad\qquad -\frac{d[A]}{dt} = k[A]$$

the rate constant has the dimensions of reciprocal time. For higher-order reactions, the constant will have units of reciprocal time multiplied by reciprocal concentration to a power that is 1 less than the over-all reaction order. There is no good uniformity in the literature as to the units of time used in reporting rate constants although strenuous efforts are currently being made to encourage the universal use of reciprocal seconds as a standard unit.[2] Complex rate laws in which the reaction order is nonintegral are known but are worth avoiding in analytical work because they usually reflect complications in reaction mechanism that may render the choice of standard reaction conditions difficult. In fact, in many analytical problems it is worth while to attempt to devise methods of converting all higher-order reactions to pseudo first order. This can be done if excesses of all except one reactant are used so that that reactant is the only species whose

[2] Committee Report, *J. Am. Chem. Soc.*, **77**, May 20 (1955).

relative concentration changes appreciably. In the above example, if the initial concentration of B is as much as ten times the initial A concentration, the concentration of B can be treated as a constant and equation 2 becomes equation 6, assuming first-order dependence on A (i.e., $n_2 = 1$):

$$(6) \qquad \frac{dx}{dt} = k([A]_0 - x)[B]^{n_2}[C]^{n_3} = k'([A]_0 - x)$$

where x = number of moles per liter of A that have reacted at time t, = number of moles per liter of products that have been formed at time t.

The kinetic laws may be utilized in differential form but are more often applied in integrated form. Note that the integration of equation 6 merely involves the integral:

$$(7) \qquad \int_0^x \frac{dx}{a-x} = \int_{t_0}^t k'\, dt$$

$$(8) \qquad 2.303 \log \frac{a}{(a-x)} = kt$$

(if $t_0 = 0$).

Integrated forms of the common rate laws are available in any textbook of physical chemistry and will not be tabulated here. Illustrations of the use of the laws will be found in the following pages.

Another descriptive quantity that is frequently reported with rate data is the activation energy of the reaction. This gives the variation of the rate constant with temperature. Although the relationship is expressed in a number of ways,[3] all the rate expressions adhere closely to the form of the Arrhenius equation:

$$(9) \qquad k = A e^{-E_a/RT}$$

It is obvious that, if a value of k is given at any temperature, a knowledge of E_a, the activation energy, permits the calculation of the rate constant at other temperatures. Alternatively, the preexponential factor A (sometimes called PZ) may be reported along with E_a. It is obvious that these two parameters permit the calculation of k at any temperature. There are two principal ways in which kinetic data

[3] K. J. Laidler, *Chemical Kinetics*, McGraw-Hill Book Co., New York, 1950, Chapter 3.

may be utilized. .First, rate constants which are available in the literature may be used to guide the choice of reaction conditions suitable for the development of a method that will discriminate among structurally similar compounds. Furthermore, if the data are not available, it may well be worth while to approach such a problem by measuring some reaction rates. Such an approach may frequently turn out to be a much faster screening method than trial-and-error experimentation. The second method of utilization is the analysis of data for the rates of reaction of mixtures of very closely related compounds.

The principles involved in the first method will be illustrated by application to a particular problem, and the second will be discussed in greater detail.

THE USE OF RATE DATA IN CHOOSING REACTION CONDITIONS

Let us first consider the general problem of estimating the minimum differences in reaction velocities which are compatible with the development of an acceptable method for the determination of one of a pair of compounds that undergo a given reaction at different rates. For the sake of simplicity, we shall consider a reaction, such as the hydrolysis of an alkyl halide, that follows the first-order rate law.

Essentially the same results are obtained for a reaction that is second order with a rate depending upon the concentration of an added reagent:

$$\frac{dx}{dt} = k_a(a - x)([R] - x)$$

In the usual case the reagent will be added in sufficient excess (twofold or more) so that the order of magnitude of the concentration of R will not change over the course of the reaction. Therefore, the value of the product $k_a[R]$ can be treated as approximately constant and the same analysis as is applied to the unimolecular reactions can be utilized.

$$(10) \qquad\qquad A \xrightarrow{k_a} \text{products}$$

$$(11) \qquad\qquad B \xrightarrow{k_b} \text{products}$$

$$(12) \qquad\qquad v_A = \frac{dx_a}{dt} = k_a(a - x_a)$$

$$(13) \qquad\qquad v_B = \frac{dx_b}{dt} = k_b(b - x_b)$$

where a and b are the initial concentrations of A and B, respectively.

The integrated equations are as follows:

$$(14) \qquad 2.3 \log \frac{a}{a - x_a} = k_a(t - t_0) = k_a t_r$$

$$(15) \qquad 2.3 \log \frac{b}{b - x_b} = k_b(t - t_0) = k_b t_r$$

where t_r is the reaction time, which will, of course, always be the same for two constituents of a mixture. These equations give the simple, time-independent relationship

$$(16) \qquad \frac{\log \dfrac{a}{a - x_a}}{\log \dfrac{b}{b - x_b}} = \frac{k_a}{k_b}$$

Let us consider the value of k_a/k_b that will make it feasible to determine A in the presence of B. A marginal case would be one in which the reaction of A was 99% complete in a period of time that is sufficient for 1% reaction of B. Substitution of these values in equation 16 gives the following:

$$(17) \qquad \frac{\log 100}{\log 1.01} = \frac{k_a}{k_b}$$

$$(18) \qquad \frac{k_a}{k_b} = 465$$

This means that A can be determined in the presence of B with fair accuracy if the rate constants differ by *only a factor of about 500.* The accuracy will be decreased if the concentration of B is larger than that of A and will be increased if A is in excess. As a rough generalization it can be stated that, if there is a thousandfold difference in the rates of reaction of two related compounds, it should be possible to develop a differential method for their determination. If the ratio of the specific rate constants lies between 200 and 1000, a fairly accurate method should be available although better accuracy can be obtained by the kinetic method described later in this chapter.

The difference in reactivity can be exploited only if the reaction times are readily controllable. Thus, even if two compounds react at very different rates, it will be impossible to exploit this difference in reactivity if the times required for complete reaction of even the slowest constituent are of the order of a few minutes.

A common problem is that of the differential determination of the constituents of mixtures of alkyl halides. According to the data of Tables 14 and 15, it should be possible to develop differential methods

TABLE 14

Rates of Solvolysis of Alkyl Halides

Halide	80% Ethanol 20% Water $k \times 10^7$ (25°) *	50% Ethanol 50% Water $k \times 10^7$ (T^0) *	40% Ethanol 60% Water $k \times 10^7$ (25°) *
CH_3Br	1.22 †	56 (50°) ‖	
C_2H_5Br	0.51 †	52.5 (55°) ‖	
i-C_3H_7Br	0.78 †	84.5 (55°) ‖	
$tert$-C_4H_9Br	3300 †		
i-C_3H_7I	0.62 ‡		
$tert$-C_4H_9Br	9000 ‡		
i-C_3H_7Cl	Very slow	0.17 ¶	
$tert$-C_4H_9Cl	92.4 §	3670 §	12,900 §

* Unimolecular rate constant from $\dfrac{dx}{dt} = k[\text{RX}]$, in sec^{-1}.

† T. W. J. Taylor, *J. Chem. Soc.*, **1937**, 992.
‡ K. A. Cooper and E. D. Hughes, *J. Chem. Soc.*, **1937**, 1183.
§ E D. Hughes, *J. Chem. Soc.*, **1935**, 255.
¶ J. D. Roberts, *J. Am. Chem. Soc.*, **71**, 1880 (1949).
‖ S. Winstein, E. Grunwald, and H. W. Jones, *J. Am. Chem. Soc.*, **73**, 2700 (1951).

TABLE 15

Rates * of Bimolecular Displacement Reactions of Alkyl Halides

R	$(CH_3)_3N + RI \rightarrow (CH_3)_3NR^+I^-$ in Benzene Solution at 40° $k \times 10^5$ †	$RCl + KI \rightarrow RI + KCl$ Acetone Solution at 60° C. $k \times 10^5$ ‡
CH_3—	53	
C_2H_5—	0.088	5.4
i-C_3H_7—	0.0054	0.041
$tert$-C_4H_9—		0.05
C_4H_9CH— $\mid$ CH_3		0.21
$cyclo$-C_6H_{11}—		0.0028

* Bimolecular rate constants, rate = $k[\text{A}][\text{B}]$, in liters mole^{-1} $\text{sec}.^{-1}$.
† K. J. Laidler and C. N. Hinshelwood, *J. Chem. Soc.*, **1938**, 858.
‡ J. B. Conant and R. E. Hussey, *J. Am. Chem. Soc.*, **47**, 476 (1925).

that allow one to distinguish clearly between tertiary halides and other classes. It is also indicated that simple methods for distinguishing quantitatively between primary and secondary halides could not be developed.

The two most important reactions of halides in general are the displacement and elimination reactions effected by basic (nucleophilic) reagents.

(19) $RX + B: \rightarrow RB + X^-$ Displacement

(20)   Elimination

Both reactions may occur by way of two alternative mechanisms.[4] These are distinctly different in extreme examples but merge into each other in borderline cases. The relative reactivities of the various halides vary quite differently under different conditions. This fact is both frustrating, because it denies the possibility of making simple and reliable generalizations, and challenging, because it opens up the possibility of developing many different discriminating methods.

Among the saturated halides it is found that a regular sequence of reactivity $1° > 2° > 3°$ is found when one observes relative rates of reaction with salts or neutral bases in nonpolar solvents. Examples are shown in Table 15. On the other hand, solvolysis reactions, such as hydrolysis, acetolysis, and alcoholysis, show the converse order of reactivity, as is illustrated by the data of Table 14. This latter sequence of reactivity is exploited by the familiar qualitative characterization procedure, using alcoholic silver nitrate.[5]

The introduction of unsaturation in the halides changes their reactivity in a striking manner. *Aryl* and *vinyl* halides, I and II, respectively, are

II

ordinarily very unreactive toward all types of displacement and elimination reactions. Even this generalization breaks down in the case of aryl halides which have unsaturated, electron-withdrawing substituents in the positions ortho and para to the halogen. Such compounds react very rapidly with strong bases as is dramatically illustrated by the picryl halides, III. These "activated" aryl halides are still inert in solvolysis reactions but undergo

---

[4] C. K. Ingold, *Structure and Mechanism in Organic Chemistry*, Cornell University Press, 1953, Chapters 7, 8 and 15.

[5] R. L. Shriner and R. C. Fuson, *Identification of Organic Compounds*, 3rd ed., Wiley, New York, 1948, p. 121.

$$O_2N \quad \overset{X}{\underset{NO_2}{\bigcirc}} \quad NO_2$$

III

very rapid displacements at low temperature with hydroxide and alkoxide ions and with aliphatic primary and secondary amines. Allylic (IV) and benzyl (V) halides are contrastingly highly reactive in all types of displacement reactions. Acid chlorides show a similar generally high reactivity.

$$\overset{\diagdown}{\underset{\diagup}{C}} = \overset{|}{\underset{|}{C}} - \overset{|}{\underset{|}{C}} - X$$

IV

$$\overset{CH_2X}{\bigcirc}$$

V

The presence of substituents in the α and β positions can lead to extreme alteration of the reactivity of halides, and so such compounds must be considered as special problems. For example, α-haloethers and β-acetoxyhalides become unusually reactive in solvolytic reactions because of the ability of the substituent groups to participate in displacement reactions.[6,7]

The development of quantitative methods for the differential analysis of a halide mixture is best done by consideration of the individual mixture. Since the chemical literature abounds with kinetic data on the rates of all types of displacement reactions, the analysis of a mixture whose constituents are known can usually be implemented by a careful study of the original literature relating to the compounds in question or to their close chemical relatives. The following examples should be considered as illustrative of the application of principles, although the methods do have intrinsic value.

Consider the problem of determination of *tert*-butyl chloride in the presence of isopropyl chloride, a typical secondary chloride. In 50% ethanol (Table 14) there is a difference of a factor of more than 10^4 in their solvolysis rates. It should, therefore, be possible to find conditions under which the tertiary halide will be solvolyzed stoichiometrically during a convenient time interval without interference from the secondary halide. Three different products are formed in the solvolysis, but the accompanying by-product is HCl in all cases.

[6] E. E. Royals, *Advanced Organic Chemistry*, Prentice-Hall, New York, 1954, p. 352.

[7] C. K. Ingold, *Structure and Mechanism in Organic Chemistry*, p. 332.

(21) $(CH_3)_3CCl + C_2H_5OH \rightarrow (CH_3)_3COC_2H_5 + HCl$

(22) $(CH_3)_3CCl + H_2O \rightarrow (CH_3)_3COH + HCl$

(23) $(CH_3)_3CCl \rightarrow (CH_3)_2C{=}CH_2 + HCl$

Therefore, a simple titration of either acid or halide ion produced in the solvolysis should be sufficient to complete the analysis. Furthermore, examination of the kinetic data provides good orientation for the choice of reaction conditions. Since there is a large difference in the reactivities of the two compounds, we can afford to aim for conditions that will lead to more than 99% reaction of *tert*-butyl chloride. From the rate law we can calculate the time required for this degree of conversion in 80% alcohol at 25°.

(24) $2.303 \log \dfrac{a}{a-x} = 9.24 \times 10^{-6} \text{ sec.}^{-1} \times t_r$

for 99.9% conversion, $\dfrac{a}{a-x} = 1000.$

(25) $t_r = \dfrac{2.303 \times 3}{9.24 \times 10^{-6}} \text{ sec.} = 1.25 \times 10^4 \text{ min.}$

The calculated reaction time is ridiculously long. There are two obvious ways of shortening the required time. The first is to raise the temperature, and the second is to increase the water content of the solvent. For the sake of an example, we choose the former for first consideration. The activation energies for the solvolysis of the chlorides in alcohol-water mixtures are nearly independent of solvent composition and are essentially the same, about 23 kcal. per mole, for both isopropyl and *tert*-butyl chloride. The definition of the activation energy is given by the Arrhenius equation:

(26) $k = Ae^{-E_a/RT}$

where E_a = activation energy and R = the gas constant.

There are two approaches to the use of activation energies in setting up revised reaction conditions. One can choose a temperature and calculate the reaction time required for a given degree of reaction, or one can set the desired time and calculate the temperature required to give the desired results. We choose the former because 80°, the reflux temperature of ethanol, is about the highest temperature that could be considered without resorting to sealed tubes. Manipulation of equation 26 gives the following:

$$(27) \qquad 2.303 \log k = 2.303 \log A - \frac{E_a}{RT}$$

$$(28) \qquad 2.303 \log \frac{k_1}{k_2} = -\frac{E_a}{R}\left(\frac{T_2 - T_1}{T_1 T_2}\right)$$

From this relationship it is quickly estimated that the value of $k_{80°}/k_{25°}$ for *tert*-butyl chloride is approximately 410. This increase in rate would decrease the time for 99.9% conversion to about 300 minutes, which is not a prohibitive reaction time but is too long for real convenience.

By changing the medium it is estimated that in 50% ethanol-water the time for 99.9% reaction will be 315 minutes and in the 40% solvent the time will be further decreased to 89 minutes. It appears that treatment of a sample with such a solvent for 1 to 1.5 hours at room temperature should effect complete solvolysis of the tertiary chloride. There is every reason to believe that a procedure such as this should be generally applicable for the determination of tertiary halides in the presence of secondary and primary halides, unless the latter are subject to activation by adjacent vinyl or aryl groups, as is the case in allyl and benzyl chlorides.

The designation of best experimental details would be dictated by matters of convenience. The determination could be completed by diluting the reaction mixture with water, extracting unreacted alkyl halide with a hydrocarbon solvent. Finally, the chloride ion left in the mixture could be titrated with standard silver nitrate. Alternatively, acid released in the reaction could be titrated directly with standard base. A base could be included in the reaction mixture to convert the acid to chloride ion. However, a careful choice of base should be made to prevent the intrusion of a bimolecular reaction between the base and isopropyl chloride. This could be done by using a sterically hindered amine such as triethylamine or an insoluble base such as calcium carbonate. The loss in base could be determined, or an arbitrary excess of base could be used and free chloride then determined in the reaction mixture.

The differentiation between primary and secondary halides by selective solvolysis would be a much more delicate problem. Bateman and Hughes [8] report that in moist formic acid the rate of solvolysis of isopropyl bromide at 100° is about 20 times that of ethyl bromide. It should, therefore, be possible to distinguish between these two compounds in this solvent with an accuracy of a few per cent, were it not

[8] L. C. Bateman and E. D. Hughes, *J. Chem. Soc.*, **1940**, 945.

for the fact that the solvolysis is reversible and does not go to completion. The addition of a formate salt to force the reaction to completion might be somewhat successful but could be complicated by a bimolecular reaction between formate ion and compounds, such as methyl halides, which react rapidly in the bimolecular displacement reaction.

Another problem that is very easily solved is that of the determination of activated aryl halides in the presence of ordinary aryl halides. Consider, for example, the reaction mixture that could be produced in the mononitration of fluorobenzene.

(29)

The combined yield of the two principal products, ortho- and para-nitrofluorobenzene could be determined readily in the presence of unreacted starting material and minor amounts of the meta isomer. Bevan and Bye report the data in Table 16 for the rates of reaction

TABLE 16

Rates of Reactions of Fluorobenzenes with Sodium Methoxide in Methanol at 49.5° *

Substituent	k_2 in liters mole^{-1} sec.$^{-1}$	log A †	E_a kcal.†
None	3.38×10^{-12}	13.0	36.4
2-NO$_2$	1.60×10^{-3}	10.7	19.9
3-NO$_2$	1.59×10^{-7}	12.8	28.9
4-NO$_2$	2.37×10^{-3}	11.0	20.1
3,5-Di-NO$_2$	4.19×10^{-3}	12.3	21.7
2,4-Di-NO$_2$	56.6	10.1	12.3

* C. W. L. Bevan and G. C. Bye, *J. Chem. Soc.*, **1954**, 3091.
† $k = Ae^{-Ea/RT}$.

of the mononitrofluorobenzenes with sodium methoxide in methanol.

By inspection of these data it is found that the activated mononitro compounds react very rapidly with methanolic sodium methoxide. At the given temperature we can calculate the rate of reaction in the presence of excess sodium methoxide at a fixed concentration. Choosing $0.1 N$ as a concentration that would be convenient for analytical purposes, we obtain the following:

$$(30) \qquad 2.303 \log \left(\frac{a}{a - x} \right) = k \times 0.1 \times t_r$$

for 99.9% conversion;

$$(31) \qquad t_r = \frac{2.303 \times 3}{k \times 0.1}$$

which gives for the activated halides

$$2\text{-}NO_2; \ t_r = 4.3 \times 10^4 \ \text{sec.}$$

$$4\text{-}NO_2; \ t_r = 2.9 \times 10^4 \ \text{sec.}$$

The reaction times are long, 8–12 hours, but could be shortened appreciably without reducing the conversions below 98%. Raising the temperature would be undesirable since this would require the use of sealed tubes. From these considerations we conclude that an approximate analysis could be obtained by dissolving about 1 milliequivalent of the total fluoro compounds in 25 ml. of standard, 0.1 N sodium methoxide, heating the sample in a stoppered flask at 50° for 6–7 hours, and, finally, titrating the unreacted base with standard acid.

Since the expected dinitration product is more reactive than the mononitro compounds by a factor of 10^4, there should be little difficulty in carrying out a selective determination of the former. At 49.5° the time for 99.9% conversion in the reaction of 2,4-dinitrofluorobenzene would be about 1 sec. However, calculation also shows that a 5-min. reaction period would be sufficient to destroy 5–10% of the mononitro compounds. Therefore, a lower temperature is indicated. By use of the Arrhenius equation one calculates the following values for the rate constants at 25°: 2-NO_2, 1.2×10^{-4}; 4-NO_2, 1.74×10^{-4}; and 2,4-di-NO_2, 11.4. A 5-min. reaction time would destroy less than 1% of the mononitro compounds, whereas the period for analytically complete conversion of the dinitro compound would still be a matter of a few seconds. The assay could be carried out by back titration of the excess base almost as soon as the sample and standard base were mixed.

It is interesting to note that the data [9] for the rates of reactions of chloronitro compounds, which are much less reactive than the corresponding fluoro compounds, indicate that the quantitative determination of 2,4-dinitrochlorobenzene in the presence of the monochloronitro compounds could be accomplished with the methanolic methoxide reagent.

Another illustration of the use of rate data to fix conditions for a

[9] J. F. Bunnett, H. Moe, and D. Knutson, *J. Am. Chem. Soc.*, **76**, 3936 (1954).

selective determination has been reported. The quantitative difference in the rates of reaction of aldehydes and related ketones in carbonyl condensation reactions was used to work out a selective process for the determination of the former in the presence of ketonic relatives by selective oximation.[10] Similar considerations led to the use of potassium iodide in acetone for selective determination of primary halides in mixtures.[11] (See Table 15.) *

THE DIFFERENTIAL KINETIC METHOD

This method of analysis makes use of rate data for the reaction of a mixture of two or more related compounds. The data are analyzed in such a way as to permit the initial concentrations of all the components of the mixture to be determined. The method has actually been used by radiochemists for many years to measure the composition of mixtures of radioactive materials that decay at different rates. The method has also been used in the course of kinetic investigations in which it is found necessary, for one reason or another, to use impure materials initially. The use of the method for the solution of other analytical problems has been most uncommon, however.

The method has great power to distinguish between closely related compounds whose chemical reactivity is closely matched. Despite the discerning eye of the infrared spectrophotometer, there are many conceivable problems that can be best handled by this procedure. Since a series of analytical determinations is really carried out over a fairly extended period of time, the method is more time consuming than are ordinary methods; also differential kinetic analysis will not be the method of choice unless consideration of the particular problem reveals that the prospects for development of a discriminating single-point procedure are not good. In actual practice the task of carrying out the analysis is less formidable than it appears at first glance. The individual analyses may be exceedingly easy, and the mathematical analysis of the data is not difficult.

Lee has presented a procedure that permits the analysis to be carried out with a single determination if suitable calibration is employed.[12]

[10] L. Fowler, *Anal. Chem.*, **27**, 1686 (1955); L. Fowler, H. R. Kline, and R. S. Mitchell, *ibid.*, 1688 (1955).

[11] H. B. Haas and P. Weber, *Ind. Eng. Chem., Anal. Ed.*, **7**, 231 (1935).

* Note the sharp contrast with the aliphatic halides. Alkyl fluorides are many orders of magnitude *less* reactive than the corresponding chlorides in all displacement and elimination reactions.

[12] T. S. Lee, *Organic Analysis*, Vol. 2, Interscience, New York, 1954.

The principle of the method is easily illustrated. Consider a mixture of two compounds (two esters, for example) that undergo a reaction (such as saponification) at different rates. In the previous section it was shown that there should be a difference of a factor of *at least* 100 in their rates of reaction if conditions are to be chosen to permit the easy determination of one in the presence of the other. Now, if the reactivity of the compounds is much more closely matched, we shall always find that, by the time the reaction of the more reactive con-stituent is approaching completion, an appreciable amount of the other will have been destroyed. However, if one patiently monitors the reaction of the mixture to high conversion, it will *inevitably* follow that during the last part of the reaction the observed rate of reaction will be essentially that of the slower component. Careful measurement of this rate will allow the *initial* concentration of the slow component to be estimated by extrapolation to zero time.

Let us take as an example two compounds, A and B, which react at rates that are separated only by a factor of 10. We simplify the problem by assuming first-order kinetics. We can calculate the con-centrations of A and B that will remain at various stages in the lifetime of A, the more reactive constituent. The results of such calculations are tabulated in Table 17.

(32) $$A \xrightarrow{k_A} products$$

(33) $$B \xrightarrow{k_B} products$$

(34) $$k_A/k_B = 10$$

The results are impressive. If we were to measure the amount of component B left after 99% of A had reacted, less than a 2% error would arise if the remaining unreacted A were included in the estimate. If such an analysis were carried out, by following the rate of disappear-ance of B during this later period of the reaction, the rate constant k_B could be determined. Using this constant and knowing the time required to reach the indicated concentration level, it becomes routine to calculate the initial concentration of B.

The method of analyzing rate data for the reaction of a mixture may be varied. That most commonly employed is to plot the data as if a single component were undergoing the reaction. The integrated form of the rate equation is used. In the case of a first-order, or pseudo first-order reaction, the function, $\log \dfrac{x_\infty}{x_\infty - x}$, where x is the total reaction

TABLE 17

Rate of Destruction of Two Compounds Whose Rates of Reaction
Differ by a Factor of 10

Time (expressed as fraction of initial A destroyed)	$[A]/[A]_0$	$[B]/[B]_0$	$[B]/[A]$ *
0	1	1	1
0.10	0.90	0.99	1.1
0.50	0.50	0.93	1.86
0.80	0.20	0.85	4.3
0.90	0.10	0.79	7.9
0.95	0.05	0.74	15
0.99	0.01	0.63	63
0.999	0.001	0.501	500
0.9999	0.0001	0.398	3980

* Estimated for equal initial concentrations.

at time t, is plotted against time. During the early part of the reaction, the plot will not be linear; but during the later stages of the reaction, when the faster component has essentially disappeared, the slope of the plot becomes constant and gives directly the rate constant for the reaction of the slower component. Graphical extrapolation of the linear portion of the curve to zero time gives the initial concentration of the slow constituent. The difference between this value and the value of x_∞ gives the initial concentration of the fast-reacting compound. A plot illustrating this method is presented in Figure 22.

A second procedure, which may yield more precise results than the first, utilizes the rate equations in their differential form. The extent of reaction is plotted against time, giving a curve that is defined completely by experimental data. A smooth curve is drawn through the points, and the slopes are measured graphically. These slopes are the instantaneous reaction rates:

$$(35) \qquad \frac{dx}{dt} = k_A[A] + k_B[B]$$

$$(36) \qquad [A] + [B] = x_\infty - x$$

When the concentration of the fast reactant A has been reduced to a negligible amount, the equations will become

$$(37) \qquad [B] = x_\infty - x$$

$$(38) \qquad \left(\frac{1}{x_\infty - x}\right) \frac{dx}{dt} = k_B$$

If the instantaneous rates are divided by $(x_\infty - x)$, the values obtained will decrease while A remains appreciable and will then become constant during the later part of a run. The rate constant, k_B, is thus determined directly, and the initial concentration of B may be calculated directly from experimental points taken late in the run:

$$(39) \qquad \log \frac{[B]_0}{[B]_0 - [B]_t} = \frac{k_B t}{2.303}$$

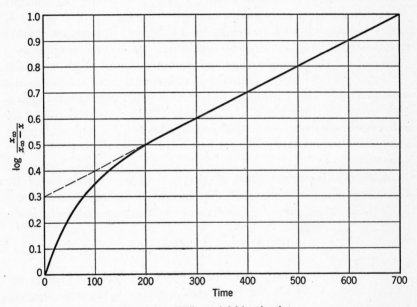

Figure 22. Differential kinetic plot.

Both methods of treatment of the data are very sensitive to the value of x_∞, and it is therefore necessary to make a very careful determination of this quantity. To do so requires that the reaction be monitored to very high conversions and that the stoichiometric relationships be precisely defined. To obtain a good experimental value of x_∞, it is necessary either to monitor the reaction to more than 99% conversion or to carry out the reaction to completion under some accelerated conditions as, for example, by heating the mixture or by adding a catalyst. The stoichiometric relationships must be determined separately with pure compounds or else they must be inferred from the chemist's independent knowledge of the reactions involved.

If the unknown sample is obtained free of extraneous impurities, the total weight of sample reacted in the kinetic experiment can be determined. This provides a useful supplement to the determination of x_∞ since the relationship

$$\text{Wt. sample} = N_A \times \text{Molec. wt. of A} + N_B \times \text{Molec. wt. of B}$$

may be used to check the values for A and B calculated from the kinetic data.

Lee's method [12] consists of making a careful calibration of amounts of the constituents of a known mixture during a specified period of time. He illustrates the procedure by the analysis of mixtures of ethyl acetate and isopropyl acetate by saponification. The rates differ by a factor of 2. He chooses a time and concentration of alkali such that the isopropyl ester is 66% hydrolyzed, whereas the same conditions and time give only 34% hydrolysis of the ethyl ester. By faithful adherence to the specification, it is possible to obtain very good results for mixtures of the two esters. The author also outlines a procedure for calculating the optimum time for best results from the individual rate constants.

Another interesting variant of the method was demonstrated by Roberts and Regan,[13] who used the reaction of diphenyldiazomethane (DDM) to determine the composition of mixtures of carboxylic acids.

$$(40) \qquad RCO_2H + (C_6H_5)_2CN_2 \rightarrow RCO_2CH(C_6H_5)_2 + N_2$$

Unfortunately, in solvents (such as ethanol) in which the kinetics are straightforward, the reaction is not stoichiometric in the sense of equation 40; and some of the diazo compound is converted to other products. DDM has an intense purple color, and so its rate of disappearance can be followed very accurately with a spectrophotometer (Chapter 10). In the presence of an excess of carboxylic acid (enough to permit the acid concentration to be treated as constant), the rate of disappearance is given by the pseudo first-order rate law.

$$(41) \qquad -\frac{d[DDM]}{dt} = k_{HA}[HA][DDM] = k'[DDM]$$

[13] J. D. Roberts and C. M. Regan, *Anal. Chem.*, **24**, 360 (1952).

or, if two acids, HA_1 and HA_2, are present,

$$(42) \qquad -\frac{d[DDM]}{dt} = k_{HA_1}[HA_1] + k_{HA_2}[HA_2][DDM]$$
$$= k''[DDM]$$

The sum of the concentrations of the two acids is easily determined independently by titration with a standard base, and so a determination of the pseudo first-order rate constant for DDM decomposition catalyzed by a mixture of acids under standard conditions provides a determination of each acid. The individual bimolecular rate constants, k_{HA_1} and k_{HA_2}, must be determined with pure acids in separate experiments. The results may be calculated as follows:

$$(43) \qquad k'' = k_{HA_1}[HA_1] + k_{HA_2}[HA_2]$$

$$(44) \qquad a = [HA_1] + [HA_2]$$

Simultaneous solution of equations 43 and 44 gives

$$(45) \qquad [HA_1] = \frac{k'' - ak_{HA_2}}{k_{HA_1} - k_{HA_2}}$$

With careful standardization of conditions, the method gave reasonably good results with acetic-benzoic acid mixtures and with mixtures of m- and p-methoxybenzoic acids. In both instances the rates differed only by a factor of 2. It seems likely that the general principle of the method may find other applications. It is certainly novel to encounter an analytical method in which the substances being determined are used in excess over the reagent.

It should be instructive to examine the details of an actual analysis that has been carried out by the differential kinetic analysis. We were confronted in the laboratory at Iowa State [14] with the problem of determining the composition of mixtures of the stereoisomeric bromides, I and II.

I   II

[14] G. S. Hammond and T. D. Nevitt, *J. Am. Chem. Soc.*, **76**, 4121 (1954).

The *trans* compound, II, could be obtained in a pure condition, but the *cis* isomer was obtainable only as a constituent of mixtures of the two isomers. By differential kinetic analysis it was possible to make a rather precise estimate of the composition of the mixtures. The first reaction that was investigated was solvolysis in methanol. As was anticipated, it was found that samples that had infrared spectra quite different from that of the pure *trans* bromide gave a kinetically homogeneous solvolysis rate which was essentially identical with the rate of the *trans* isomer. This indicated that the reactivity of the two isomers in this reaction was very nearly the same. However, the results did serve to indicate that no compounds other than tertiary bromides were present in the mixtures.

Recourse was then had to the bimolecular elimination reaction.

$$(46) \qquad \begin{matrix} & Br \\ & | & | \\ -C-C- \\ & | & | \\ & H \end{matrix} + B^- \rightarrow \quad \begin{matrix} \diagdown & \diagup \\ C{=}C \\ \diagup & \diagdown \end{matrix} + BH + Br^-$$

By analogy to previous work it was expected that the *trans* isomer would be more reactive than its stereoisomer in this process. The rates of the elimination reactions of the *trans* bromide were measured in two media. The first was a solution of sodium methoxide in methanol. It was found that, if the concentrations of the base were maintained low enough to make the reaction rate measurably slow, the unimolecular, solvolytic reaction competed appreciably with the second-order reaction. This observation guaranteed that kinetic separation would not be feasible since the expected difference in reactivity, if it existed, would make the rate of the bimolecular reaction of the *cis* isomer slow in comparison with the nondiscriminating unimolecular reaction.

Upon investigation of the reaction in ethanol, a solvent in which solvolysis was slower, a much more favorable situation was encountered. In 98% ethanol containing $3 N$ base (sodium hydroxide-ethoxide), the second-order reaction was approximately one hundred times as fast as solvolysis in the absence of an added base. The rates of reaction of the mixtures of stereoisomeric bromides were, therefore, measured in this solvent. The reaction was monitored by removing aliquot samples which were quenched by 5:1 dilution with cyclohexane. The resulting mixture was extracted twice with aqueous nitric acid, and the free bromide in the aqueous extract was titrated by the Volhard method. The value of the infinite titer was determined by accelerating the solvolysis by dilution of an aliquot with 4 to 5 volumes of water. After the resulting solution was allowed to stand for 24 hours, it was acidified and the bromide ion was titrated.

The data were analyzed by plotting the function log $[Br^-]_t/[Br^-]_\infty -$ $[Br^-]_t$ against time. The linear portion of the curve was extrapolated to zero time, giving the initial concentration of *cis* bromide. The slope of this portion of the curve was used to calculate the value of the rate constant for this *cis* compound, which was found to be about one-twelfth that of the *trans* isomer. For routine analysis, data were collected beginning at the time calculated for 99% destruction of the *trans* isomer. From the relationships

(47)
$$\frac{d\mathrm{A}}{d\mathrm{B}} = \frac{k_\mathrm{A}[\mathrm{A}]}{k_\mathrm{B}[\mathrm{B}]}$$

(48)
$$\frac{k_\mathrm{B}}{k_\mathrm{A}} \log [\mathrm{A}] \doteq \log [\mathrm{B}]$$

it is readily calculated that approximately 68% of the *cis* isomer originally present remained at this point in the reaction. For mixtures that contained 50% or more *cis* bromide, it is estimated that the error involved in the determination was no more than 1.5%.

In the course of the study it was of interest to determine accurately the composition of mixtures that contained only traces (2% or less) of *cis* bromide. The differential kinetic method would have given relatively poor results for such mixtures since the values of x would have been very close to x_∞ during the critical periods of the rate runs. Recourse was had to an infrared method for solution of this problem. A series of mixtures of known composition that were lean with respect to the *cis* bromide were made up by dilution of the *cis*-rich mixtures, which had been analyzed by the kinetic method, with pure *trans* bromide. These were used to calibrate the infrared method. This unusual procedure was chosen because of very practical considerations. The procedures for making the *cis*-rich samples were only adaptable for small-scale operations whereas it was relatively easy to prepare large amounts of the pure *trans* isomer. If the synthetic situation had been reversed, it would have been very easy to take advantage of the analytical data to prepare pure *cis* bromide. The elimination reaction could have been run on a large scale and quenched after the 99% mark in the destruction of the *trans* bromide. Unreacted bromide recovered after the selective destruction would have been essentially pure *cis* bromide suitable as a standard for calibration of analytical procedures.

Examples of applications of differential kinetic analyses are not to be found in large numbers in the literature although they are more common than is ordinarily realized. The best examples are usually "hidden" in papers that have the primary purpose of reporting rate studies for other than purely analytical purposes. As a consequence, useful analyses are worked out but never find their way as such into the abstract literature and the indices thereto.

The radiochemical literature,[15] as was mentioned earlier, provides examples of the methods of analysis of rate data in great abundance.

Brown and Fletcher[16] presented a fine example of the method for the determination of the composition of mixtures of the two isomeric tertiary halides, III and IV. They used solvolysis in 80% ethanol

[15] G. B. Cook and J. F. Duncan, *Modern Radiochemical Practice,* Oxford University Press, London, 1952, p. 54*ff*.

[16] H. C. Brown and R. S. Fletcher, *J. Am. Chem. Soc.,* **73**, 1318 (1951).

$$
\begin{array}{ccc}
CH_3 & CH_3 & CH_3 \\
| & | & | \\
CH_3C\text{----}CH\text{----}CHCH_3 \\
| \\
Cl
\end{array}
\qquad
\begin{array}{ccc}
CH_3 & CH_3 & CH_3 \\
| & | & | \\
CH_3CH\text{----}C\text{----}CHCH_3 \\
| \\
Cl
\end{array}
$$

III   IV

at 25° to differentiate the two and obtained a very clean separation as judged by the high precision indicated in the calculation of the rate constant for IV, the faster component. Similarly, Bartlett and Swain [17] resolved the compositions of two and three component mixtures of halides produced by the reaction of hydrogen chloride with several highly branched alcohols.

Connor and Wright [18] used methoxymercuration, equation 49, to analyze mixtures of the ethyl esters of oleic and elaidic acids. Ethyl

$$
(49) \quad \text{>C=C<} + Hg^{++} + 2CH_3OH \rightarrow
\begin{array}{c}
OCH_3 \\
| \\
\text{----}C\text{--------}C\text{----} \\
| \\
HgOCH_3
\end{array}
$$

oleate, the *cis* isomer, reacts four times as fast as its stereoisomer. The reaction is so rapid with both isomers that it was necessary to use rather dilute solutions in order to render the reactions measurably slow. The kinetics were not clean at high conversions; but by using a procedure similar to Lee's method (p. 162), reasonably good results were achieved.

SUMMARY

Kinetic data can be of great service in the analysis of mixtures of closely related compounds. In the easier cases, information about reaction rates may facilitate the choice of conditions suitable for selective analysis, and, if the reactivity of the different compounds is too closely matched in all reactions to permit single-determination analysis, the problem may be handled by collecting kinetic data for some reaction of the mixture of compounds.

The original kinetic literature is well reported and indexed in *Chemical Abstracts*, and much rate data and references thereto are to be found in textbooks of theoretical organic chemistry such as *Structure and Mechanism in Organic Chemistry* by C. K. Ingold. A rather complete compilation of kinetic data through the late 1940's is to be

[17] P. D. Bartlett and M. S. Swain, *J. Am. Chem. Soc.*, **77**, 2801 (1955).
[18] T. Connor and G. F. Wright, *J. Am. Chem. Soc.*, **68**, 256 (1946).

found in the National Bureau of Standards publication *Tables of Rate Constants of Homogeneous Chemical Reactions*. It should also be borne in mind that the collecting of kinetic data is not an excessively arduous task and should be considered a practical approach to setting up an analytical procedure.

In the event that the introduction of kinetics into analysis strikes the student as being unduly complicated, we should reemphasize that the methods described in this chapter are uniquely applicable where other simpler procedures fail. It is the opinion of the authors that the analyses described in which the differential kinetic procedure was used could not have been solved by any other method of comparable simplicity.

PROBLEMS

1. From the data of Reference 9 calculate suitable conditions for the determination of 2,4-dinitrochlorobenzene in the presence of 2- and 4-nitrochlorobenzene.

2. Triphenylmethyl chloride, $(C_6H_5)_3CCl$, is frequently contaminated with triphenyl carbinol, $(C_6H_5)_3COH$. Devise an easy procedure for assaying the purity of the halide. By consulting the literature, determine whether your method would also be satisfactory for the determination of triphenylmethyl chloride in the presence of benzhydryl chloride, $(C_6H_5)_2CHCl$.

3. Work out *the details* of a procedure for following the rate of the nitration of fluorobenzene with excess nitric acid in nitromethane as the solvent.

4. How would you determine the composition of the mixture of monochlorination products formed in the photochemical chlorination of each of the following hydrocarbons:

$$CH_3CHCH_3$$
$$|$$
$$CH_3$$

$$CH_3CH_2CH_2CH_3$$

$$CH_3$$
$$|$$
$$CH_3C—CH_2CH_2CH_3$$
$$|$$
$$CH_3$$

10.

SPECTROPHOTOMETRIC

METHODS

INTRODUCTION

The development of spectrophotometers capable of functioning in the ultraviolet and infrared regions of the electromagnetic spectrum has extended the scope of the standard technique of colorimetry in a remarkable manner. Applications can be made throughout the field of chemistry, and no real distinction should be made between the determination of organic compounds, the subject of this chapter, and spectrophotometry in general. The one exception to this generalization is emission spectroscopy which is uniquely applicable to problems in general chemistry since it deals with the emission of light during the cascade of excited electrons to subvalence levels. As a consequence, emission spectra are principally valuable in the quantitative determination of the elements. This can ordinarily be accomplished more easily by chemical methods for those elements that occur commonly in organic compounds.

GENERAL PRINCIPLES

The basic law governing the absorption of light by any species is the Beer-Lambert law,

$$(1) \qquad \log \frac{I_0}{I} = A_s = a_s bc$$

where I_0 is the intensity of the light incident on the sample, I is the light transmitted by the sample, A_s is the *absorbancy* (or optical density), a_s is the *absorbancy index* (or extinction coefficient), b is the path length of the light, and c is the concentration of the absorbing species in the sample. When b is expressed in centimeters and c in moles per liter, a_s becomes a_M, the *molar absorbancy index*. The subscripts to A_s and a_s are used to indicate the use of logarithms to the base 10 in equation 1. In the exponential form of the equation

$$(2) \qquad \frac{I}{I_0} = e^{-kbc} = e^{-2.303 a_s bc}$$

The proportionality factor k is related to a_s by the multiplicative constant 2.303. Much confusion exists in the literature as to the significance of various terms used to express results of absorption measurements. Through the efforts of the National Bureau of Standards, there has been a fortunate tendency to standardize terminology, and their recommended terms [1] are those used above. Because of this confusion of terms and for other reasons discussed below, it is very highly recommended that the absorption characteristics of substances to be assayed should be redetermined by the analyst before he attempts to utilize them for quantitative work.

THE SPECTRA AND SPECTROPHOTOMETERS

Figure 23 shows the principal regions of the electromagnetic spectrum and indicates the kinds of excitation that occur when radiation of the various types is absorbed by molecules. The common names of the spectral regions and the designations in terms of both wave numbers and wavelength are included.

The regions of principal interest in organic analysis are the near ultraviolet, the visible, and the near infrared. The two former regions should be considered one continuous region since they arise from a common origin and give similar types of information. By contrast, infrared spectra have rather different characteristics and give quite different information. Both types of spectra can be used profitably in quantitative determinations.

Instrumentation is, of course, a major problem which must be taken

[1] National Bureau of Standards, *Letter Circular LC-857* (1947).

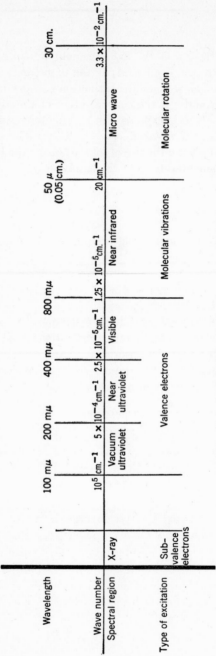

Figure 23. Principal regions of the electromagnetic spectrum.

care of before application can be made to analytical problems. At the present time there are a large number of excellent spectrophotometers which are commercially available. Nearly all spectroscopic studies reported in the current literature are carried out with factory-made instruments. Their construction is sufficiently complex to require that most servicing be carried out by an expert. No attempt will be made to describe instruments in any detail, but it is worth while to consider the general design of spectrophotometers.[2] Figure 24 is a schematic representation of a spectrophotometer. Most prism

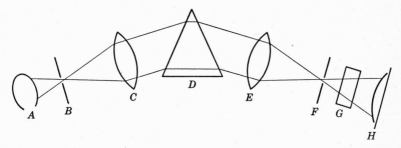

Figure 24. Schematic representation of a prism spectrophotometer. *A*, radiation source; *B*, entrance slit; *C*, collimating lens; *D*, dispersing prism; *E*, telescope lens; *F*, exit slit; *G*, sample cell; *H*, detecting unit.

spectrophotometers actually have optical parts, such as mirrors, other than the essential elements shown.

The radiation source varies with the wavelength of light desired. A tungsten lamp is usually used for the visible region; a hydrogen discharge lamp overlaps the former in its output and is used down to 200 mμ, the limit of nonvacuum spectrophotometers. For the infrared region, a black body radiator such as a Globar serves as a source. The two slits and the dispersing prism serve to provide a narrow beam of nearly monochromatic light. Slit width is one of the variable adjustments on most spectrophotometers. As the slit is cut down, less light is passed through the system and the light becomes more nearly monochromatic. It is often necessary to open the slits wider than would otherwise be desirable in order to obtain a signal of sufficient strength from the detecting cell, when work is being done in a region in which the output from the source is low and/or there is appreciable

[2] For an excellent and easily understood discussion, see G. R. Harrison, R. C Lord, and J. R. Loofbourow, *Practical Spectroscopy*, Prentice-Hall, New York, 1948.

absorption by the solvent in which the sample is obtained. The monochromator varies according to the wavelength of light used. Table 18 shows the regions of partial transparency of prism materials and the spectral regions for which each are recommended.

Quartz monochromators are used in most of the high-dispersion visible-ultraviolet spectrophotometers. Sodium chloride prisms are used most frequently in infrared spectrophotometers, but useful increases in resolution and extension of the working region into the 15-to-25-micron region is obtained by replacing the rock salt optics by other materials as indicated in Table 18.

TABLE 18

Transparency of Prism Materials

Material	Useful Region in Microns	Recommended for
Glass	0.35 – 2.5	
Quartz	0.185– 3.5	0.2– 3.5
Lithium fluoride	0.12 – 6.5	3 – 6
Calcium fluoride	0.12 – 9	5 – 9
Sodium chloride	0.20 –16	8 –15
Potassium chloride	0.20 –21	15 –20
Potassium bromide	0.21 –38	19 –25
Potassium iodide	0.25 –31	

Sample cells with quartz or glass windows, respectively, are used in the ultraviolet and visible regions. Sodium chloride cells are most commonly used for infrared spectra. The latter restrict usage to water-free samples, a fact that has been impressed with vigor on research workers who have committed the heinous crime of submitting wet samples for infrared analysis. Work with aqueous solutions can be carried out with silver chloride cells, which, however, are optically inferior to sodium chloride.

Photoelectric cells are used almost exclusively for detectors in the visible and ultraviolet regions. They are of little use in the infrared region, although a lead selenide photocell has been provided by the Beckmann Company that extends the use of their visible-ultraviolet spectrophotometer to the limit set by the quartz optical system. Thermopiles or bolometers are used for detectors in infrared spectrophotometry. In both, the radiation is converted to heat on a blackened metal surface. In a thermopile, the receiver is attached to one end of a thermocouple. The current thus produced is measured. In the bolometer, the blackened metal strip is made one arm of a Wheatstone bridge and the detection consists of measuring the change in the resistance of that branch of the circuit. The signals from either detector may be amplified through one or more photomultiplier tubes. The gain that is attained in the response of the instrument also increases the noise level of the instrument. This gives rise to one of the most difficult problems in quantitative infrared spectrophotometry since the noise is a random phenomenon that cannot be compensated.

In quantitative studies of solutions, it is necessary to carry out a calibration in which the absorption by constituents of the solution, other than the unknown sample, is measured and compensated for. In double-beam instruments the monochromatic light from the dispersing prism is split by one means or another,* and one half is passed through the reference solution and the other traverses the unknown solution. Compensation can then be made by electronic subtraction of the signals from two detecting units. In single-beam instruments the sample and reference solution are introduced alternately in the light path. If the instrument is used with a recorder that plots the spectrum on a strip chart, it is necessary to go through the spectrum first with the reference solution and either adjust the detecting circuit to an apparent zero response or plot on the chart a "base line" which can be later used to correct the readings from the unknown. If the spectrophotometer is manually operated, the compensation is carried out by balancing the circuit with the reference solution in the light path for each wavelength setting. Manual operation *has an advantage for quantitative work* in that the balancing and reading of the unknown can be repeated as many times as is desired to detect and correct for electronic instability of the instrument.

Manually operated spectrophotometers for the visible-ultraviolet region have been available for some time. More recently several excellent automatic-recording spectrophotometers for this region have also appeared on the market. At the other end of the expense scale are found the junior spectrophotometers and photoelectric colorimeters. There is little question in the mind of the authors that the best instruments for general application to analytical problems are the manually operated spectrophotometers. Unless expense is a very critical factor, the greater precision and versatility of these instruments, as compared with cheaper instruments, make the added investment a wise expenditure. Furthermore, there are real advantages to manual

---

* In one of the newer ultraviolet instruments, the Beckmann Model DK, the entire beam is switched back and forth between two optical paths at a high frequency by means of rotating mirrors.

operation as compared with automatic recording in quantitative assays. This is in no way intended to impeach the obvious advantages of the automatic machines for scanning spectra for purposes of characterization or to follow the progress of fast reactions. In quantitative analysis it is often the practice to make readings at one or only a few wavelengths, and so the disadvantages of manual operation disappear. An added advantage of some manual instruments is the fact that they permit the introduction of four, rather than two, samples in the cell housing. These can be placed alternately in the light beam so that three samples may be compared with the reference at a single setting. This is of great convenience to the analyst because it permits two or three determinations to be carried out simultaneously or allows one to make continuous comparison with a solution of known composition. The latter procedure, as will be shown later, is of aid in detecting or compensating for absorption by interfering substances.

CHOICE OF WAVELENGTH(S) FOR ANALYSIS

It is trite to say that determination of a particular compound requires that a spectral region must be found in which it has appreciable absorption and where absorption by the other constituents of the mixture is limited. It should be equally evident that the scanning of the visible-ultraviolet region and/or the infrared should be carried out before a great deal of time has been consumed in speculation as to the prospects. If the identity of contaminants is known, their spectra should also be scanned.

Two generalizations can be drawn comparing the potential value of the two spectral regions. First, the intensities associated with infrared absorption are much lower than those found for many visible and ultraviolet bands. Second, the maxima in the infrared are far more numerous and distinctive than those in the visible and ultraviolet. It can be guaranteed that any organic compound will have several observable bands in the infrared, but many saturated compounds do not have useful absorption short of the inaccessible vacuum ultraviolet region. Because intensities are often higher, visible-ultraviolet spectra offer the better possibilities for highly sensitive assays and the precision to be expected is greater. On the other hand, infrared analysis offers much more general application and permits the possibility of distinguishing between compounds that are closely related structurally. The precision attainable in infrared analysis is better than is commonly realized, but good results are often attainable only after a considerable struggle with the problem of establishing the best method of correcting for the wandering of the base line from the 100% transmission mark on the strip chart. A disadvantage arises from the low intensity of infrared bands. This necessitates either the use of inconveniently long cells or analysis at concentration levels at which the Beer-Lambert law may become inexact because of the interactions between solute molecules.

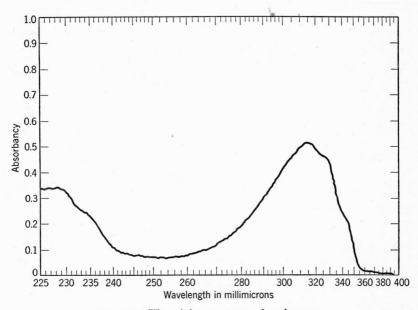

Figure 25. Ultraviolet spectrum of azobenzene.

The choice of wavelength for analysis in a single-setting determination is dictated by many considerations. Some of these will develop in the discussion of spectral characteristics (p. 191), and others relate specifically to the consideration of the contours of absorption bands. Typical plots of ultraviolet and visible spectra of organic compounds are shown in Figs. 25 and 26. The spectrum of azobenzene presents several interesting possibilities for determination. There is a broad low intensity band in the visible region. This would probably often be the region of choice for many analytical problems. Interferences would be less common (*vide infra*), and the fact that A_s changes only gradually with wavelength will minimize errors due to irreproducible wavelength setting and variation in the slit width. However, the low intensity of the band limits application to solutions in which the azobenzene concentration is of the order of 10^{-4} M or greater, if 1-cm. cells are used in the analysis. For the determination of trace amounts, the band with a maximum at 319 mμ might be much more useful since there is a potential gain of a factor of about 20 in the sensitivity at the more intense maximum. In the total absence of interfering substances, one would choose a setting coincident with the maximum for the analytical determination. Since the band is nearly symmetrical,

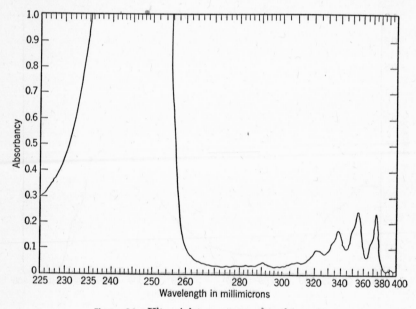

Figure 26. Ultraviolet spectrum of anthracene.

this will minimize the error arising from variation in the slit width. The band is not exceptionally sharp, but there is enough variation of A with wavelength to necessitate care in setting. This latter error can, of course, be compensated by running a control with the same setting. If there is interference from absorbance by another species, one should look for the spectral region where the difference between the absorbancy indices of azobenzene and the offending substance is largest. If it develops that this point occurs at a wavelength (e.g., 330 mμ) where the absorbance of azobenzene is changing rapidly, successful analysis essentially demands that a control solution be measured with the same setting of the spectrophotometer.

The spectrum of anthracene, shown in Fig. 26, presents other interesting possibilities. The numerous sharp, intense peaks nearly guarantee that a good assay can be developed for most mixtures. Precision setting will be demanded at almost any useful wavelength, and so the choice will be dictated almost entirely by the question of interference.

In Fig. 27 the spectra of several nitrobenzene solutions are shown. The intense absorption around 260 mμ certainly would be useful for analysis in mixtures that are free from interference or in which the interference is readily controlled. However, it will often be of interest to determine nitrobenzene in mixtures that include varying

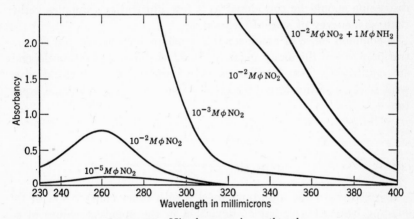

Figure 27. Nitrobenzene in methanol.

amounts of other aromatic substances. The solution of such problems may be implemented by the use of the low-intensity "tail" of the absorption band which runs out into the visible region of the spectrum. This absorption is responsible for the pale yellow color of nitrobenzene, and measurement at about 350 mμ can give good values for the nitrobenzene content of solutions in which the nitrobenzene is $10^{-2}\,M$. The flat tails of absorption bands must, however, be used with care. They are frequently altered by the presence of large amounts of other constituents of the mixture which form molecular complexes with the absorbing species. This is illustrated by the curve in Fig. 27 that shows the influence of the addition of aniline to the solution. The occurrence of such a disturbance can be detected by adding known amounts of nitrobenzene to the solution and measuring the absorption at the wavelength of choice. If the absorbancy readings, including the assay solution, fit the Beer-Lambert law and extrapolate to zero absorbancy at zero concentration, it can be assumed that the result is correct.

DETERMINATION UNDER NON-IDEAL CONDITIONS

The scope of spectrophotometric assays can be broadened by the resourceful analyst to include many determinations in solutions that show no spectral region in which the routine application of the Beer-Lambert law, equation 1, does not give good results. The possibilities are so varied that there is no substitute for the careful consideration of the individual problem and the exercise of personal ingenuity in setting up some sort of a compensating procedure. The following discussion should be considered as a few illustrative examples rather than as a survey of special techniques.

A common cause of nonlinear relationships between A_s and concentration arises if the assay species is involved in concentration-dependent equilibria. Two familiar examples are the ionic dissociation of weak acids, equation 3, and the dissociation of hexaphenylethane, equation 4.

$$(3) \qquad\qquad HA \underset{\overleftarrow{}}{\overset{K_i}{\rightleftharpoons}} H^+ + A^-$$

$$(4) \qquad\qquad (C_6H_5)_6C_2 \underset{\overleftarrow{}}{\overset{K_d}{\rightleftharpoons}} 2(C_6H_5)_3C \cdot$$

Association of the absorbing species with other constituents of the solution can also give rise to deviation in the apparent values of a_s. These complications can be handled if they are recognized and a proper number of calibrating measurements are made. Consider, for example, the case of the weak-acid ionization. It will be necessary to measure the absorbancy indices of both HA and A^-; and in the general case one must take into account absorption by both species, although in some instances the proper choice of the wavelength of the light used for analysis will allow neglect of the absorption by one of the species.

Let us consider the case of the partially dissociated weak acid in which the analysis desired is the total of $HA + A^-$.

$$(5) \qquad A_{s(obs)} = A_{s(HA)} + A_{s(A^-)} = b(c_{HA}a_{s(HA)} + c_{A^-}a_{s(A^-)})$$

$$(6) \qquad\qquad c_{HA} + c_{A^-} = T_{HA}$$

$$(7) \qquad\qquad K_i = \frac{c_{H^+}c_{A^-}}{c_{HA}}$$

The ratio of c_{A^-} to c_{HA} is dependent on the hydrogen ion activity of the solution. If this can be fixed by buffering, the problem becomes relatively simple if $a_{s(HA)}$ and $a_{s(A^-)}$ can be determined independently from measurements made, respectively, in highly acidic and highly basic solutions. In unbuffered solutions the problem is essentially unmanageable unless it is known that HA is the only source of H^+. Then the following relationships hold:

(8) $$c_{H^+} = c_{A^-}$$

(9) $$c_A = \frac{-K_i + \sqrt{K_i^2 + 4K_i T_{HA}}}{2}$$

(10) $$c_{HA} = T_{HA} - \frac{-K_i + \sqrt{K_i^2 + 4K_i T_{HA}}}{2}$$

(11) $$A_{s(obs)} = b \left\{ a_{s(HA)} \left(T_{HA} - \frac{-K_i + \sqrt{K_i^2 + 4K_i T_{HA}}}{2} \right) \right.$$

$$\left. + a_{s(A^-)} \left(\frac{-K_i + \sqrt{K_i^2 + 4K_i T_{HA}}}{2} \right) \right\}$$

If $a_{s(HA)}$, $a_{s(A^-)}$, and K_i are known, equation 11 can be used to calculate T_{HA} from absorption measurements. Furthermore, if HA is available in pure form and $a_{s(HA)}$ and $a_{s(A^-)}$ can be determined independently, the value of K_i can be determined spectrophotometrically by absorption measurements with solutions at varying T_{HA}. It is also possible to use extensive data covering a range of concentrations to determine all the values from a single set of measurements even if HA is not readily isolable. The method has too limited a scope, however, to warrant the development of the details in this discussion.

It is always necessary to take account of the absorption by other constituents of the mixture. By suitable choice of the wavelength of the light used in the analysis, it may be possible to avoid competitive absorption entirely. To guarantee that this has been accomplished in a particular problem necessitates either a complete knowledge of the identity of *all* other constituents of the sample or the development of some means of carrying out independent measurements to fortify the assumption. Consideration of the history of the sample will determine whether the analyst knows all of its constituents. No such knowledge could be assumed about any sample derived from natural sources or about the crude products of organic reactions in general. However, it may be known that the material has already undergone preliminary purification which is known to remove all, or all except a few, closely related impurities. Fractions collected from a standardized chromatogram would fall in this category. Awesome errors may well be introduced by indiscriminate application of colorimetric methods for trace amounts of material in complex mixtures of unknown composition.

There are several ways of checking the reliability of a determination of a single constituent of a mixture, but the most generally applicable is to carry out absorption measurements at a series of wavelengths at which the absorbancy index of the substance to be determined varies significantly. The probability that the interfering materials will have absorption curves with exactly the same shape as that of the assay substance is much smaller than is the chance that there will be competitive absorption. If the same result is indicated by calculations from readings at a series of wavelengths, it is reasonably safe to assume that the result is reliable. The data in Table 19 show an application of

TABLE 19

Determination of Benzophenone in the Presence of Unknown, Absorbing Impurities *

Wavelength in mμ	A_x	A_0 †	A_0/A_x
370	0.090	0.268	2.98
365	0.125	0.370	2.96
360	0.160	0.482	3.01
355	0.176	0.525	2.98
350	0.197	0.582	2.96
345	0.214	0.627	2.93
340	0.211	0.610	2.88
335	0.206	0.584	2.83
330	0.199	0.538	2.70
325	0.185	0.467	2.53
320	0.171	0.401	2.35

Average ‡ $= 2.98 \pm 0.01$
$C_x = 0.0298$

* W. P. Baker and G. S. Hammond, unpublished data.
† $C_0 = 0.1000\ M$.
‡ 350–370 mμ.

this procedure. It was desired to determine the residual benzophenone in toluene solutions after the partial photochemical reduction of the compound. It was known that the reaction took the courses indicated by equations 12 and 13 for the most part.

None of the indicated products have significant absorption in the

(12) $(C_6H_5)_2C{=}O + C_6H_5CH_3 \xrightarrow{h\nu}$

$$(C_6H_5)_2C\underset{\underset{OH}{|}}{\quad}C\underset{\underset{OH}{|}}{\quad}(C_6H_5)_2 + (C_6H_5CH_2)_2$$

(13) $(C_6H_5)_2C{=}O + C_6H_5CH_3 \xrightarrow{h\nu} (C_6H_5)_2\underset{\underset{OH}{|}}{C}CH_2C_6H_5$

region of the ultraviolet spectrum between 300 and 380 mu. However, traces of oxygen divert a very small fraction of the material to unknown substances that absorb in this region. Since the amounts of oxygen present varied, there was no easy way of correcting for the interference. Therefore, readings were taken at a series of different wavelengths. In order to minimize instrumental errors, readings were determined at the same settings for a solution of benzophenone in toluene of known concentration. The ratio of the values of A_s for the known and unknown solutions should give the ratio of concentrations. The data show that the values of the absorbancy ratio in the sample determination are quite constant at the longer wavelengths but begin to deviate badly in the region 300 to 340 mμ. The presumption was made that there was no significant interference from by-products at the longer wavelengths, and the average of the values of A_x/A_0 determined in the range 350 to 370 mμ was used to calculate the concentration of benzophenone in the unknown solution.

EXAMPLES OF SPECTROPHOTOMETRIC ANALYSES

Hundreds of spectrophotometric analyses have been reported in the literature, and it would be out of the question to make any attempt to survey the field in a comprehensive manner. However, examination of the details of a few representative methods will be useful to the student. The examples are drawn largely from the authors' experience merely because it is physically easier to assemble the details for such a problem.

Benzidine Rearrangement Mixtures

Carlin, Nelb, and Odioso [3] developed an elegant spectrophotometric method for following the course of the rearrangement of hydrazobenzene, I, to a mixture of benzidine, II, and diphenyline, III.

(14)

[3] R. B. Carlin, R. G. Nelb, and R. C. Odioso, *J. Am. Chem. Soc.*, **73**, 1002 (1951).

All three aromatic amines have absorption maxima in the ultraviolet but the positions of the maxima are found at different wavelengths, as is shown by the data of Table 20.

TABLE 20

Molar Absorbancy Indices

Compound	245 mμ	270 mμ	285 mμ
Benzidine	22.0	101.9	134.5
Diphenyline	79.2	52.0	32.2
Hydrazobenzene	110.0	12.9	19.2

Measurements were made at each wavelength, and the concentrations were calculated by solution of the following set of simultaneous equations:

(15) $A_{245} = 22.0[B] + 79.2[D] + 110.0[Hy]$

(16) $A_{270} = 101.9[B] + 52.0[D] + 12.9[Hy]$

(17) $A_{285} = 134.5[B] + 32.2[D] + 19.2[Hy]$

The original report did not indicate the precision of the results, but in the repetition of the method [4] it has been found that the results are accurate to $\pm 1\%$ or better.

Examples of Infrared Methods

The consideration of two problems in which infrared methods have been useful is instructive. In one case the solution turned out to be simplicity itself; and, in the other, even a reasonably good answer was attainable only after struggle. In the first instance, the problem was that of finding the distribution of isomers produced in the nitration of compound IV.[5]

[4] G. S. Hammond and W. Grundemeier, *J. Am. Chem. Soc.*, **77**, 2445 (1955).
[5] G. S. Hammond, F. J. Modic, and R. M. Hedges, *J. Am. Chem. Soc.*, **75**, 1388 (1953).

The spectra of the three products and the starting material, in carbon disulfide solution, are shown in Fig. 28. The clear definition of the characteristic bands and the base line of the spectra made the analysis very easy. Weighed samples were made up to volume in carbon disulfide, and the spectra were run in a Baird Associates single-beam instrument. The correction for background was made by drawing a straight line between the two minimum points on either side of a band to establish a base line. Since the chart was calibrated in per cent transmission, the values of the base line and maxima were read, converted to logarithms and subtracted to give the absorbancy due to the solute. Analysis of synthetic mixtures showed that each peak followed the Beer-Lambert law, even in mixtures. Table 21 shows

TABLE 21

Determination of a Synthetic Mixture

1,X-(NO$_2$)$_2$-2,5-Cl$_2$—C$_6$H$_2$ Isomers

Compound	Frequency of Characteristic Band (cm^{-1})	Per Cent in Sample	Found
V	822	48.3	46.6
VI	842	16.7	16.9
VII	718	34.9	36.5

typical results for the determination of the composition of a synthetic mixture of products.

This accuracy is typical of that which may be expected from an

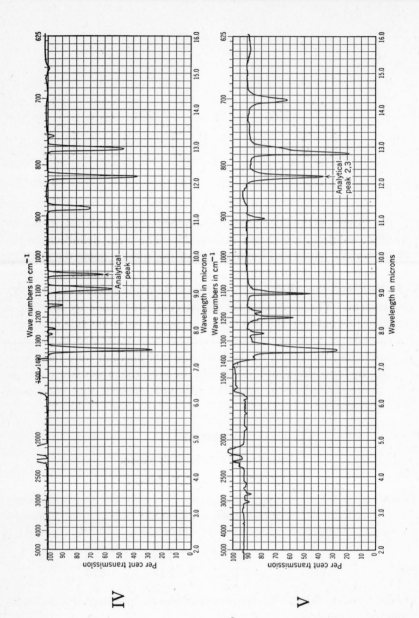

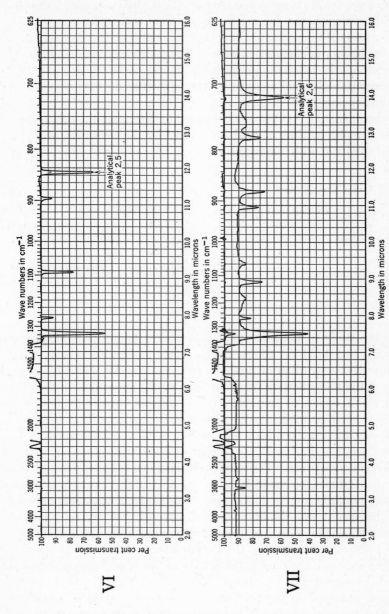

Figure 28. Infrared spectra of compounds IV, V, VI, and VII.

unrefined infrared determination in the best cases. Some improvement in precision could probably have been attained by the use of a double-beam instrument, but the results shown were sufficiently accurate for the purposes of the particular experiment. Although the accuracy may seem to be poor in comparison with that regularly attainable by chemical methods in inorganic analysis, it should be borne in mind that a differential chemical analysis of the particular mixture would be a nearly hopeless task.

In another study [6] it became necessary to determine the composition of the complex mixture of products formed by the treatment of γ-bromobutyronitrile with strong bases.

$$BrCH_2CH_2CH_2CN \xrightarrow{B^-}$$

$$\underset{\text{VIII}}{BCH_2CH_2CH_2CN} + \underset{\text{IX}}{CH_2=CHCH_2CN} +$$

$$\underset{X}{\overset{CH_2}{\underset{CH_2}{\diagdown}}}CHCN \rightarrow \underset{XI}{CH_3CH=CHCN}$$

In the study of the reaction it was desired to utilize a number of solvents, and it did not appear that it would be feasible to carry out a quantitative separation of products from the reaction solvents. Since most of the solvents were found to have strong absorption in the 800–1600 cm^{-1} region of the spectrum, it did not appear at first that analyses could be made at all. However, it was found that the $C\equiv N$ stretching frequencies which fell between 2080 and 2380 could be resolved, using a Perkin-Elmer Model 112 spectrophotometer with a calcium fluoride prism. The various solvents had sufficient background, due to overtones, to make it necessary to match unknown solutions against carefully prepared mixtures. This analysis was never actually used because it was simultaneously discovered that several bands at lower frequencies were free from interferences from the solvent and were sufficiently resolved by the Perkin-Elmer Model 112 spectrophotometer to permit their use in the determination of cyclopropyl cyanide, X, and crotononitrile, XI. It was further found that, if a slight excess of base was used in the reaction, the isomerization of allylcyanide, IX, to XI was complete. No general method could be developed for

[6] D. H. Hogle and G. S. Hammond, unpublished results.

the products, VIII, formed by displacement. Therefore, the analysis was developed for X and XI with the view that their absolute determination would give a tentative value for VIII by difference, since the total reaction was easily estimated by extraction with water and titration of bromide ion liberated. It ultimately turned out that with bases strong enough to give appreciable amounts of the elimination products, X and XI, the tentative value for VIII was always zero. For the purposes of the particular investigation, it was sufficient to know that the value was very small, so no further analyses were made.

The previous paragraph could certainly imply much greater simplicity in the determination of X and XI than was actually experienced, and an account of the details of procedure is in order. Such details are best worked out by the analyst in connection with a particular problem, but it should be instructive to consider the problems that arose in a particular case and the ways in which they were solved. The bands used for analysis in the various solvents are listed in Table 22, and re-

TABLE 22

Infrared Bands Used for Analysis of Crotononitrile, X, and
Cyclopropyl Cyanide, XI, in Various Solvents

Wavelength in Microns

Solvent	Crotononitrile	Cyclopropyl Cyanide
Benzene	10.54	9.6, 10.76
Nitrobenzene	10.54	9.6, 10.76
Benzonitrile	6.1, 10.54	10.76
n-Butanol	6.1	10.76
sec-Butanol	6.1	9.6, 10.76
t-Butanol	6.1	10.76
Dimethylformamide	10.54	10.76

productions of actual spectra of the two nitriles are shown in Fig. 29. It will be observed that the bands are not sharply defined and that the background on either side of the analytical peaks is characterized by significant absorption. This is due largely to the impossibility of attaining perfect matching of solvent absorption in the unknown sample and the reference solution.

The method chosen for reading the spectra is indicated by the tie lines drawn in Fig. 30. Solutions containing known concentrations of the two nitriles in the particular solvent system were made up and their spectra were run. In order to shift the spectra to a common

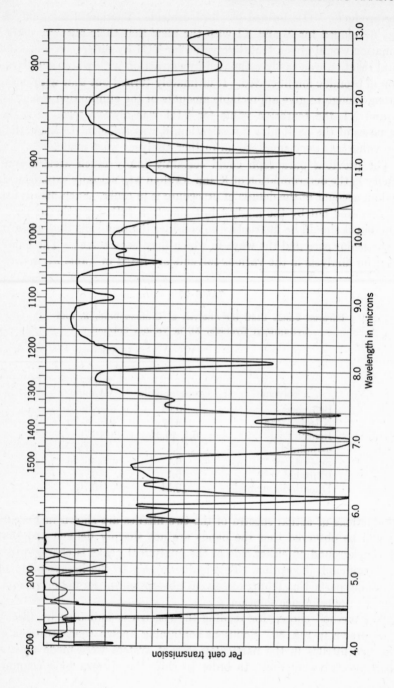

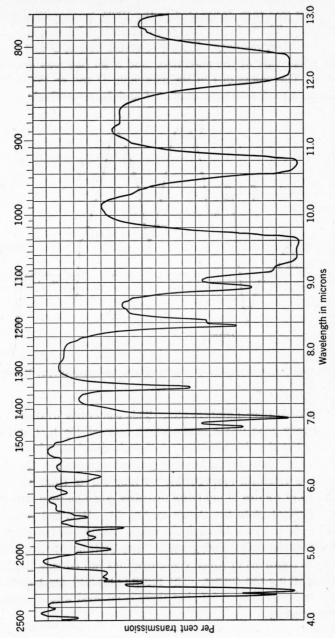

Figure 29. Infrared spectra in *n*-butanol. Top curve, crotononitrile; bottom curve, cyclopropyl cyanide.

background, a point A was chosen at which absorption was low. This
reference point was then designated as the 100% transmission level in
all the spectra. The value of I at the reference point was subtracted
from all other chart readings. Then two stable points, B and C, were
chosen on either side of the maximum, and a tie line was drawn between them. The values of I at the maximum D and on the base line
(point E) were read and were used as I and I_0, respectively, in con-

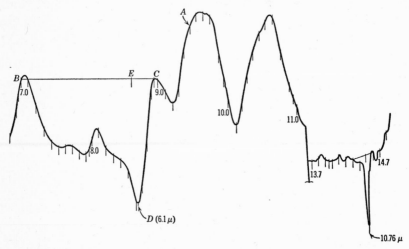

Figure 30. Partial infrared spectra of crotononitrile and cyclopropyl cyanide in
n-butanol.

structing a pseudo Beer-Lambert plot. This somewhat irrational procedure gave very good linear relationships between log I_0/I and concentrations of the absorbing species. Although absorbancy indices calculated from such data would have no general significance, the procedure seemed to establish reproducible working curves from which the
concentrations of solutes in unknown mixtures could be read with good
accuracy. Typical plots are shown in Fig. 31. It is not surprising
that the lines do not pass through the origin because of the empirical
nature of the correction for background. Such plots should not be used
for analysis of solutions in which concentrations fall outside the limits
used in establishing the curves. The results obtained are believed to
be accurate to better than ±5%, but there is no good way of checking
the accuracy exactly.

CONSTITUTIONAL EFFECTS

Before starting to set up a method, the spectra of the compound to be determined and those of other substances that are expected as constituents of the reaction mixture should be examined. However, certain generalizations about the correlations of structure with spectra can serve as a useful guide in the choice of a method. These correlations are treated in much more detail in specialized literature [7] than

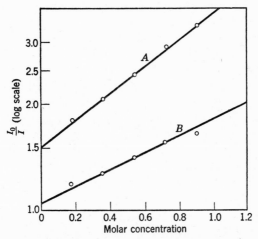

Figure 31. Pseudo Beer-Lambert plots. Curve A, 10.76μ band of cyclopropyl cyanide in benzonitrile; curve B, 6.1μ band of crotononitrile in benzonitrile.

can be done in this book. However, some orienting generalizations seem in order.

There is a large difference in origin and in characteristics between infrared spectra on the one hand and visible and ultraviolet spectra on the other. Absorption of infrared radiation results in the excitation of the molecule to higher vibrational states. That is, it is the heavy nuclei in the molecule that are involved. In the visible and ultraviolet region, absorption is due to the excitation of electrons to higher molecular levels. The two spectra give rather different types of information concerning molecular structure which are very useful in qualitative characterization of materials of unknown structure. Some

[7] F. A. Miller in *Organic Chemistry, An Advanced Treatise,* H. Gilman, Editor, Vol. III, Wiley, New York, 1955, and bibliography cited therein; L. J. Bellamy, *The Infra-Red Spectra of Complex Molecules,* Wiley, New York, 1954; L. N. Ferguson, *Chem. Revs.,* **43,** 385 (1948).

knowledge of these characteristics can also be of aid in choosing an analytical method for a known substance.

In general, it can be said that infrared spectra are more selective but less sensitive. The first fact arises from the great complexity of infrared spectra and the second from the fact that the intensities of infrared absorptions are much lower than the intensities of allowed transitions in the electronic spectrum.

For most molecules there will be $3n - 6$ degrees of vibrational freedom where n is the number of atoms in the molecule. If the molecule has no symmetry, there will be a corresponding number of fundamental absorption frequencies in the infrared spectrum. In addition, there will be overtone and combination bands. If the molecule possesses symmetry, there will be a smaller number of infrared active transitions for two reasons. First, certain of the motions will become degenerate or identical to each other since they involve identical motions of indistinguishable atoms. Thus, in a symmetrical molecule such as n-butane, the various C—H stretching and bending frequencies will fall into two groups, those characteristic of the CH_2 groups and those characteristic of the CH_3 groups. Nearly the same behavior will be observed if a molecule has some sort of pseudo symmetry. All methyl groups in molecules, for example, will contribute some very similar frequencies from those motions that approximate the deformation of the C—H bonds alone. The second reason for the reduction of the number of absorption bands in symmetrical molecules is that the excitation of some vibrations by absorption of radiation is said to be forbidden. In order to be allowed, it is necessary that the excitation process change the dipole moment of a molecule. It is easily seen that some vibrations will not effect such a change. Consider the case of the *cis-* and *trans-*2-butenes, XII and XIII. The stretching of the carbon-carbon double

$$\begin{array}{ccc} \text{H} & \quad \text{H} & \qquad \text{H}_3\text{C} \quad \text{H} \\ \diagdown \quad \diagup & & \diagdown \quad \diagup \\ \leftarrow\text{C}=\text{C}\rightarrow & & \leftarrow\text{C}=\text{C}\rightarrow \\ \diagup \quad \diagdown & & \diagup \quad \diagdown \\ \text{H}_3\text{C} \quad \text{CH}_3 & & \text{H} \quad \text{CH}_3 \\ \text{XII} & & \text{XIII} \end{array}$$

bond in XIII cannot change the dipole moment since the center of the bond is a center of symmetry of the molecule. In *cis*-butene this motion can be infrared active since the dipole moment of the molecule will be altered by the motion. The simplicity of the infrared spectra of highly symmetrical molecules is often useful in their characterization but does tend to limit the use of spectra for their quantitative determination.

Because of the usual complexity of the infrared spectra of organic molecules, a complete theoretical assignment of the observed frequencies has been made only in a few especially simple cases. Therefore, an analyst cannot ordinarily make a final decision as to the applicability of an infrared method to the solution of a particular problem until he has actually examined the spectra of all the principal constituents of the mixture.

There are, however, certain "group frequencies" which are characteristic of particular functional groups. These can be associated with vibrations that involve the particular group and not the other atoms in the molecule. Rather comprehensive reviews of these group frequencies are to be found in the specialized literature.[7] Most infrared spectrometers cover the range from 5000 to 300 cm^{-1} (with suitable changes in the optics). The highest group frequency that recurs commonly is the O—H stretching mode which is found in the region 3700 to 3500 cm^{-1} in all compounds containing this group in which it is not involved in hydrogen bonding. Acids, alcohols, and phenols can, therefore, be determined in nonoxygenated solvents by analysis of this band, although corrections for the formation of hydrogen-bonded dimers may be necessary. The most useful of the other group frequencies are as shown in Table 23.

TABLE 23

Some Group Frequencies

Group	Frequency in cm^{-1}	Comment
$\diagdown$N—H$\diagup$	3500–3300	Position sensitive to hydrogen bonding
$\diagdown$—C—H$\diagup$	3030–2880	Careful analysis can separate much substructure
—C≡C—	2260–2200	
—C≡N	~2250	
$\diagdown$C=O$\diagup$	1850–1625	Much variation with structure within the region—very intense
$\diagdown$C=C$\diagup$	1680–1600	
—NO$_2$	1650–1500	Very intense

The exact positions of the maxima within the limits quoted vary a great deal with the structure of the compounds. However, these variations are normally quite reproducible, and very narrow limits can be set for the expected position of the bands associated with most of the functional groups if the immediate environment is fixed. Thus, it would normally be possible to determine a saturated aliphatic ketone and an α,β-unsaturated ketone individually in a mixture that contained both species. There are many other group frequencies that have been identified, but one cannot depend upon utilizing them for analysis since the spectra of most compounds below 1600 cm^{-1} is ordinarily replete with bands arising from "skeletal" vibrations. Many determinations can be made using this spectral region as is illustrated by the examples discussed previously, but the possibilities can be evaluated only after the spectra of the material to be determined and of other constituents of the mixture have been examined in detail.

The absorption of visible and ultraviolet light results in the excitation of electrons and, therefore, reflects the electronic structure of molecules. Although there are a limited number of exceptions, it is generally found that only unsaturated molecules give strong absorption in the visible and near ultraviolet. Even the singly unsaturated groups such as C=C, C≡C, C=O, C≡N, etc., show only end absorption above 210 mμ. It is interesting to note that all the above groups, which have been studied in the vacuum ultraviolet, have maximum absorption between 175 and 185 mμ. This demonstrates that ultraviolet absorption is more characteristic of the extent of a π electron system than it is of the specific nature of the atoms in the system. As additional unsaturation is added in the conjugated arrangement, the first maximum moves to longer wavelengths. Conjugated dienes and α,β-unsaturated esters, acids, aldehydes, and ketones all have strong maxima in the region 205 to 230 mμ. Exact positions vary with the character of substituents attached to the unsaturated system. In general, the addition of electron-donating groups such as alkyl or alkoxyl shifts the absorption to longer wavelengths (bathochromic shift), and electron-attracting groups have the opposite effect (hypsochromic shift). Steric strains can also exert a profound influence as in 1,3-cyclohexadienes which absorb at about 260 mμ, the region where the first maxima of triply unsaturated, conjugated systems usually absorb. Continued extension of the unsaturated systems results in additional bathochromic shifts. A surprising feature is the close association of open-chain trienes (260 mμ) and benzene (265 mμ and pyridine (250 mμ). The location of the first *strong* ultraviolet or visible maximum gives a rough characterization of the extent of the conjugated unsaturated system in a molecule. The significance in analytical work is the prospect of distinguishing spectrophotometrically between unsaturated molecules which differ significantly in the extent of their conjugated systems.

The absorption bands that have been considered in the previous paragraph are the intense, allowed transitions which are ordinarily characterized by having absorbancy indices between 2000 and 40,000. Exceptions are found with highly symmetrical molecules such as benzene in which the first transition is forbidden ($a_{max.} = 250$). In addition to these excitations of unsaturation electrons, certain other very low-intensity absorption is found in some molecules. This is usually associated with the excitation of nonbonding electrons of oxygen and nitrogen atoms. The long wavelength maximum in the spectrum of azobenzene (Fig. 26) belongs to this class as does the weak band at 280 to 290 mμ in the spectra of aliphatic aldehydes and ketones. These forbidden bands may be an annoyance or a curiosity to spectroscopist but are often of great service to the analyst since they are found at wavelengths much longer than those of the strong absorption bands. This permits the development of many specific assays. A familiar example is found in the analyses for quinones, which have forbidden absorption near 440 mμ.

11.

SEPARATIONS

In principle it is always more convenient to carry out quantitative determinations directly on portions of the original sample. Many times, however, the analytical methods available are not sufficiently selective to permit this direct approach. In such cases the use of preliminary separations will often greatly simplify the analytical problem. This is especially true when complex mixtures of many components are being analyzed.

The separation process may be at the same time a method of determining one or more of the sample constituents. For example, when a substance is separated by quantitative distillation, that substance may be determined quantitatively simply by weighing the distillate. When the various constituents of a mixture are separated by vapor-phase chromatography, the monitoring device commonly used is such that a very good quantitative estimation is obtained of the amount of each constituent present.

Complete separations are always preferred, of course, but they are not always required. Merely a reduction in the quantity of foreign substances present is often enough to simplify the subsequent analytical task. Partition analysis, discussed on page 207, makes use of separations that are incomplete but the extent of which are precisely known.

DISTILLATION

If there is a large difference in the volatility of the sample components, a simple distillation may be sufficient to achieve the desired separation. In most cases, however, fractional distillation must be employed. Depending on the nature of the separation required, fractional distillation may involve the use of a very simple column packed with glass beads, or it may demand an extremely elaborate column such as the Podbielniak equipment used extensively in the petroleum industry. In choosing apparatus and in carrying out analytical distillations, several principles should be recalled.

The process of fractional distillation may be thought of as a series of distillations being carried out simultaneously in various sections of the column. Each distillation produces a vapor which is richer in the lower-boiling constituent than the original liquid, so that as the sample progresses up the column it becomes enriched in the lower-boiling constituent and depleted of the higher-boiling constituent. The vapor from the top of the column is drawn off, condensed, and collected, and this, if a good separation is achieved, consists almost exclusively of the lower-boiling constituent. In order not to upset the efficient progress of this entire operation, a steady rate of heating the still pot is necessary. Good insulation of the column is also necessary to avoid drafts and excessive cooling. The packing of the column should be designed to provide good contact between the rising vapors and the descending condensed liquid. At the same time the packing should permit the condensed liquid to return as rapidly as possible to the still pot and thus avoid excessive holdup. Again to keep the holdup to a minimum, the column chosen should be as short as possible to give the desired fractionation. Finally it is necessary to maintain a sufficiently high reflux ratio (ratio of the volume of condensed liquid returned to the still pot to the volume distilled and collected). Even a column having many theoretical plates will give poor separation if the distillation is carried out at too rapid a rate. The best condition for separation is to operate at nearly total reflux, but since this greatly prolongs the time required for the distillation some compromise is clearly in order.

One of the problems in using distillation in quantitative analysis is obtaining complete separation. In order to separate *all* of the more volatile constituent from the mixture *A-B*, it becomes necessary to continue the distillation to the point where some of the higher boiling *B* will also be found in the distillate. If the purpose of the distillation is to permit quantitative determination of *A*, it is often possible to weigh the total fraction collected and correct for the relatively small amount of B present. One specific example of this is the determination of ethyl benzene in crude acetophenone.[1] Distillation is carried out in a 30-by-400-mm. column packed with stainless steel turnings using a 3:1 reflux ratio. The distillation is stopped when the head temperature reaches 175° C. (the b.p. of ethylbenzene is 136° C. and the b.p. of acetophenone is 202° C.). The entire fraction is weighed and the acetophenone content is then determined by a hydroxylamine method.

If it is not convenient to determine the minor constituent in a distillate by functional group methods, it may be possible to apply an empirical correction. For example, in determining small amounts of diethyl ether (0 to 2%) in ethyl alcohol, the ether is distilled off under closely standardized conditions, and a correction for the alcohol in the distillate is applied from an empirically determined curve of correction vs. the uncorrected volume of distillate.[2] Small amounts of benzene do not interfere in this determination.

A complete separation of A and B is often made possible by adding a liquid C, of intermediate boiling point as a carrier, or "chaser" for A. In this case the distillate will contain all the A present in the original sample plus some of the C added; the still pot will contain all the B plus some C. A specific example is found in separation of butadiene from its dimer (4-vinyl-1-cyclohexene), using chloroform as the carrier.[3] Although the advantages of this technique are immediately obvious, it is necessary to employ considerable care in selecting a suitable carrier. For one thing, the effect of the added liquid on the subsequent analysis of the distillate and residue must be considered. If a judicious choice is not made, distillation with a carrier may actually complicate the analytical task rather than simplify it. The prospective carrier should be screened for possible side reactions with the various components of the sample. Finally it is necessary to check for azeotrope formation between the added liquid and one or more of the sample components. If the liquid C forms an azeotrope with the lower-boiling constituent A, complete separation of A from B is still possible, but it may be necessary to add a larger amount of C than would otherwise be necessary. Azeotrope formation between C and B will cause the separation to be unsatisfactory unless that azeotrope contains such a low percentage of B that the amount of B distilled in flushing A from the column is insignificant.

[1] Carbide and Carbon Chemicals Co., unpublished method.
[2] W. E. Shaefer, *Anal. Chem.*, **20**, 651 (1948).
[3] J. L. Jezl and C. P. Hablitzel, *Anal. Chem.*, **21**, 1046 (1949).

Azeotrope formation is often a major limitation in employing distillation as a separation even if no "carrier" is involved. The boiling point of the pure substances A and B may be many degrees apart, but, if they form an azeotrope when mixed (that is, a mixture that boils at a lower point than either pure constituent), quantitative separation by ordinary fractional distillation will be impossible. Actually azeotrope formation is a very common phenomenon. One of the most extensive compilations of azeotropic data is given in a publication by the American Chemical Society.[4]

The behavior that prevents one separation sometimes makes another one possible. Thus the formation of azeotropes can often be used to advantage. Suppose A and B have similar boiling points so that separation by ordinary fractional distillation is not feasible. By adding a liquid C that boils somewhat below A and B and forms an azeotrope with A (or with B) that boils lower than B, a complete separation of A and B can be achieved. The separation of small amounts of benzene from ethyl alcohol is a practical illustration of this principle.[5] Benzene boils at 80.2° C., and absolute ethyl alcohol boils at 78.4° C. Water, however, forms an azeotrope with ethyl alcohol boiling at 78.1° C. and an azeotrope with benzene (containing 8.9% water) that boils at 69.3° C. The boiling point of benzene-water azeotrope is therefore sufficiently below that of the alcohol-water to permit separation by fractional distillation. The benzene is then isolated from the distillate by extraction with hexane.

Some compounds that have high boiling points or that are unstable at temperatures near their boiling point can be separated by steam distillation. The apparatus used is essentially the same as for simple distillation except that a stream of steam is passed into the sample to carry the vapors of the volatile constituent(s) into the condenser.

The theoretical basis of steam distillation is as follows. In a mixture of immiscible liquids, each exerts its own vapor pressure independently of the other. An intimate mixture of water and an insoluble organic liquid will boil when the *sum* of the vapor pressures of water and the organic liquid is equal to the atmospheric pressure. This is shown graphically in Fig. 32. The boiling point is at temperature c, which is determined by moving line ab (the length of which represents the atmospheric pressure) along the temperature axis until it just touches

[4] L. H. Horsley and co-workers, *Azeotropic Data*, American Chemical Society, Washington, 1952.

[5] D. L. Kouba, L. R. Kangas, and W. W. Becker, *Anal. Chem.*, **20**, 1063 (1948).

the vapor pressure curves of both water and the organic liquid.   In
the distillate the ratio of organic liquid to water is theoretically equal
to the ratio of line bc to line ac in Fig. 32.   It is seen that, in order for
a given liquid to be steam distilled, it must neither react with water

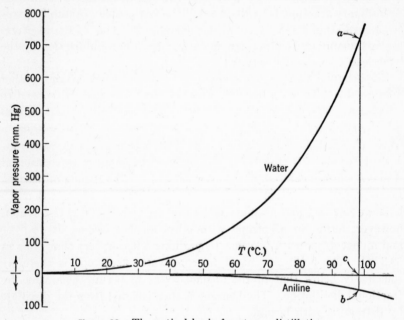

Figure 32.   Theoretical basis for steam distillation.

nor be soluble in water; also it must have an appreciable vapor pressure at temperatures near the boiling point of water.

ION EXCHANGE

Some of the applications of ion exchange resins in determining certain substances by indirect acidimetric methods were discussed in
Chapter 4.   In addition ion exchange resins may be very useful in
separating organic compounds or groups of compounds in order to
simplify their analysis.   In general almost any organic compound that
is ionic or can be made ionic can be separated from nonionic substances
by ion exchange.

An important use of cation exchange columns is in the separation
of amines.   Strongly acidic, sulfonated resins in the hydrogen form
will take up amines generally, even those that are quite weakly basic.
The reaction is:

(1) $$RNH_2 + R_s\!\!-\!\!H^+ \rightarrow R_s\!\!-\!\!RNH_3^+$$

If the amine solution added to the column is sufficiently acidic to convert the amine to its salt, the ion exchange resin may be in the ammonium or alkali form and still remove the amine quantitatively.

(2) $$RNH_3^+ + R_s\!\!-\!\!Na^+ \rightarrow R_s\!\!-\!\!RNH_3^+ + Na^+$$

Hydrogen ions also present in the sample added to the column will compete with the alkyl ammonium ions for occupancy of the active positions of the resin. If the concentration of hydrogen ions is not too great the amine will still be taken up quantitatively, but if the excess acidity is greater than about $0.05\,M$ some or all of the amine will pass through the column.

Weakly acidic resins of the carboxylic acid type will retain moderately basic amines but not the very weakly basic ones. This permits some separation of different types of organic bases, especially if buffers are used so that some of the resin is in the acid form and some in a neutralized form such as sodium. The resin thus serves as a buffer in the pH region of about 4 to 7 and can quantitatively take up alkyl ammonium in this pH range without appreciably affecting the pH of the solution. By contrast sulfonic acid resins have little buffer capacity in this pH range, and it is difficult to maintain a given acidity during the exchange process. Another advantage of the carboxylic acid resin is that, after the exchange step, the greater affinity of this resin for hydrogen ions permits elution of the amines from the column with only a small amount of dilute acid.

Some typical examples of the use of cation exchange column in separation processes may be cited. Quinine sulfate and nicotine (the free base) can be separated by means of a carboxylic acid resin column in the sodium form.[6] Only the quinine is taken up by the resin. If the same resin is used in the hydrogen form, both alkaloids are retained. Amino acids which have an isoelectric pH higher than the pH of the resin phase will be taken up by a cation exchange column. All types of amino acids are retained by hydrogen form sulfonic acid resins, even polycarboxylic amino acids. Only the basic amino acids are taken up from a 5% acetic acid solution by carboxylic acid resins.[7] It is necessary, however, to wash the column with 20% acetic acid to remove all

[6] J. C. Winters and R. Kunin, *Ind. Eng. Chem.*, **41**, 460 (1949).
[7] A. Tiselius, B. Drake, and L. Hagdahl, *Experientia*, **3**, 21 (1947).

the neutral and acidic amino acids. Separation of individual amino acids can be accomplished by ion exchange chromatography.[8]

Anion exchange columns are also useful in effecting certain separations. Anion exchange resins containing the tetraalkyl ammonium group are the most useful. In the hydroxide form this resin is quite a strong base and is able to exchange with anions of weak acids. Numerous instances may be found where anion exchange columns have been used to separate amino acids, ascorbic, citric, formic, fumaric, malic, oxalic, succinic, and sulfonic acids from cations and from non-electrolytes such as alcohols, aldehydes, sugars, etc. It appears likely that many phenols, enols, imides, and other acidic organic compounds may also be taken up quantitatively by anion exchange columns.

Samuelson and his co-workers have reported a very interesting method for separating aldehydes and methyl ketones from alcohols and other organic matter. They found that an anion exchange column in the bisulfite form will quantitatively retain aldehydes and certain ketones by virtue of forming their bisulfite addition products.[9, 10]

$$(3) \qquad R_s\!-\!HSO_3{}^- + RCHO \rightarrow R_s\!-\!RCH(OH)SO_3{}^-$$

They found that acetaldehyde, benzaldehyde, crotonaldehyde, furfural, glyoxal, salicylaldehyde, and vanillin are taken up readily. Acetone and methyl ethyl ketone form less stable bisulfite addition products than aldehydes and therefore require a longer column. The bisulfite addition product of formaldehyde is more stable than that of other aldehydes, yet formaldehyde requires a longer column and slower flow rate than other aldehydes. This is probably owing to the greater tendency of formaldehyde to polymerize or become hydrated.

Washing the column causes some decomposition of the bisulfite addition products. The free carbonyl compound then moves down the column to where the bisulfite ion concentration is greater; here the carbonyl compound reacts and is again taken up by the column. The net effect of washing is thus a slow movement of the carbonyl compounds down the column. Aldehydes and methyl ketones can be separated by elution of the column with hot (75° C.) water. The bisulfite addition products of the ketones are rapidly eluted from the column under these conditions, but the aldehydes are moved only slightly down

[8] For a discussion of this topic, see O. Samuelson, *Ion Exchangers in Analytical Chemistry*, Wiley, New York, 1953, pp. 216–20.

[9] G. Gabrielson and O. Samuelson, *Svensk Kem. Tidskr.*, **62**, 214 (1950); *Acta Chem. Scand.*, **6**, 729, 738 (1952).

[10] E. Sjostrom, *Svensk Kem. Tidskr.*, **64**, 301 (1952).

the column. The aldehydes can then be removed from the column by elution with 1 M sodium chloride.

Many sugars can be converted into ionic species by complexation with a dilute borate solution. A strongly basic resin in the hydroxide form is used for the separation.[11] Any other ionic material is removed from the sugars by ion exchange before the ion exchange separation in the presence of borate.

Phosphate esters (except trialkyl phosphates) are acidic and can be taken up by anion exchange resins. For example, glucose-1-phosphate has been separated from dextrins and proteins by means of a weakly basic anion exchanger.[12]

Very large organic ions are not readily taken up by ion exchange resins. This is especially true if highly cross-linked resins are employed. In such resins it becomes mechanically impossible for the large ions to penetrate beyond the surface; smaller ions can, however, diffuse rapidly through the individual resin particles and exchange with ions in the interior of the resin. Actually only a very small fraction of the capacity of ion exchange resins is at the surface, especially if resin of rather large particle size is used.

A practical example of this principle is the purification of cellulose xanthate before determining the degree of substitution.[13] Ionic impurities such as sulfide and trithiocarbonate are quantitatively removed by a strongly basic anion resin, but essentially none of the large cellulose xanthate molecules are retained. A highly cross-linked resin of large particle size is used. In order to prevent decomposition of the cellulose xanthate during its passage through the column, the solution is cooled and a rapid flow rate is employed. Another use is in separating large sulfonate dye molecules from their impurities. Richardson[14] states that molecules having a diameter of 30 A will not be taken up by anion resins.

EXTRACTION

Extraction may be defined as the selective transfer of certain components of a gaseous, solid, or liquid sample to a solvent that is in intimate contact with the sample. Two phases must remain after the extraction, and the transfer of the various components of the sample

[11] J. X. Khym and L. P. Zill, *J. Am. Chem. Soc.*, **73**, 2399 (1951).

[12] R. M. McCready and W. Z. Hassid, *J. Am. Chem. Soc.*, **66**, 560 (1944).

[13] O. Samuelson and F. Gartner, *Acta Chem. Scand.*, **5**, 596 (1951).

[14] R. W. Richardson, *Nature*, **164**, 916 (1949); *J. Chem. Soc.*, **1951**, 910.

must take place to a different extent, otherwise the process merely becomes that of dissolution.

Extraction of gaseous and solid mixtures is usually a simple process. A gas is commonly passed through a liquid solvent, using a bubbler or diffuser of porous glass to increase the amount of contact between the two phases. The separation of olefins from a hydrocarbon mixture by extraction with concentrated sulfuric acid is a typical example. Another method is to introduce a solid material into a mixture of gases which will selectively react with various constituents of the mixture and thus transfer those constituents from the vapor phase to the solid phase. By either of these methods certain mixtures can be analyzed (as well as separated) by measuring the volume of gas before and after extraction.

Solid samples are usually extracted by agitating the sample with the extractive solvent and then filtering off the undissolved solid. In some cases, as with vegetable matter or other natural products, the use of a mechanical mixer such as the Waring Blendor is helpful in attaining the best possible contact between the solid and the solvent. If it is desired to extract a substance that is only slightly soluble in the extractive solvent, the use of some continuous extractor such as the Soxhlet extractor is recommended.

Although extraction of solids and gases is a thoroughly useful separative technique, extraction of a liquid with a second immiscible liquid (e.g., liquid-liquid extraction) is even more important and widely used. A discussion of the basic principles of liquid-liquid extraction follows.

If a solute dissolved in solvent 1 is thoroughly agitated with an equal volume of immiscible solvent 2 and the phases are allowed to settle, some of the solute will be found in each layer. For such a process the *partition coefficient* is defined:

$$(4) \qquad\qquad P_{1\text{-}2} = \frac{c_2}{c_1}$$

where $P_{1\text{-}2}$ is the partition coefficient for extraction of the solute from solvent 1 to solvent 2, and c_1 and c_2 are the concentrations of solute in the respective solvent. The per cent of solute extracted after one extraction is given by the expression

$$(5) \qquad \% \text{ Extracted} = 100 \left(\frac{c_2}{c_1 + c_2} \right) = 100 \left(\frac{P}{1 + P} \right)$$

If the different volumes of the two solvents are used the per cent extracted is

(6) $$\% \text{ Extracted} = 100 \left(\frac{PR}{1 + PR} \right)$$

where R is the volume ratio of solvent 2 to solvent 1.

If a % is extracted in one extraction and it is assumed that P is constant over the entire concentration range used, then after n extractions with fresh solvent the *total* per cent of the original solute extracted is given by the expression

(7) $$\% \text{ Extracted} = 100 \left[1 - \left(\frac{100 - a}{100} \right)^n \right]$$

If more than about 90% of the desired solute is extracted each time, an essentially complete separation can be achieved after two or three extractions with fresh solvent. These operations may be carried out manually using an ordinary separatory funnel. When the partition coefficient is less favorable, complete separation may still be possible if a sufficient number of extractions with fresh solvent are used. To do this with convenience requires the use of a continuous extractor.[15]

A solvent for a given extractive separation should not be chosen solely on the basis of a favorable partition coefficient. The analytical steps that are to follow the separation process often place additional requirements on the extractive solvent. For example, if the extracted substances are to be determined by ultraviolet or infrared spectroscopy, the solvent should be transparent in the spectral region to be used. If a nonaqueous acid-base titration is to be the basis of the subsequent analysis, a solvent with desirable properties should be chosen (see Chapter 3). Sometimes a very low-boiling solvent is advantageous, as in the determination of fat in dairy products. Here the sample is extracted, and then the solvent is removed, using gentle heat and reduced pressure. Finally, the extracted fat is weighed.[16] Everything else being equal, it is more convenient to extract with a heavy solvent because there is less manipulation when several extractions with fresh solvent are carried out. Solvents should be avoided if they require excessive time to form a sharp interface with the other liquid phase.

In choosing a solvent for a given extraction, the rule that "like dissolves like" is often a useful guide. Salts and other polar substances are soluble in solvents of high dielectric constant such as water, and

15 M. Schmall, C. W. Pifer, and E. G. Wollish, *Anal. Chem.*, 24, 1446 (1952); 26, 1670 (1954).

16 Mojonnier and Troy, *The Technical Control of Dairy Products*, Chicago, Mojonnier Bros. Co., 1925.

are generally insoluble in nonpolar organic solvents. Nonpolar organic substances are insoluble in water but soluble in solvents of low dielectric constant such as benzene, chloroform, and carbon tetrachloride. It is often possible to adjust conditions so that a substance will either be extracted or not extracted by a given solvent. For example, at high pH values phenols exist as the phenolate ion, whereas in solutions of lower pH the free phenol is present. The former is quite soluble in water and insoluble in nonpolar organic solvents; the latter is more soluble in organic solvents. A practical illustration of this is in determining phenols in oil refinery waste water.[17] The sample taken for analysis is adjusted to pH 12, and the oil present is extracted with carbon tetrachloride. The pH is then adjusted to 5, and the phenols are extracted with carbon tetrachloride. The phenol content of the extract is determined spectrophotometrically in the ultraviolet region. In a similar manner a proper adjustment of pH will usually permit or prevent the extraction of amines, carboxylic acids, enols, imides, thiophenols, and other acids and bases from water into nonpolar organic solvents.

An interesting technique is extraction with a solvent containing a solute that will react chemically with the extracted species. If the product of this reaction is more soluble in the extractive solvent, the partition coefficient will be more favorable than otherwise. The extraction of furfural from lubricating oil into aqueous bisulfite illustrates this point.[18] Furfural is appreciably soluble both in organic liquids and in water, but the bisulfite addition product, being ionic, is much more soluble in water than in the organic phase.

Another example of this principle is the separation of aromatic hydrocarbons from aliphatics by extraction into a 22% solution of picric acid in nitrobenzene.[19] Picric acid has a chemical affinity for aromatic hydrocarbons as evidenced by the formation of aromatic picrates of definite composition and melting point. The polar nature of aromatic picrates makes them difficultly soluble in aliphatic hydrocarbons. The relatively high dielectric constant of nitrobenzene and its chemical similarity to picric acid (both are nitro aromatics) make it an ideal solvent for aromatic picrates.

The discussion thus far has dealt with situations where one component of a mixture can be extracted quantitatively and the extraction

[17] L. J. Schmauch and H. M. Grubb, *Anal. Chem.*, **26**, 308 (1954).

[18] W. C. Woelfel, W. D. Good, and C. A. Neilson, *Petroleum Engr.*, **24**, C42 (1952).

[19] E. A. Pasquinelli, *Anal. Chem.*, **26**, 329 (1954).

of the other components is essentially nil. Unfortunately such a favorable situation does not always exist. Simple extraction may still be used to advantage where there is a significant difference in the partition coefficients of a mixture, even though this difference is not sufficient to effect a quantitative separation. This method is based on the principle that each component of a mixture is extracted by a given solvent to the same extent as if it were the only substance present.

Consider the extraction of a mixture of A and B, where A has a partition coefficient (P_{1-2}) P_A and B has a P_{1-2} value of P_B. After one extraction with an equal portion of solvent 2, the fractions of A and B remaining in solvent 1 are $\dfrac{1}{1 + P_A}$ and $\dfrac{1}{1 + P_B}$, respectively. If a quantitative determination of the sum of A and B is made before and after extraction, the amount of each constituent in the original sample can be calculated from the equations,

$$(8) \qquad\qquad\qquad A + B = m$$

$$(9) \qquad\qquad\qquad aA + bB = n$$

where m = sum of A and B before extraction, as determined by analysis,

n = sum of A and B after extraction, as determined by analysis,

$a = \dfrac{1}{1 + P}$, the fraction of A not extracted by solvent 2,

$b = \dfrac{1}{1 + P}$, the fraction of B not extracted by solvent 2.

This principle has been used by Osburn and Werkman [20] and more recently by Tsai and Fu [21] for determining some of the lower carboxylic acids in binary and ternary mixtures. They used the solvent system, water-isopropyl ether, for their studies. Where three acids are extracted, two extractions (and chemical analysis of the unextracted portion) are necessary to provide sufficient data for calculating the composition of the original sample. The second extraction may be another extraction of the aqueous phase with the ether, or the ether phase from the first extraction may be back-extracted with pure water.

Some care is required in selecting a solvent for extractions of this type. In the example mentioned an extractive solvent in which carboxylic acids are extensively dimerized will cause anomalous results.

[20] C. L. Osburn and C. H. Werkman, *Ind. Eng. Chem., Anal. Ed.*, **3**, 264 (1931).
[21] K. R. Tsai and Y. Fu, *Anal. Chem.*, **21**, 818 (1949).

It was found that association of dilute solutions of the lower carboxylic acids in isopropyl ether is apparently negligible, but is considerable in isoamyl ether. It is also important that the extractive solvent chosen should give as large a difference as possible in the extraction coefficients (the fraction of each solute which is not extracted); otherwise the accuracy of the method may be unsatisfactory.

Gordon and Jones have applied the distribution law to the polarographic determination of aldehyde mixtures.[22] Excellent results were obtained in the analysis of binary and ternary mixtures of acetaldehyde, propionaldehyde, and butyraldehyde. The analysis of such a mixture is ordinarily considered quite difficult because of the similarity of half-wave potentials and chemical properties of these compounds. It should be possible to extend this principle to the analysis of other mixtures of similar compounds.

COUNTERCURRENT EXTRACTION

If a system can be found where the differences in the partition coefficients of the various solutes are very large, separation can be readily achieved by simple extraction. Where the differences in partition coefficients are smaller, simple mixtures can often be analyzed by the partition method just described, but the separation is incomplete. By means of countercurrent extraction it is possible to separate solutes having only slightly different partition coefficients, and the separation can usually be made quantitative, or very nearly so.

The all-glass Craig apparatus is probably the most suitable for analytical separations.[23] This is a series of glass tubes mounted on a rack in such a manner that a whole set of batchwise extractions can be carried out at the same time. When the solvent layers have separated, the rack can be tilted so that the upper layer of each tube is transferred to the next tube in the series. At the start of a run all tubes are partly filled with pure solvent 1 except tube 0, which contains the sample dissolved in this same solvent. A lighter, immiscible solvent 2 is added to tube 0, and the solvents are mixed and allowed to settle. The upper layer is transferred to tube 1, fresh solvent 2 is added to tube 0, and extractions are carried out simultaneously in both tubes. Then the upper layers from tube 1 and tube 0 are simultaneously transferred to tubes 2 and 1, respectively, fresh solvent 2 is added to tube 0, and

---

[22] B. E. Gordon and L. C. Jones, *Anal. Chem.*, **22**, 981 (1950).

[23] An excellent description of the construction, theory, and use of the Craig apparatus is given by H. Diehl and G. F. Smith, *Physical Chemical Methods of Analysis,* 3rd preliminary edition, Ames, Iowa, 1956.

the entire process is repeated. The scheme of transfer is shown in Fig. 33. Since only the upper layers are transferred after each set of simultaneous extractions, the only way the solutes can travel along the series of tubes is by extraction into the lighter solvent. The rate at which the various solutes progress along the series of tubes depends on their partition coefficients; the one most readily extracted by the lighter solvent moves at the greatest rate, etc.

If the partition coefficient is known, the amount of a particular solute in each tube after n extractions can be calculated. After one extraction the fraction of the original solute in the upper layer of tube 0 is

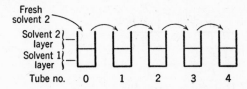

Figure 33. Scheme of transfer in Craig countercurrent extraction.

$P/(1 + P)$ and the fraction in the lower layer is $1/(1 + P)$. The amount of solute in the upper and lower layer of the various tubes after each of four extractions is shown in Table 24. It will be noted that the amount of solute in the upper layer of any tube after each extraction is equal to $P/(1 + P)$ times the *total* solute in that tube after the transfer from the previous extraction. Similarly the solute in the lower layer is $1/(1 + P)$ times the total amount of solute in that tube. The *total* solute in each tube after the transfer following the fourth extraction is also given in Table 24. The total solute in each tube after the transfer following the nth extraction is given by the terms of the binomial expansion

$$\left[\left(\frac{1}{1 + P} \right) + \left(\frac{P}{1 + P} \right) \right]^{n}$$

A theoretical plot of the fraction of solute in each tube after 16 and 64 extractions is shown in Fig. 34. This illustrates the fact that the solute with the greater partition coefficient "travels" faster along the series of tubes, also that separation of the two solutes is more nearly complete after a larger number of extractions and transfers. In actual practice most systems adhere very closely to the theoretically calculated behavior.

TABLE 24

Tube Number

	0	1	2	3	4
$n = 1$	$\dfrac{0}{1}$				
	$\dfrac{P}{1+P}$				
	$\dfrac{1}{1+P}$				
$n = 2$	$\dfrac{0}{1}$ $\dfrac{1}{1+P}$	$\dfrac{P}{1+P}$ 0			
	$\dfrac{P}{(1+P)^2}$	$\dfrac{P^2}{(1+P)^2}$			
	$\dfrac{1}{(1+P)^2}$	$\dfrac{P}{(1+P)^2}$			
$n = 3$	$\dfrac{0}{1}$ $\dfrac{1}{(1+P)^2}$	$\dfrac{P}{(1+P)^2}$ $\dfrac{P}{(1+P)^2}$	$\dfrac{P^2}{(1+P)^2}$ 0		
	$\dfrac{P}{(1+P)^3}$	$\dfrac{2P^2}{(1+P)^3}$	$\dfrac{P^3}{(1+P)^3}$		
	$\dfrac{1}{(1+P)^3}$	$\dfrac{2P}{(1+P)^3}$	$\dfrac{P^2}{(1+P)^3}$		
$n = 4$	$\dfrac{0}{1}$ $\dfrac{1}{(1+P)^3}$	$\dfrac{P}{(1+P)^3}$ $\dfrac{2P}{(1+P)^3}$	$\dfrac{2P^2}{(1+P)^3}$ $\dfrac{P^2}{(1+P)^3}$	$\dfrac{P^3}{(1+P)^3}$ 0	
	$\dfrac{P}{(1+P)^4}$	$\dfrac{3P^2}{(1+P)^4}$	$\dfrac{3P^3}{(1+P)^4}$	$\dfrac{P^4}{(1+P)^4}$	
	$\dfrac{1}{(1+P)^4}$	$\dfrac{3P}{(1+P)^4}$	$\dfrac{3P^2}{(1+P)^4}$	$\dfrac{P^3}{(1+P)^4}$	
Totals after transfer	$\dfrac{1}{(1+P)^4}$	$\dfrac{4P}{(1+P)^4}$	$\dfrac{6P^2}{(1+P)^4}$	$\dfrac{4P^3}{(1+P)^4}$	$\dfrac{P^4}{(1+P)^4}$

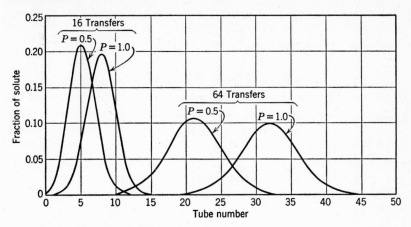

Figure 34. Theoretical distribution of solutes in countercurrent extraction.

CHROMATOGRAPHY

Chromatography may be defined as a separation technique by which various substances are made to move at different rates of speed through a column. A given constituent of the mixture may thus be concentrated in one portion of the column and separated partially or completely from the other substances present. Essentially the separation is based on the differences in affinity of the column material for the different constituents of the sample. The process is very similar to a countercurrent extraction of many stages or to a distillation of many plates. The sample is in one phase (liquid or vapor) moving down the column, and the column packing constitutes a second solid or liquid phase. This phase is actually stationary, but relative to each other the two phases are moving in opposite directions, or countercurrently.

Chromatographic methods may be divided into three classifications. Ion exchange chromatography involves differential elution of ionic substances from columns of ion exchange resins. In adsorption chromatography the column is packed with an adsorbent such as alumina or activated charcoal. Partition chromatography involves partition of the solutes between two liquid phases or between a liquid and a gas. One of these phases is held immobile by absorbent material in the column such as silica gel.

In any of these methods the sample, dissolved in an appropriate solvent, is applied to the column. The substance for which the resin or adsorbent has the greater affinity is somewhat concentrated near the top of the column during this step, but no appreciable separation is effected unless the column material has a much greater affinity for one constituent or group.

The next step is the differential elution of the solutes on the column. This is sometimes called "developing" the chromatograph. There are two general possibilities for this process. One of these is to elute with a solvent or reagent for which the column material has somewhat less affinity than for the solutes. This is often called elution chromatography. Consider the chromatographic separation of solutes A and B by such a process. When the eluting reagent comes in contact with the band of mixed A and B, both A and B will be somewhat displaced down the column by the mass effect of the eluting reagent. If the column material has a greater affinity for A than for B, then B will be moved down the column at a faster rate than A. First B concentrates in the front edge of the mixed band, then B and A separate into distinct bands, and the separation is thus complete. If at this point the column contains adherent material such as silica gel, it can be extruded from the column and cut into sections corresponding to the location of the bands. If this is not possible (as with ion exchange resins) or is otherwise not desirable, the elution is continued until the bands move off the column. Fractions are taken, and the amount of A or B in each fraction is determined. From this information a curve of the type shown in Fig. 35 can be plotted. The data for plotting such a curve may require the collection of a rather large number of fractions, and in such cases an automatic fraction collector becomes almost a necessity.

A second general method, known as displacement chromatography, is to elute with a reagent that is more strongly taken up by the column than any of the sample components. This may be considered a kind of chemical piston which pushes A and B down the column. In this case A and B are gradually separated into distinct bands that are adjacent to each other. Once they are separated into bands, A and B proceed at the *same speed* down the remainder of the column. Even if the interface between bands A and B is sharp, it is not possible to recover *all* of one constituent without getting some of the other. However, this method does have the advantage that higher concentrations of solute are possible; also less eluting reagent is required, and the separation is usually more rapid than when a more weakly adsorbed substance is used as the eluting reagent.

A third general method known as frontal analysis is less frequently used. Here a rather large sample is fed continuously into the chromatographic column. Soon the column becomes saturated, and the fastest moving constituent appears first in the effluent. In later portions of the effluent, the other sample components appear in the order of their mobilities on the column. This technique seldom gives quantitative separations.

So many variations and combinations of chromatographic columns, eluents, types of sample, flow rates, etc., have been used that the selection of optimum conditions for a given chromatographic separation is very confusing. Many of the methods in the literature appear to

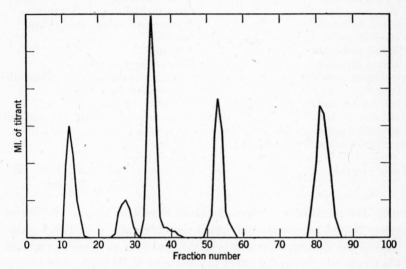

Figure 35. Chromatographic elution curve.

have been arrived at through a combination of copying the conditions of previous methods and personal prejudice. Indeed this may sometimes be the most efficient way to select conditions. Certain generalities can, however, be made as an aid to systematic choice of conditions. In adsorption chromatography, organic substances that are more polar are usually more strongly adsorbed. Strain [24] has prepared a graded series of eluting solvents for adsorption chromatography. He has also listed absorbents in the order of their adsorbing ability (see Table 25). More subtle variation in the affinity of eluents for adsorbents can be achieved by employing mixtures of varying proportions. It should be emphasized that these series are generalities and that the order is often different under various conditions.

To predict the conditions for separation by partition chromatog-

[24] H. H. Strain, "Chromatographic Adsorption Analysis," New York, Interscience, 1942, pp. 50, 66.

TABLE 25

Graded Series of Adsorbents and Eluents [24]

Chromatographic Adsorbents in Order of Increasing Adsorbing Power	Solvents in Approximate Order of Increasing Eluting Power
Sucrose, starch	Carbon tetrachloride
Inulin	Cyclohexane
Magnesium citrate	Carbon disulfide
Talc	Ether (anhydrous, alcohol-free)
Sodium carbonate	Acetone (anhydrous, alcohol-free)
Potassium carbonate	Benzene
Calcium carbonate	Toluene
Calcium phosphate	Esters of organic acids
Magnesium carbonate	1,2-Dichloroethane, chloroform, dichloromethane
Magnesia (Merck)	
Lime (freshly and partially slaked)	Alcohols
Activated silicic acid	Water (variations with pH and salt concentration)
Activated magnesium silicates	
Activated alumina, charcoal and magnesia (Micron brand)	Pyridine
Fuller's earths	Organic acids
	Mixtures of ·acids and bases with water, alcohol, or pyridine

raphy, the partition coefficients involved should be known. A solvent system should be selected for which the difference in partition coefficients of the various constituents of the sample is as great as possible. It is frequently worth the effort to determine these coefficients experimentally in order to select a reasonably suitable eluting solvent.

The scope and principles of chromatographic separations in organic analysis can perhaps be best illustrated by describing a few of the numerous methods appearing in the current literature. One of these is a system for separating monocarboxylic acids (C_2 to C_{16}) and dicarboxylic acids (C_2 to C_{22}) on a silica gel column.[25] Methyl Cellosolve-water (9:1) equilibrated with the developing solvent is used as the internal phase. Skelleysolve B, then Skelleysolve B–n-butyl ether, and finally n-butyl ether is used as the eluting solvent. Fractions are collected with the aid of an automatic drop-and-time-counting fraction collector, and the carboxylic acid content of each fraction is determined by alkalimetric titration. By this method complete separation of the individual acids is accomplished. This requires about 24 hours' time, but separation of less complex mixtures is accomplished more rapidly.

A method for the quantitative determination of organic acids in

[25] V. Zbinovsky, *Anal. Chem.*, **27**, 764 (1955).

cured tobacco employs a variety of separative techniques.[26]   The solid sample is homogenized in a Waring Blendor, and the acids and other water-soluble material are extracted with dilute sodium hydroxide. After filtering, the extract is passed through an anion exchange column in the carbonate form to remove the organic acids.   This step eliminates interfering substances such as sugars, pigments, and cations.   The acids are eluted from the anion exchange column with ammonium carbonate, then the excess ammonium carbonate is decomposed by heating to 70° C.   A portion of this solution is then passed through a cation exchange column in the hydrogen form, and the total acid content is determined by titration with standard sodium hydroxide.   An aliquot of the eluate from the anion column is acidified and transferred to a column containing silica gel which had previously been treated with water-saturated chloroform.   The column is then eluted with different eluents in the order listed in Table 26.

TABLE 26

Elution Schedule for Separating Acids in Tobacco Extracts

Eluent	Ml. of Eluent	Acid Eluted
Chloroform (H$_2$O saturated)	50	None
Chloroform–8% t-butanol	75	Fumaric
Chloroform–13% t-butanol	75	Succinic
Chloroform–20% t-butanol	115	Oxalic
Chloroform–25% t-butanol	90	Malic
Chloroform–30% t-butanol	110	Citric

Using this elution scheme, only one fraction must be collected for each acid and all of that acid is in one fraction.   On a routine basis this separation is comparatively simple and rapid.   In order to determine this schedule originally, however, it was necessary to patiently collect and analyze many small fractions.   It was also necessary to ascertain that varying the proportions of the individual acids in the sample within reasonable limits did not affect the volume of eluent required for each acid.

In the separation just described the use of eluents containing a gradually increasing ratio of t-butanol to chloroform is interesting.   It is probable that a solvent containing 8% t-butanol would eventually have eluted all the acids from the column, but a much larger volume of eluent would have been required.

[26] F. E. Resnik, L. A. Lee, and W. A. Powell, *Anal. Chem.*, **27**, 928 (1955).

A very simple chromatographic method is stated to determine the total aromatic content of petroleum products.[27] The column used is a tube approximately 9 mm. in inside diameter by 1000 mm. long and is carefully packed with oven-dried silica gel. A trace of a fluorescent, hydrocarbon-soluble impurity is added to a 2-to-5-ml. sample. The sample is added to the column and then eluted farther down the column by an equal volume of alcohol. When viewed under ultraviolet light the fluorescent impurity imparts a fluorescence to the entire hydrocarbon band. The aromatic constituents are more strongly fluorescent and are clearly seen as a separate band. The per cent of aromatics in the sample is simply the length of the purple aromatic band times 100, divided by the length of the entire sample. This method requires a maximum of only 45 minutes per determination and is reproducible to ±2%.

GAS CHROMATOGRAPHY

Chromatographic methods have been developed for the separation and analysis of substances that are gases or that can be vaporized. In gas chromatography (also called vapor-phase chromatography) as well as in liquid-phase chromatography, both adsorption and partition methods have been used. Gas-liquid partition chromatography seems to give better separations for a larger number of cases than do gas-adsorption chromatographic methods. Several authors have already discussed the principles and typical applications of gas chromatography, and the literature on this subject is growing at a rapid pace.[28-33]

Gas chromatography has been used extensively only since about 1954 but already it is being hailed as the most important advance in analytical chemistry of the last 10 or 20 years. There are sound reasons for this enthusiasm. For one thing gas chromatography affords a much more rapid separation than is generally possible by liquid-phase chromatographic methods. Often a complete separation of a multicomponent sample can be achieved in only 15 or 20 minutes. The decreased resistance of column packing to gaseous substances permits

[27] A. L. Conrad, *Anal. Chem.*, **20**, 725 (1948).

[28] A. I. M. Keulemans, A. Kwantes, and P. Zaal, *Anal. Chem. Acta*, **13**, 357 (1955).

[29] H. W. Patton, J. S. Lewis, and W. I. Kaye, *Anal. Chem.*, **27**, 170 (1955).

[30] D. H. Lichtenfels, S. A. Fleck, and F. H. Buroco, *Anal. Chem.*, **27**, 1510 (1955).

[31] M. Dimbat, P. E. Porter, and F. H. Stross, *Anal. Chem.*, **28**, 290 (1956).

[32] E. M. Fredericks and F. R. Brooks, *Anal. Chem.*, **28**, 297 (1956).

[33] F. T. Effersten, H. S. Knight, and S. Groennings, *Anal. Chem.*, **28**, 303 (1956).

use of much longer columns than would be practical with liquids. In gas chromatography a column length of 10 or 12 feet is common, and columns 50 to 75 feet in length have been used successfully. Long columns permit the separation of compounds that are very closely related in their chemical and physical properties. An excellent automatic device (thermal conductivity) is available for measuring and recording the composition of the gas emerging from the column, and this permits

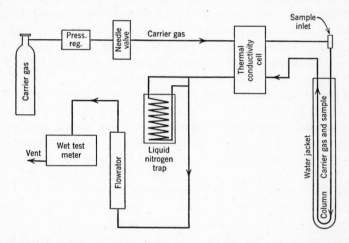

Figure 36. Schematic diagram of apparatus. (Reprinted from *Analytical Chemistry* with permission.)

a rapid quantitative estimation of the various components of a sample mixture.

A schematic diagram of the apparatus typically used in gas-liquid partition chromatography is shown in Fig. 36. A continuous flow of carrier gas (helium, nitrogen, or hydrogen) is supplied to the system from a gas cylinder. A constant flow rate is obtained by a series of reducing valves; the rate of flow is indicated by a rotameter and can be measured with a wet-test meter. The liquid nitrogen trap (or a trap containing a cooled solvent such as carbon disulfide) is used only if sample fractions are to be collected for further analysis. A typical column is ¼ inch in diameter and is wound in a spiral for compactness. It is packed with an inert, porous material (such as Celite, crushed firebrick, or the detergent Tide) which has been coated with a high-boiling organic liquid. The entire column (and often the thermal conductivity cell also) is enclosed in a water jacket or air bath to maintain constant temperature and to permit operation at elevated or reduced temperatures if desired.

The sample is injected into the stream of carrier gas by means of a hypodermic syringe. The maximum sample size employed is usually about 1 ml. for liquid samples or 10 to 15 ml. for gaseous samples. High-boiling samples are flash-volatilized by means of a preheater. The mixture of carrier gas and sample flows into the packed column where the individual components of the sample are partitioned between the gas phase in the pore space of the column packing and the liquid coating of the column packing. As elution with the carrier gas continues, the sample components move with individual velocities which are less than that of the carrier gas. The rate at which each component moves is dependent upon its partition coefficient.

The gas stream leaving the column is usually analyzed by a thermal conductivity method. Before the run the electrical bridge of the thermal conductivity cell is balanced with carrier gas passing through both the reference channel and the sample channel. As the effluent stream passes through the sample, the electrical bridge of the thermal conductivity cell is thrown out of balance. The voltage resulting from this unbalance is transmitted to a recording potentiometer which automatically plots the detector response as a function of time. A recording of a typical chromatographic analysis is shown in Fig. 37.

Identification of the components of a mixture is accomplished by noting the retention volume (the volume of gas that flows through the detector cell between the time the sample is injected and the time the sample peak appears) or the retention time. This is far from infallible as a qualitative method because two or more compounds may have almost identical retention volumes under a given set of conditions. However, at least a tentative identification is possible by this method, and a sure identification can be made by collecting the fraction in question and subjecting it to infrared analysis. A good estimate of the quantitative composition of a sample is made by measuring the area under each peak of the chromatogram. This may be done by multiplying the peak height by the width halfway between the peak and the base line. Another quantitative method is to simply measure the various peak heights.

The scope of gas chromatography appears to be very broad indeed. A general rule is that any compound is susceptible to separation and determination by gas chromatographic methods provided it has a vapor pressure of at least 10 mm. of mercury at the temperature employed.

With apparatus now available which permits operation up to 150° C. (or up to 250° C. with one instrument), the number of compounds that fall into this class is tremendous. It should be pointed out, however, that there is a marked decrease in sensitivity of the thermal conductivity detection device at elevated temperatures.

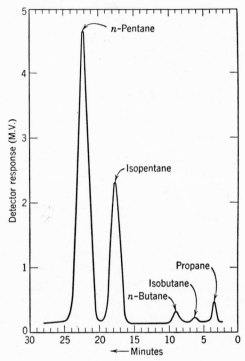

Figure 37. Typical gas chromatographic curve. (Reprinted from *Analytical Chemistry* with permission.)

Gas chromatography has thus far been used most extensively in the analysis of hydrocarbon mixtures, but increasing application is now being made to mixtures containing alcohols, ethers, water, and components of many other types. Applications are not limited to the determination of the major constituents of a sample. It is comparatively easy to separate and measure small amounts of a substance in the presence of a less volatile major constituent. The reverse situation is more difficult but can frequently be accomplished. For example, by a simple modified base-line technique, a cyclohexanol concentration of the order of 50 p.p.m. in toluene can be measured.

The column packing is an important variable in gas chromatography. By changing the stationary liquid used in the column, the degree of separation of various substances may be considerably altered. In some cases a change in the liquid used will actually cause a reversal in the order of elution of certain compounds. If the stationary liquid is a chemically inert substance such as a hydrocarbon vacuum pump oil, the order of elution of the sample components is almost strictly a function of their boiling points. Dimethylsulfolane, I, as illustrated, has

$$CH_3—CH——CH_2$$
$$CH_2 \quad CH—CH_3$$
$$S$$
$$O \quad O$$

I

a greater attraction for olefins than for saturated hydrocarbons and therefore gives excellent separation of olefins and paraffins having the same number of carbon atoms. The molecular compound from fluorene and picric acid has been shown to be advantageous as the stationary liquid for separation of aromatic hydrocarbons, and diglycerol has been employed for the separation of oxygenated substances.[28] Many other liquids will undoubtedly be proposed. The stationary liquid is definitely an important variable although the proper choice is still essentially a matter of trial and error.

Some thought should be given to the column length to be employed. Long columns are capable of better separations than shorter columns but, of course, prolong the time required for separation. Because of the time factor it is sometimes convenient to chromatograph a sample quickly on a rather short column. This will effect a complete separation of some, but not necessarily all, of the sample components. The incompletely separated fractions may then be subjected to infrared or chemical analysis, or rechromatographed to achieve complete separation. It should also be mentioned that, by connecting two short columns in series which contain different types of packing, a better separation will frequently be obtained than would be possible with a single long column.

TRACER DILUTION METHODS

An analytical method that has nearly universal scope in principle is the tracer dilution technique. Although the technique is applicable to the quantitative solution of an enormous number of problems, it is definitely not adaptable to routine application. It will be mainly useful for the solution of problems of theoretical interest. In essence it consists of taking a crude mixture, adding to it a purified sample of one of the products, and then reisolating the particular product. Either the original mixture or the added material must be tagged in some way that permits the examination of the finally purified product, so as to determine what fraction of it came from the mixture and what fraction was recovered from the added substance. The losses during purification can then be calculated accurately from a knowledge of the amount of the tracer added before isolation.

The procedure has usually utilized isotopic tracers and is for that reason commonly referred to as *isotopic dilution analysis*. The procedure is not actually restricted to isotopic tracers; hence it seems better to use the more general term, *tracer dilution analysis*.

The application of the method is best explained by the consideration of specific examples. Klapproth and Westheimer [34] wished to determine accurately the composition of the mixture of isomers produced in the mercuration of toluene.

(10)

(where $x = OAc^-$ or ClO_4^-).

To analyze the mixture of ortho, meta, and para isomers, they converted the mixed aryl mercuric compounds to aryl bromides with radioactive bromine. There is every reason to believe that the reactions used in this conversion were quantitative.

(11) $ArHgx \xrightarrow{\text{NaBr}} ArHgBr$

(12) $ArHgBr + Br_2^* \longrightarrow ArBr^* + HgBr_2^*$

The mixture of radioactive bromotoluenes was analyzed by the dilution principle as indicated by the accompanying flow sheet.

[34] Wm. J. Klapproth and F. H. Westheimer, *J. Am. Chem. Soc.*, **72**, 4461 (1950).

Dissolve and remove
↓ aliquot portions

Aliquot 1	Aliquot 2	Aliquot 3
↓ Add a grams inactive o-$C_6H_4(CH_3)Br$	↓ Add b grams inactive m-$C_6H_4(CH_3)Br$	↓ Add c grams inactive p-$C_6H_4(CH_3)Br$
↓ Oxidize with MnO_4^-	↓ Oxidize with MnO_4^-	↓ Oxidize with MnO_4^-
Mixture of bromobenzoic acids	Mixture of bromobenzoic acids	Mixture of bromobenzoic acids
↓ Recrystallize ortho to radio chemical purity	↓ Recrystallize meta to radio chemical purity	↓ Recrystallize para to radio chemical purity
X grams with radioactivity some fraction of that of original bromine	Y grams with radioactivity some fraction of that of original bromine	Z grams with radioactivity some fraction of that of original bromine

To calculate original yield of ortho isomer,

$$x \frac{\text{activity}}{\text{original activity}} = \text{radioactive bromo acid in purified product} = \gamma$$

$$x - r = \text{inactive bromo acid in purified product}$$

$$\frac{x - r}{a} = \text{fraction recovered in work-up}$$

$$\frac{ar}{x - r} = \text{amount of radioactive ortho isomer in original aliquot}$$

Roberts *et al.*[35] have applied isotopic dilution to the determination of isomer distribution in the nitration chloro-, bromo-, and iodobenzenes.

An ingenious variant of dilution analysis has been developed by Boozer and Lewis.[36] Actually it is consideration of their method that has prompted the writers to extend the nomenclature for designation

[35] J. D. Roberts, J. K. Sanford, F. L. J. Sixma, H. Cerfontain, and R. Zagt, *J. Am. Chem. Soc.*, **76**, 4525 (1954).

[36] C. E. Boozer and E. S. Lewis, *J. Am. Chem. Soc.*, **76**, 794 (1954).

of this method of analysis. They were concerned with the study of the decomposition of secondary alkyl chlorosulfites and wished to determine accurately the absolute yield of secondary halide produced. The fact that by-products were formed in the reaction necessitated the

$$\begin{array}{c} \text{RCHCH}_3 \rightarrow \text{RCHCH}_3 + \text{SO}_2 \\ | \qquad\qquad | \\ \text{OSOCl} \qquad \text{Cl} \end{array}$$

(13)

direct determination of the chloride produced. Advantage was taken of the fact that the secondary carbon atom was an asymmetric center in all the systems studied. The decomposition of a racemic chlorosulfite led, of course, to the formation of racemic chloride. The yield of chloride was then determined by adding a sample of optically active chloride to the reaction mixture. The chloride fraction was then worked up by distillation.* Measurement of the optical activity of the purified product then gave the dilution ratio, and the recovery of the active constituent gave a quantitative measure of the losses entailed in the isolation of the chloride sample. This elegant method must always be subjected to careful control to ensure that no racemization of the active material occurs during the isolation.

It is noteworthy that the reversal of the optically active tracer dilution analysis is not always possible. For example, it is known that the decomposition of optically active chlorosulfites is accompanied by varying amounts of racemization and inversion of configuration. This would invalidate any attempts to analyze reaction products from active starting materials by dilution with racemic chlorides.

It is possible to foresee many applications of this analytical method, as it is not restricted exclusively to compounds that have asymmetric centers. If nonasymmetric products can be converted quantitatively to derivatives that are asymmetric, the latter can be diluted with active material and worked up for analysis. For example, a mixture of carboxylic acids might be converted to sec-butyl esters with racemic sec-butanol. A sample of the optically active form of one of the esters could be added allowing the determination of that particular constituent by a dilution analysis.

* Note that isolation by recrystallization would not be trustworthy in such an analysis. The common occurrence of solid, racemic compounds would often lead to fractionation of the mixture. In principle the same behavior might lead to error in the isolation of liquids by distillation or extraction procedures. However, liquid racemate and the corresponding optically active compounds usually form ideal solutions.

PROBLEMS

1. Klapproth and Westheimer [*J. Am. Chem. Soc.*, **72**, 4461 (1950)] also studied the mercuration of nitrobenzene. They analyzed the products by conversion to mixtures of nitrobromobenzenes. The mixed halides were then allowed to react with piperidine under conditions that led to selective displacement on the ortho and para nitro-compounds.

This gave values for the ratio, $(o + p)/m$, in the mercuration reaction but did not give the o/p ratio.

Devise methods for the determination of the o/p ratio based upon:

a. Isotope dilution.

b. Dilution analysis using optically active amines.

c. Differential kinetic analysis (see Chapter 9, and consult *Chemical Abstracts* for rate data that may be pertinent to the problem).

Compare the relative merits of the various methods and state any preferences that you might have among them. In evaluating *a* and *b*, remember to take into account the time required to prepare tracer materials.

2. Devise methods for carrying out either a partial or a total separation of the following mixtures in order to facilitate the total analysis. What chemical methods would you use to supplement the separations in each case?

a. $CH_3CHOHCH_3$, CH_3COCH_3, .

b. $n\text{-}C_7H_{16}$, $C_6H_5CH_3$, C_6H_6.

c. $CH_3CO_2CH_2C_6H_5$, CH_3CO_2H, $CH_3CO_2C_2H_5$, C_2H_5OH, $C_6H_5CH_2OH$.

12.

PHYSICAL

AND

POLAROGRAPHIC METHODS

PHYSICAL METHODS

It is often possible to use physical properties such as the refractive index, density, viscosity, freezing point, boiling point, solubility, and miscibility as a basis for analyzing organic samples. These methods are usually limited to two- and three-component systems, but many actual samples requiring analysis are of this type. Analysis of such samples by physical methods or by combined physical and chemical methods is often more rapid and convenient than by chemical methods alone. Determinations based on physical measurements are often empirical and require rather extensive preliminary calibration. This type of method is well suited to the routine analytical laboratory but is less convenient when only an occasional determination is desired.

Many other methods that are primarily physical in nature find considerable use in organic analysis. Analytical methods based on measurement of absorption spectra are discussed in Chapter 10. Separations based on physical properties are discussed in Chapter 11. It is not within the scope of this book to discuss certain other very useful but specialized techniques such as mass spectrometry, microscopy, x-ray diffraction analysis, etc.

Refractive Index. The refractive index of a single drop of liquid can be determined conveniently and accurately with an Abbé refractometer. A broad range, 1.3000 to 1.7000, is covered with a precision of ±0.0001. The scale of this instrument is calibrated to read the refractive index directly.

With larger samples the immersion-type refractometer may be used. This instrument has less range (N_d 1.325 to 1.367, or to 1.492 with an auxiliary prism) but is capable of somewhat greater precision and accuracy than is the Abbé instrument. Temperature control is necessary for good work with either instrument because the temperature coefficient for most substances is about 0.0004 per 1° C.

A good discussion of the elementary principles of refractometry is given by Willard, Merritt, and Dean.[1] Operating directions for refractometers may be obtained by consulting either their textbook or the manufacturer's instruction sheet accompanying the instrument.

The interferometer is also used for measurement of refractive index. This instrument compares the refractive indices of two similar substances or solutions, one of which may be a standard. The interferometer is extremely sensitive to small differences in refractive index. This makes it useful for detecting small *changes* in the concentration of a solution, such as those involved in adsorption studies,[2-4] where the change in concentration due to adsorption is slight and must therefore be measured very accurately. The basic principles of interferometry are also discussed in the textbook cited above.[1]

Density. Density may be determined approximately and rapidly with a suitable hydrometer or, more accurately, with a Westphal balance. Probably the most commonly used accurate method, however, is to weigh a known volume of liquid, using a pycnometer.

The pycnometer is dried and weighed empty (or filled with distilled water if specific gravity is to be determined). It is then nearly filled with the liquid to be measured, capped, and placed in a thermostat. When temperature equilibrium has been attained, the plug is inserted and the liquid that is pushed out through the capillary is carefully wiped off. The pycnometer and contents is then weighed, and the density (or specific gravity) is calculated. A micro pipet serves as a

[1] H. H. Willard, L. L. Merritt, Jr., and J. A. Dean, *Instrumental Methods of Analysis*, 2nd ed., New York, Van Nostrand, 1951, p. 146.

[2] F. E. Bartell and C. K. Sloan, *J. Am. Chem. Soc.*, **51**, 1637 (1929).

[3] R. F. Hansen, Ying Fu, and F. E. Bartell, *J. Phys. & Colloid Chem.*, **53**, 769 (1949).

[4] R. F. Hansen and R. P. Craig, *J. Phys. Chem.*, **58**, 211 (1954).

convenient pycnometer when only a small quantity of sample is available.

Freezing Point. Freezing-point determinations are most commonly used to estimate the purity of organic liquids containing not more than 5 or 10 per cent impurities. If such a mixture is frozen slowly and the

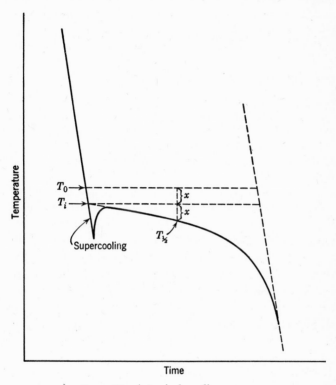

Figure 38. A typical cooling curve.

temperature is plotted against time, a "cooling curve" of the type shown in Fig. 38 is obtained. The temperature T_i (the intersection of the lines of linear extrapolation of the steep and flat portions of the curve) represents the true freezing point of the mixture. As more of the pure solvent freezes out, the freezing point of the remaining solution is lowered because the concentration of impurities in the mother liquor is increased.

If the system obeys Raoult's law, the mole fraction of impurities present can be calculated from the freezing points of the mixture and of the pure major constituent, using the expression:

(1) $$x = \frac{\Delta H_{\text{fus.}}}{RT_0{}^2} (T_0 - T_i) = K\Delta T$$

where x = the mole fraction of impurities present,
T_0 = the freezing point of the pure major constituent,
T_i = the freezing point of the mixture.

Often the freezing point of a pure liquid (T_0) is not available in the literature to as high a degree of accuracy as needed. In such cases T_0 can be determined accurately from the cooling curve of the slightly impure liquid.

(2) $$x = \frac{\Delta H_{\text{fus.}}}{RT_0{}^2} (T_0 - T_i)$$

(3) $$2x = \frac{\Delta H_{\text{fus.}}}{RT_0{}^2} (T_0 - T_{1/2})$$

Combining and solving for T_0:

(4) $$T_0 = 2T_i - T_{1/2}$$

In this derivation it is assumed that all the impurity stays in the mother liquor during most of the freezing process. When one-half of the pure compound has been frozen, the mole fraction of impurities in the mother liquor, x, will therefore be twice the original concentration, or $2x$.

Cooling curves are often recorded automatically and used to determine the purity of an organic substance.[5] A very simple method for determining the freezing (or congealing point) is given in procedure 7, page 271.

Viscosity. The viscosity of liquids is commonly measured by an Ostwald viscometer (rate of flow through a capillary), by a rotating-cylinder viscometer (which measures the torque required to rotate a cylinder at a given speed in the liquid), or by the velocity at which a sphere falls through the liquid. A discussion of these methods may be found in Daniels et al.[6] and in other standard physical chemistry textbooks.

Analysis of Binary Mixtures

If no third substance is present, only one measurement is required to establish the composition. The measurement chosen should be a property in which the two constituents differ as much as possible.

[5] C. R. Witschonke, *Anal. Chem.*, **24**, 350 (1952); **26**, 562 (1954).

[6] F. Daniels et al., *Experimental Physical Chemistry*, 4th ed., New York, McGraw-Hill, 1949, pp. 433–436.

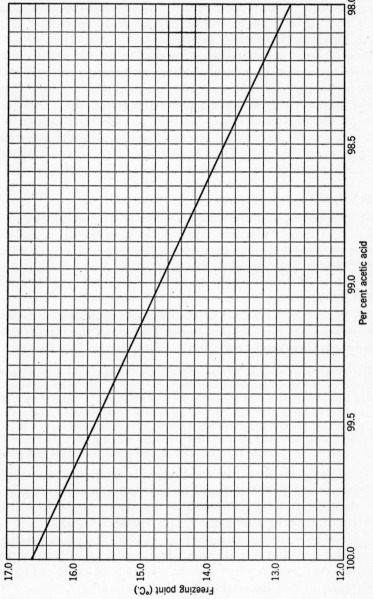

Figure 39. Calibration curve for acetic acid.

The usual procedure is then to prepare a series of known synthetic mixtures and to measure the density, refractive index, or other property of each mixture. A plot of the property chosen against the composition gives a working curve to be used in the analysis of unknowns. This curve is usually a straight line, or nearly so.

Figure 39 shows a calibration curve used to determine the purity of glacial acetic acid by measurement of its freezing point. Here it is only necessary to determine the freezing point within $\pm 0.05°$ C. to give the per cent purity of acetic acid accurate to $\pm 0.03\%$. Other examples of the analysis of binary mixtures by physical measurements are the analysis of ethyl alcohol-water mixtures by refractive index and determination of the composition of propylene glycol-water binaries [7] by density or refractive index, depending on the composition range.

Analysis of Ternary Mixtures

Two independent measurements are sufficient to establish the composition of a ternary mixture. One of the most useful methods is based on chemical determination of one constituent plus a phase titration.[8] Consider a mixture of A, B, and C, where A and B are immiscible and C is a solvent for both A and B. A practical example would be A = chlorobenzene, B = water, and C = methanol. The mixture may be titrated with either A or B to the first permanent turbidity. At the end point of this titration, the composition of the titrated mixture lies somewhere on the curve in the phase diagram (see Fig. 40).

The choice of A or B as titrant depends on the original composition of the mixture. For a sample of composition 1 in Fig. 40, titration with B would shift the composition toward pure B as indicated by the arrow. The intersection of the arrow and composition line is nearly a right angle, thus indicating that the end point would be sharp. If a mixture of composition 2 it titrated with B, it will be seen that turbidity will appear only gradually as B is added. In this case titration with A would give a sharper end point.

If the amount of one of the constituents is determined chemically on a separate sample and corrected for the change in composition due to the phase titration, the composition of the mixture can be calculated. For example, suppose a 50-gram sample contains 8 grams of A by chemical analysis and requires 10 grams of B for the phase titration. The weight per cent of A in the titrated mixture is $8/(50 + 10) \times 100 = 13.3\%$. On the curve where $A = 13.3$, there is 23.7% B and 63.0% C after titration. In the original sample, therefore:

[7] G. MacBeth and A. R. Thompson, *Anal. Chem.*, **23**, 618 (1951).
[8] S. Siggia and J. G. Hanna, *Anal. Chem.*, **21**, 1087 (1949).

(5) $\qquad A = \frac{8}{50} \times 100 = 16.0\%$

(6) $\qquad B = \left[\dfrac{(0.237 \times 60) - 10}{50} \right] \times 100 = 8.4\%$

(7) $\qquad C = \dfrac{(0.63 \times 60)}{50} \times 100 = 75.6\%$

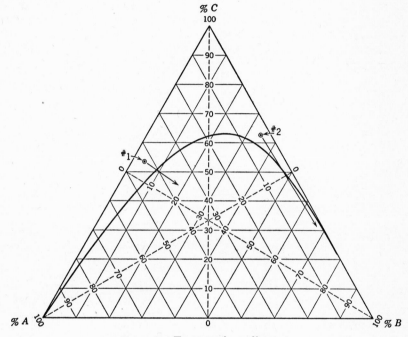

Figure 40. Ternary phase diagram.

In addition to the example cited above, the following systems have been analyzed by the method of phase titration and chemical determination: acetic acid-carbon tetrachloride-water, glycerol-acetic acid-benzene, pyridine-ethyl ether-monoethanolamine, benzaldehyde-dioxane-water, water-pyridine-benzene, and ethyl vinyl ether-ethanol-water.

Chemical analysis for one constituent plus measurement of one physical property of the sample can also be used to determine the composition of a ternary. The physical property chosen should be almost identical for two of the components, and this value should be considerably different from that of the third component. The component determined chemically must be one of the two possessing the similar physical property.

Using this principle,[9] Frere and Busz analyzed mixtures (from the hydrogenation of diacetone alcohol) containing isopropyl alcohol, diacetone alcohol, and 2-methyl-2,4-pentanediol. The physical prop-

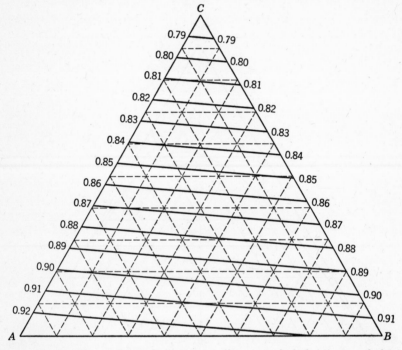

Figure 41. Specific gravities of the system diacetone alcohol (A), 2-methyl-2,4-pentanediol (B), and isopropyl alcohol (C). (Reprinted from *Analytical Chemistry* with permission.)

erty chosen for measurement was the specific gravity. Using triangular coordinates, a working curve is plotted with lines drawn to indicate various compositions having equal specific gravity (see Fig. 41). The specific gravity of the mixture is determined at 25° C., and the diacetone alcohol is determined chemically by the hydroxylamine hydrochloride method. The point at which the diacetone alcohol composition line intersects the specific gravity line represents the composition of the sample.

[9] F. J. Frere and J. J. Busz, *Anal. Chem.*, **21**, 616 (1949).

Data for preparing the working curve is obtained by adding varying amounts of isopropyl alcohol to fixed binary mixtures of diacetone alcohol and 2-methyl-2,4-pentanediol and measuring the specific gravity of these mixtures. By treating the binary mixture as a single component, the specific gravity (or any other suitable physical property) can be plotted against composition, using rectangular coordinates. From several plots of this type, ternary solutions of variable composition but with the same specific gravity can be selected. This information plotted on triangular coordinates permits construction of a working curve as shown in Fig. 41.

POLAROGRAPHY

In contrast to the situation in the field of inorganic chemistry, no large array of electrochemical methods has been applied to organic analysis. This is due in large part to the fact that most organic systems do not achieve the rapid equilibrium required for many electrochemical measurements. Also, the technique of electrodeposition does not seem well suited to organic compounds since their solubilities are not often changed appreciably on undergoing oxidation or reduction. Furthermore, high overvoltages are often required in electrolytic reduction and oxidation of many organic molecules. The one outstanding exception to these generalizations is found in polarography, which is applied to an ever-increasing number of organic analytical problems.

Polarography is a method in which small amounts of material are reduced (or in some cases oxidized) electrolytically. The current which flows through the cell during the electrolysis is measured at various applied voltages, and a current-voltage curve is plotted manually or recorded automatically. A plateau region exists in the current-voltage curve where the current is proportional to the concentration of reducible (or oxidizable) substance present. With the aid of suitable calibrations, the concentration of compounds containing the reducible group can thus be calculated. Because reduction of various functional groups occurs at different applied potentials, the polarographic method of analysis is capable of considerable selectivity.

In the following section some of the basic principles of polarography are presented, and the scope of polarography as applied to quantitative organic analysis is discussed. It is not within the scope of this book to go into the complexities of polarographic theory and instrumentation. A very complete treatise on this subject is available,[10] and ade-

[10] I. M. Kolthoff and J. J. Lingane, *Polarography*, 2nd ed., New York, Interscience, 1952.

quate discussions can be found in standard textbooks on instrumental analysis. The biannual reviews on polarography in *Analytical Chemistry* are helpful in checking for recent applications.

Basic Principles of Polarography

The basic circuit used in polarography is shown in Fig. 42. The voltage applied to the electrolytic cell is varied by adjustment of resistance R and by means of the slide wire which acts as a voltage

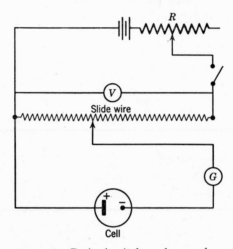

Figure 42. Basic circuit for polarography.

divider. The current that flows through the cell is measured in microamperes by means of galvanometer G. The solution in the cell is in contact with a dropping mercury electrode and with a calomel reference electrode of rather large area. A typical polarographic cell is shown in Fig. 43.

> Sometimes a rotating platinum electrode is used in place of the dropping mercury electrode. It is possible to use higher (more negative) reduction potentials with the mercury electrode owing to the high hydrogen overvoltage on mercury. A dropping mercury electrode has the advantage that a fresh, clean surface of mercury is being continuously presented.

The electrolysis cell contains the following substances:

1. The sample to be determined dissolved in an appropriate solvent. The concentration of the sample should be 0.01 M or less. Concentrations of the order of 10^{-3} to 10^{-4} M are commonly used.

2. A "supporting electrolyte," the concentration of which must be at

least 100 times that of the sample in order to minimize the migration current. Because a buffer of the desired pH is usually necessary when organic substances are being determined polarographically, it is common practice to use a buffer at sufficiently high concentration for it to serve the dual function of buffer and supporting electrolyte. If a buffer is unnecessary, a solution of inert salts such as a tetraalkylammonium halide or lithium chloride may be used.

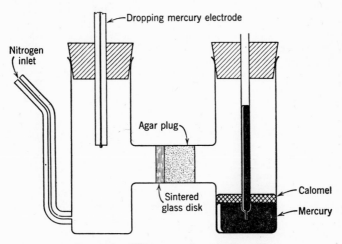

Figure 43. "H"-type polarographic cell.

3. A maximum suppressor such as methyl red is usually required to prevent the current from going through a maximum before returning to the plateau region of the current-voltage curve.

Before making virtually any polarographic determination it is necessary to remove dissolved oxygen. This is accomplished by bubbling nitrogen through the cell for several minutes before each run. The polarogram is obtained by applying increasingly negative potentials to the dropping mercury electrode, measuring the current that flows through the cell at each potential, and plotting a current-voltage curve.

> The dropping mercury electrode takes on the potential applied and is thus said to be polarized. The potential of the reference electrode is independent of the applied voltage, and this electrode is thus said to be depolarized.

A typical polarogram obtained manually is illustrated in Fig. 44.

> Many commercially available polarographs plot the current-voltage curve automatically. The curve has the general shape of that shown in Fig. 44 but shows an oscillating current instead of being smooth. This is because

the current changes continuously as each drop of mercury grows. In the manual instrument, the galvanometer has a period 3 to 4 times longer than the drop time; hence oscillations of the current are averaged out.

At applied voltages too low to cause a chemical reaction to occur, virtually no current flows. In practice a small current known as the residual current (region A in Fig. 44) is observed. When a critical

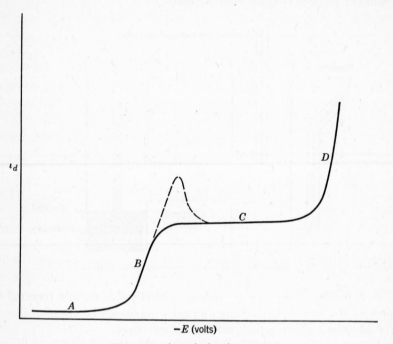

Figure 44. A typical polarogram.

applied potential known as the "decomposition potential" is attained, reduction starts to occur and a significant increase in current is observed. Further increases in the negative potential of the dropping mercury electrode result in increased current. This is region B in Fig. 44. With further increase in the applied negative potential, the current levels off to a constant value called the limiting current (region C). This leveling-off is due to depletion of reducible ions in the region of the cathode. In unstirred solution the rate of reduction (and thus the magnitude of the limiting current) is controlled by the rate at which reducible ions from the bulk of solution reach the surface of the cathode. The limiting current is thus proportional to the concentration of reducible ions in the bulk of solution, also to the diffusion coefficient of these ions.

If a maximum suppressor is not added a polarogram will often take the course shown by the dotted line in Fig. 44. The cause of this is not definitely known, but it has been found that certain surface-active agents are effective in preventing this phenomenon.

With still further increases in applied negative potential, the current again rises rapidly corresponding to the start of a second reduction wave (region D in Fig. 44). This is due to reduction of the supporting electrolyte or of impurities in the solvent. The voltage at this point represents the maximum that can be employed for this system.

It was stated above that the magnitude of the limiting diffusion current is proportional to the concentration of reducible substance and to the rate at which the reducible substance diffused from the bulk of the solution to the surface of the electrode. The current is also affected by the electron change in the reduction step, the mass of the mercury drop, and the drop time. These relationships are stated quantitatively in the Ilkovic equation,

$$(8) \qquad\qquad i_d = 706nCD^{\frac{1}{2}}m^{\frac{2}{3}}t^{\frac{1}{6}}$$

where i_d is the diffusion current in microamperes, 706 is a combination of numerical constants, n is the number of electrons involved in the reduction (or oxidation), C is the concentration of reducible (or oxidizable) substance in millimoles per liter, D is the diffusion coefficient in square centimeters per second, m is the mass of mercury flowing per second, and t is the time in seconds between drops.

If all the other variables are known, the amount of a given substance can be calculated quantitatively from the Ilkovic equation by simply measuring the diffusion current. In actual practice, however, it is usually more convenient and accurate to determine organic compounds quantitatively by a more empirical method. Known concentrations of the compound to be determined are polarographed, and a plot is made of the limiting current against concentration. The resulting curve is essentially a straight line and can be used to calculate the results when the same compound is being determined in actual samples.

Polarography of Organic Substances

Many of the conditions for quantitative polarography of inorganic ions apply without change to organic compounds. For example, the optimum concentration for both organic and inorganic substances is

10^{-3} to $10^{-4} M$. Both frequently require the addition of surface-active agents as maximum suppressors. In all cases close control of temperature and other variables is important in order to obtain consistently accurate quantitative results.

Several points pertaining primarily to organic polarography should, however, be mentioned. Water is usually employed as the solvent when working with inorganic material, but most organic compounds must of necessity be determined in a partially or completely nonaqueous system. Solvents such as methyl and ethyl alcohols, dioxane, acetic acid, and Cellosolve have found wide use. In completely nonaqueous solution the ratio of diffusion current to concentration of reducible substance is often considerably less than in water; also polarographic waves sometimes have smaller slopes in nonaqueous media. Because of this most quantitative work with organic compounds has been done in alcohol-water or dioxane-water containing not more than 50 to 75% by volume of the nonaqueous solvent.

Oxygen is more soluble in solutions containing a nonaqueous solvent than it is in water alone. For this reason it is necessary to purge the nonaqueous solution longer with nitrogen to ensure complete removal of oxygen. It is well to presaturate the nitrogen stream with the solvent mixture used in order to prevent changes in the solvent composition of the sample during the purging operation.

The supporting electrolyte must, of course, be soluble in the solvent mixture used. In some cases it is necessary to work at highly negative applied potentials which would cause reduction of the alkali metal salts commonly used as supporting electrolytes. In this situation tetraalkylammonium salts (usually the iodide or the hydroxide) are useful. They are soluble in most organic solvents and permit the use of highly negative applied potentials.

> Quaternary ammonium compounds must be carefully purified to remove reducible impurities such as tertiary ammonium compounds. It is very disconcerting to find that considerable amount of work has been invalidated because of interfering impurities in the supporting electrolyte. For the same reason it is apparent that careful purification of all organic solvents used will be necessary.

Unlike inorganic polarography, the large majority of organic compounds are reduced irreversibly. Quinones and a few other compounds are exceptions. The half-wave potential has less exact significance in the case of irreversible processes but is nevertheless a convenient (and widely used) method for comparing the relative ease of reduction (or oxidation) of organic compounds.

The half-wave potential of many organic substances changes considerably with a change in pH. Even though the pH is maintained essentially constant in the bulk of the solution, there may be a considerable change in pH in the immediate region of the electrode during the reduction. This may lead to serious and undetected errors in quantitative determinations. This can be avoided by carrying out all determinations in well-buffered solutions. Solutions of strong acids or bases which are 0.05 to 0.1 M are also satisfactory because they will supply a sufficient excess of hydrogen or hydroxyl ions to prevent any significant concentration polarization in the vicinity of the electrode.

Polarography of organic compounds is often complicated by various types of kinetic processes. For example, formaldehyde is highly hydrated in aqueous solution, but only the nonhydrated form is polarographically reducible. The magnitude of the current therefore depends on the concentration of free formaldehyde, which in turn depends on the concentration of the hydrated form and on the rate of dehydration in the sense of equation 9.

$$\text{(9)} \qquad \underset{\diagdown OH}{\overset{\diagup OH}{H-CH}} \quad \rightleftharpoons \quad \overset{O}{\overset{\diagup\diagup}{H-C}}-H + H_2O$$

Scope of Organic Polarography

The major types of organic compounds that can be determined polarographically are listed in Table 27. A considerable number of miscellaneous compounds have also been determined. In Table 28 the half-wave potentials of several classes of compounds are summarized. These are only intended to serve as a general guide because substituents in the parent compound or variation in the supporting electrolyte will often change the reduction potential considerably. A convenient and extensive table of half-wave potentials or organic compounds has been compiled by Zuman.[11]

One of the most important advantages of the polarographic method is that it permits more selective reduction (and in some cases, oxidation) than is usually possible by chemical means. If two substances differ by 0.2 volt in their half-wave potentials, it is usually possible to determine the more easily reducible (A) in the presence of rather large quantities of the other (B). If A is the minor constituent or if

[11] P. Zuman, *Collection Czechoslov. Chem. Communs.*, **15**, 1107 (1950).

TABLE 27

Polarographically Reducible Organic Compounds

Classification	Type Formula	Remarks
Acids		
Conjugated unsaturated	$-CH{=}CH-\overset{\displaystyle O}{\overset{\|}{C}}-OH$	
α-Keto	$-\overset{\displaystyle O}{\overset{\|}{C}}-\overset{\displaystyle O}{\overset{\|}{C}}-OH$	
Aldehydes		
Aliphatic, saturated and unsaturated	$R\overset{\displaystyle O}{\overset{\|}{C}}-H,\ -CH{=}CH-\overset{\displaystyle O}{\overset{\|}{C}}-H$	
Aromatic	$Ar\overset{\displaystyle O}{\overset{\|}{C}}-H$	
Sugars	....	
Halides	RX, ArBr, ArI, etc.	Most organic halogen compounds are reducible. Polyhalogen compounds are reduced more easily than mono. Ease of reduction: I > Br > Cl.
Hydrocarbons Conjugated aliphatic Phenyl substituted olefins and acetylenes	$-CH{=}CH-CH{=}CH-$ $Ar-CH{=}CH-$ $ArC{\equiv}C-$	Half-wave potential independent of pH. Benzene, simple olefins, and saturated hydrocarbons not reducible. A few polynuclear aromatics fail to give well-defined waves and cannot be determined polarographically.
Polynuclear aromatic	, etc.	
Ketones		
Aromatic	$ArC\overset{\displaystyle O}{\overset{\|}{}}-R,\ ArC\overset{\displaystyle O}{\overset{\|}{}}-Ar$	Aliphatic ketones not reducible directly but can be determined after reaction with Girard's reagent, phenylhydrazine, etc.
Conjugated unsaturated	$-CH_2{=}CH-\overset{\displaystyle O}{\overset{\|}{C}}-R$	
Diketones	$-\overset{\displaystyle O}{\overset{\|}{C}}-\overset{\displaystyle O}{\overset{\|}{C}}-,\ -\overset{\displaystyle O}{\overset{\|}{C}}-CH_2-\overset{\displaystyle O}{\overset{\|}{C}}-$	
Nitro compounds Aliphatic Aromatic	RNO_2 $ArNO_2$	
Nitrogen heterocylics Alkaloids	....	
Amine oxides	$-\overset{\|}{N}{\to}O$	
Many other miscellaneous types	....	
Peroxides and hydroperoxides	$RC\overset{\displaystyle O}{\overset{\|}{}}-O-O-\overset{\displaystyle O}{\overset{\|}{}}CR$	
Quinones		
Miscellaneous Disulfides Nitroso compounds	$-S-S-$ $-N{=}O$	

TABLE 28

Half-Wave Potentials of Some Organic Compounds

Compound or Group	Formula	Medium	$-E_{\frac{1}{2}}$
Benzoquinone		pH7, H_2O	0.0
Aromatic nitro compounds	$ArNO_2$	0.05 M H_2SO_4, 10% EtOH	0.2 to 0.4
Aliphatic nitro compounds	R—CH— $\quad$NO$_2$	0.05 M H_2SO_4, 10% EtOH	0.6 to 0.7
Aromatic aldehydes	ArCHO	0.05 to 0.1 M Base	1.5 to 1.65
Formaldehyde	HCHO	0.05 to 0.1 M Base	1.5 to 1.65
Saturated aliphatic aldehydes	RCHO	0.05 to 0.1 M Base	1.85
Diaryl ketones	ArCOAr	0.05 to 0.1 M Base	1.4
Monoaryl ketones	ArCOR	0.05 to 0.1 M Base	1.65
Methyl chloride	CH_3Cl		2.2
Methyl bromide	CH_3Br		1.6
Methyl iodide	CH_3I		1.6
Methylene chloride	CH_2Cl_2		2.3
Chloroform	$CHCl_3$		1.7
Carbon tetrachloride	CCl_4		0.8, 1.7
Hexachloroethane	CCl_3CCl_3		0.6, 1.7, 2.0
Aryl substituted olefins and acetylenes	ArCH=C— ArC≡C—	Dioxane-H_2O, $R_4N^+I^-$	2.1 to 2.5
Polynuclear aromatic hydrocarbons	, etc.	Dioxane-H_2O, $R_4N^+I^-$	2.3 to 2.6
Conjugated aliphatic hydrocarbons	—CH=CH—CH=CH— —C≡C—C≡C— —CH=CH—C≡C—	Dioxane-H_2O, $R_4N^+I^-$	2.3 to 2.6

A and B are present in approximately equal concentrations, then both can be determined individually. If A is present in large excess over B, it is usually only possible to determine A.

Only dilute solutions can be determined polarographically; the usual range determined is about 10^{-3} to $10^{-5} M$. This makes the polarographic method very useful for analyses where only a small sample is available. It is also a valuable method for determining certain minor constituents in larger samples, such as traces of nitrobenzene in aniline. For this type of analysis polarographic and spectrophotometric methods (Chapter 10) are the most widely applicable. It is sometimes advantageous to determine major constituents in macro samples polarographically. In this case careful dilution and measurement of the diffusion current is required to avoid excessive error. With reasonably careful work a relative precision and accuracy of about 2% is attainable.

The following specific examples have been chosen more or less at random to further illustrate the practical use of quantitative polarographic methods.

1. Determination of naphthalene and substituted naphthalenes in petroleum fractions.[12] Monocyclic aromatics, olefins, naphthenes, and mono olefins do not interfere. A preliminary separation from higher polynuclear aromatics is required.

2. Analysis for small amounts of phthalate esters (used as plasticizers) in plastics.[13]

3. Determination of acrolein in the presence of formaldehyde and acetaldehyde.[14]

4. Individual determination of trichloroacetic acid and dichloroacetic acid in mixtures.[15] A large excess of monochloroacetic acid or acetic acid causes no interference.

5. Dissolved oxygen in petroleum fractions can be determined polarographically.[16] Only 10 to 15 minutes is required for each analysis.

6. A method for quantitatively determining ethylene glycol and 1,2-propylene glycol in a mixture uses a preliminary oxidation with periodate.[17,18] The formaldehyde from oxidation of ethylene glycol, and the acetaldehyde from oxidation of 1,2-propylene glycol are determined polarographically.

7. Carbon tetrachloride in tetrachloroethylene, carbon tetrachloride and chloroform in mixtures with methyl and methylene chloride, and several other organic halides in mixtures have been determined polarographically.[19]

Use and Development of Polarographic Methods

Quantitative polarography is a convenient tool only if all the necessary equipment is always assembled and available for use. As a minimum, the permanent set-up should include the following:

[12] R. E. Burdett and B. E. Gordon, *Anal. Chem.*, **19**, 843 (1947).
[13] G. C. Whitnack, *Anal. Chem.*, **25**, 553 (1953).
[14] R. W. Moshier, *Ind. Eng. Chem., Anal. Ed.*, **15**, 107 (1943).
[15] P. J. Elving and C. S. Tang, *Anal. Chem.*, **23**, 341 (1951).
[16] M. E. Hall, *Anal. Chem.*, **23**, 1381 (1951).
[17] B. Warshowsky and P. J. Elving, *Ind. Eng. Chem., Anal. Ed.*, **18**, 253 (1946).
[18] W. A. Cannon and L. C. Jackson, *Anal. Chem.*, **24**, 1053 (1952).
[19] M. von Stakelberg and W. Stracke, *Z. Elektrochem.*, **53**, 118 (1949).

1. Polarograph.
2. Dropping mercury electrode complete with capillary, leveling bulb, etc.
3. Polarographic cells.
4. Constant-temperature bath.
5. Nitrogen system for removing dissolved oxygen from the solutions used.

It is frequently found that capillary constants and certain other conditions change from time to time. This reduces the accuracy to be expected and may necessitate checking of calibration curves. A very simple procedure developed by Allen [20] eliminates many of these difficulties. At the start of each day a standard chromate solution is polarographed at a suitable applied potential, and the height of the mercury column is adjusted until the diffusion current attains a certain predetermined value. This standardizes the experimental conditions so that polarographic determinations run at various times are reproducible even though the capillary is changed or an entirely different polarographic instrument is used.

Correction factors have been worked out which enable comparison of results obtained using instruments of different manufacturers. With this system no correction is required for different instruments of the same model by a single manufacturer.

In developing a method for determining a new compound or in adapting known analytical methods to a new situation, the following general approach is suggested:

1. Consider the nature of the problem and decide whether a polarographic approach appears feasible. Consult the literature for methods that may have been used for analogous problems. Weigh the comparative advantages of the polarographic, titrimetric chemical, spectrophotometric, and other approaches.

2. If polarography appears promising, run polarograms of the substance to be determined in various media. It is suggested that each of the following supporting electrolytes (in alcohol-water solution) be tried: 0.1 M hydrochloric acid, pH 4 acetate buffer, pH 7 phosphate buffer, pH 9 phosphate buffer, and 0.1 M sodium hydroxide. The concentration of the buffer is such that, after dilution of an aliquot of test solution with buffer, the final concentration of buffer is about 0.1 M. It is rare that buffers at pH values other than those listed above are necessary to find any unusual polarographic behavior associated with

[20] W. Allen, Meeting in Miniature, North Jersey Section, A.C.S., Jan. 24, 1955.

a given substance. If the substance is reducible only at very negative potentials, it may be necessary to use a tetraalkylammonium salt as the supporting electrolyte.

3. Using the medium selected, determine the effect of all possible impurities on the curve of the constituent to be determined. Do not be concerned with substances that are very unlikely to be present in the type of sample you intend to analyze.

4. Standardize polarographic conditions by the chromate method described above. Using the applied voltage selected from previous experiments, run a series of standards and plot a calibration curve of current vs. concentration. From the slope of this line obtain a factor by which the current reading of an unknown may be multiplied to calculate the concentration of the substances determined.

13.

SOLVING NEW
ANALYTICAL PROBLEMS

GENERAL APPROACH

No aspect of this work compares in importance with the subject of devising methods to meet the demands of a particular situation. The hopelessness of the encyclopedic approach to organic analysis is treated in Chapter 1. An analyst will, for the most part, find it necessary to live by his wits when he is confronted with problems involving new compounds or different and often complicated combinations of known compounds. It would be unwise to attempt to prescribe a universal approach to such problems because the sequence of events should be different as the nature of the problem is varied. However, we can indicate in a general way a line of attacking a new problem. In many actual cases the order of consideration would be altered somewhat, but most of the following steps would be found as ingredients in a judicious approach to a new problem.

1. State the Problem Clearly

This can save a great deal of pain and frustration. Find out what information is really desired and what analyses are necessary to give this information. Is a total analysis, assay for one or more minor constituents, or simply the assay for a single major constituent necessary? Enough determinations should be made to ensure accuracy and confidence, but analyses that do not give any pertinent information should be avoided.

The accuracy necessary to give an unequivocal quantitative answer to the problem should be considered. Choose a method that will give extra accuracy only if this can be done without sacrificing speed or convenience. It is wasteful to insist on results accurate to $\pm 0.1\%$ when a much shorter analytical method would give results accurate to $\pm 2.0\%$, if the latter would be equally valuable in interpreting the analytical results.

The circumstances under which the samples for analysis will be produced should be known. Variation in solvents or the presence of additives, such as stabilizers, can render a method worked out on a pilot basis ineffective. For example, it would be discouraging to have worked out a fine procedure for determining a particular amine by a nonaqueous titration, using a new indicator, and then be presented with samples from a production line that were a dark-brown color. It would be of little comfort to be assured that this color was due to a trace impurity which could be safely ignored. In this case, the procedure might be readily adapted by using either a potentiometric titration or a fluorescent indicator to determine the end point. In another case, a feasible adaptation might be more difficult and much of the developmental work would have to be repeated.

2. Check Known Methods

Consult the literature in order to ascertain whether there is an established method that should serve the desired purpose. Such a survey might well begin with a scrutiny of textbooks and reference books but should not end without a thorough search of the periodical literature. If the analytical literature already provides a solution to a closely related problem, the further adaptation may be relatively simple. If an analytical scheme for a more distantly related problem is available, it may be applicable with suitable modification in various details.

In selecting an analytical method from the literature, choose one that appears to be rapid and convenient. This is especially important if the method is to be used routinely. Also consider the feasibility of the method in the light of the competence of the personnel who will be using it.

3. Consider Preliminary Separations

If available methods are lacking in selectivity, recourse to simple preliminary separations may greatly simplify the analytical task (see Chapter 11). A separation step often effects a simultaneous quantitative analysis for one or more of the constituents. By reducing the number of interfering compounds, separation almost always increases the number of standard quantitative methods that can be applied. Preliminary separation is often advisable in any case where the sample is of highly complex chemical composition (as with many natural products, for example) or is highly contaminated with tar, rust, or dirt in general.

4. If Existing Methods Are Inadequate, Devise New Methods

If an existing method is available that looks very mediocre, a fresh, new approach may be worth while. This is especially true if a large number of analyses are to be made. If only a few determinations are contemplated, it may be better to struggle along with a somewhat inferior method if it will give the desired results.

If it appears that an entirely new method will be needed, the general literature of organic chemistry should be consulted in order to learn as much as possible concerning the chemical behavior of the compounds involved in the problem. Elementary textbooks are of relatively little value for various reasons. The writers of such textbooks have a natural tendency to be somewhat conventional in the selection of examples of reactions, and those chosen will not necessarily be the cleanest for a given class of compounds. Furthermore, a high degree of selection must be exercized in preparing an elementary text since inclusion of any substantial fraction of the known organic reactions would make a book grow to completely unmanageable proportions. Much better sources of inspiration are advanced texts such as those by Fuson[1] and Royals[2] Such books often give some hint as to the influence of structural variations on the course and/or rate of a particular reaction. However, there is usually no substitute for the original literature in evaluating possible useful reactions of a particular compound or set of compounds. If the assay substance is either new or little known, it will be necessary to seek information concerning analogous substances.

Herein lies a major oversimplification. The term "analogous substance" is about as sophistical an expression as any that can be found in respectable

[1] R. C. Fuson, *Advanced Organic Chemistry*, Wiley, New York, 1950.
[2] E. E. Royals, *Advanced Organic Chemistry*, Prentice-Hall, New York, 1954.

scientific writing. The basis for chemical analogy shifts in a subtle way as one considers different reactions. For example, neopentyl chloride, $(CH_3)_3CCH_2Cl$, is classified as a primary chloride. Since a rather bulky group is attached to the functional carbon atom, the question arises as to what other chlorides should be considered analogous to neopentyl chloride. No unequivocal answer can be given to such a question. If one specifies a reaction to be carried out under a particular set of conditions, the choice can be made but it may be very different from that which would be made from other reactions. For example, the rate of hydrolysis in moist formic acid,

$$RCl + H_2O \xrightarrow{HCO_2H} ROH + HCl$$

is about the same with neopentyl halides as it is with ethyl halides. However, in the halide exchange reaction,

$$RCl + KI \xrightarrow{dry\ acetone} RI + KCl$$

neopentyl halides react more slowly than ethyl halides by a factor of about 10^6. In this reaction neopentyl chloride is more nearly analogous to tertiary butyl chloride in its behavior.

In devising a new method it is always well to look for the unique characteristics of the compound to be determined. Does the compound undergo any reactions that are not shared by the other substances present? Are any of these reactions stoichiometric, or nearly so? If a yield greater than about 90% is reported in preparative work, it is probable that the reaction can be made essentially stoichiometric. This is true because most yields of organic reactions are based on the isolation and weighing of the product. If a suitable reaction is found, how can it be monitored? Consider finally whether the compound has any unique physical properties that can be measured.

5. Plan an Experimental Program

A series of experiments should be carefully designed to test the reaction(s) chosen as potential analytical methods. Such an experimental program must also be carried out if an existing analytical method is to be modified for use in a new analytical situation. The series of experiments should include investigation of interference by other compounds that are known or suspected to be present in the samples to be analyzed. The effect of varying experimental conditions should be studied. This enables the analyst to find the optimum conditions and also to establish the permissible limits of these conditions. This should be done even if early attempts seem to give good results. Although many experimental conditions are interrelated, it is best whenever possible to vary but one condition at a time, keeping all others constant.

Often an analytical method is worked out or proved on synthetic samples of known composition. This is good practice if the effect of possible impurities present in actual samples is also considered. Another approach is to use the proposed method to determine the desired constituent in actual samples of unknown composition. One can then analyze aliquots of the same sample to which varying but known amounts of the pure constituent being determined are added. If recovery of the added material is quantitative (allowing for the amount of the same compound previously found in the unknown), the method usually can be assumed to be valid.

At the risk of seeming to be unduly impressed with the importance of their own experiences, examples of problems that have been studied in the authors' laboratories will be discussed. The only particular value of these examples is that the authors know intimately the details of their development. It will be obvious from problems that have not yet been brought to satisfactory completion that these experiences are not to be considered models in every respect.

Determination of Benzpinacol in a Reaction Mixture

In the course of a particular research program it became necessary to develop an accurate assay for the amount of benzpinacol, I, produced in the photoreduction of benzophenone in toluene solution. The authors began with the certain conviction that the reaction took, at least in part, the path indicated by equation 1. This was readily confirmed by the isolation and identification of I from reaction mixtures. After a somewhat tedious isolation procedure, it was found that diphenylbenzyl carbinol, II, was also produced in substantial amounts.

(1) $2(C_6H_5)_2C{=}O + 2C_6H_5CH_3 \xrightarrow{h\nu}$

$$(C_6H_5)_2\underset{\underset{\text{I}}{OH}}{\overset{|}{C}}{-}\underset{OH}{\overset{|}{C}}(C_6H_5)_2 + C_6H_5CH_2CH_2C_6H_5$$

(2) $(C_6H_5)_2C{=}O + C_6H_5CH_3 \xrightarrow{h\nu} (C_6H_5)_2\underset{\underset{\text{II}}{OH}}{\overset{|}{C}}CH_2C_6H_5$

The problem could then be stated. It consisted of the determination of a 1,2-glycol in toluene in the presence of benzophenone and II, a tertiary carbinol. This immediately eliminated from consideration all methods based upon hydroxyl determination since it will be noted that the carbonyl group of each benzophenone molecule reacting is converted to a tertiary hydroxyl whether it reacts by reaction 1 or reaction 2.

Among the standard analytical procedures in the literature there is one that is designed specifically for the determination of vicinal diols. This is the metaperiodate oxidation which has found wide application in the carbohydrate field (Chapter 5). However, the reagent is not soluble in organic media, and I is not soluble in water. It is possible that a mixed solvent could have been developed and used but this hardly seemed like a profitable approach since it would have certainly necessitated the removal of the toluene from the reaction mixture.

Turning then to the general literature of organic chemistry, the authors found that there is a reagent, lead tetraacetate, which is used regularly as a complement to metaperiodic acid for the cleavage of water-insoluble glycols. At a very early stage it seemed evident that this reagent held the solution to the problem although the authors actually indulged in some speculation concerning the application of the pinacol rearrangement, reaction 3.

(3) $(C_6H_5)_2COHCOH(C_6H_5)_2 \xrightarrow{\text{acid}} (C_6H_5)_3CCOC_6H_5$

Although no experiments were conducted along these lines, it seems very probable that a method could have been developed since it is reported that the treatment of I with iodine in acetic acid gives a 96% yield of benzpinacolone.[3] Since the latter is a very highly hindered ketone, there is little doubt that it could have been differentiated from benzophenone.

An experimental program was then set up to evaluate reaction 4 as an analytical procedure.

(4) $(C_6H_5)_2COHCOH(C_6H_5)_2 + Pb(OAc)_4 \rightarrow$

$$2(C_6H_5)_2CO + Pb(OAc)_2 + 2HOAc$$

This part of the work was rendered almost trivial in its ease by an assist from the literature. Criegee [4] has studied the rate of the cleavage reaction of various glycols, including benzpinacol, in acetic acid solution. Moreover, he specifically included mention of the effect on the

[3] *Organic Syntheses*, Collective Vol. 2, Wiley, New York, 1943, p. 73.
[4] R. Criegee, *Ber.*, **64B**, 264 (1931).

reaction rate of using a mixed solvent made by addition of benzene to acetic acid. By making the reasonable assumption of the equivalence of solvent effects from toluene and benzene, the authors found that their problem had actually been solved rather nicely in 1931. From the published rate data, it was possible to calculate that the reaction would, at the concentration levels involved, be essentially complete in 24 hours at 25°. In order to check on interference from benzophenone and the by-product, II, and the equivalence of benzene and toluene as solvent, several rate runs were carried out in toluene-acetic acid mixtures. The only problem that developed was a very minor one relating to the end point in the iodometric assay for residual lead tetraacetate. No serious consideration was given to speeding up the analysis by carrying out the reaction at a higher temperature since the literature gives ample evidence that the thermal decomposition of lead tetraacetate becomes quite rapid at elevated temperatures. At room temperature it was barely observable and required only a small blank correction.

Determination of Crotononitrile and Its Isomers

On another occasion the authors were confronted with the problem of determining the composition of a reaction mixture that might have been composed of compounds III, IV, and V. A logical line of attack could

$$CH_2{=}CHCH_2CN \qquad\qquad CH_3CH{=}CHCN \qquad\qquad \begin{array}{c} H_2C \\ | \diagdown \\ | CH{-}CN \\ | \diagup \\ H_2C \end{array}$$

III   IV   V

be based upon the unsaturation of the molecules. The literature provides a number of procedures, such as bromination (Chapter 5), epoxidation (Chapter 5), and hydrogenation (Chapter 6), for the determination of unsaturation. Furthermore, it is well known that a conjugated system such as that in crotononitrile, IV, will be much slower in bromination or epoxidation than an unconjugated compound such as vinyl acetonitrile, III. Less is known about the rates of ring opening of cyclopropanes, but there is a strong implication that they are very sluggish in this reaction.

Hydrogenation was discarded from consideration without trial because it is known that the nitrile function can be hydrogenated. A sufficient problem in relative reactivities was at hand without introducing further complications. Bromination was chosen as a method of investigation since the reactivity of bromine solutions may be regulated by the addition of mercuric sulfate as a catalyst. The experimental program was laid out on a logical-empirical basis.

First, samples of all compounds, including the *cis* and *trans* isomers of crotononitrile, were prepared for test purposes. Each was treated with a solution of bromine (released from standard bromide-bromate mixture with sulfuric acid) in acetic acid. By carrying out rough rate studies it was observed that vinyl acetonitrile was brominated at a reasonable rate whereas its isomers were completely unreactive. Attention was then turned to catalyzed bromination. At the outset the results were exceedingly confusing. However, controlled experiments revealed that the order of addition of materials exerted a remarkable effect on the results. Unless the bromine is released in the presence of the mercuric ion *before* the addition of the sample, the catalyst undergoes some irreversible reaction with the nitriles and very little bromine is consumed. This behavior was not anticipated and was only revealed by a systematic experimental program.

It was found that both of the crotononitriles were brominated fairly rapidly at room temperature and that cyclopropyl cyanide was completely inert under these conditions. It was also observed that even at the ice temperature the bromination of vinylacetonitrile was essentially instantaneous in the presence of the catalyst. On repeating the bromination of the crotononitriles at the lower temperature, it was found that the reaction was very slow. These observations allowed the authors to determine III by low temperature bromination and to obtain the sum of III and IV by carrying out the reaction at room temperature. If the samples had been free of impurities, they could then have estimated V by difference. Since this was not the case they attempted to open the cyclopropane ring by raising the temperature. However, controls showed that the rate of bromination of the solvent was easily competitive with the rate of addition to V. Since rate measurements indicated that bromine was taken up faster in the presence of the nitrile than in the blanks, they could probably have developed a method by changing the solvent. However, an infrared analysis had been programmed in parallel with the chemical method, and it was worked out successfully (see Chapter 10). For this reason the somewhat unpromising chemical procedure was dropped as a means of ultimate analysis.

Despite the fact that bromination was abandoned as a method for cyclopropyl cyanide, it may be interesting to consider the possibilities that would have been considered had it seemed profitable to continue the study. A solvent would have been needed that was at the same time a good solvent for the catalyst and chemically inert toward bromine. The number of such solvents is rather limited, and the chief candidates would have been media, such as acetonitrile and nitromethane, which have high enough dielectric constants to make them reasonably good solvents for electrolytes and which have functional groups that are not susceptible to oxidation or bromine addition. Changes in the nature of the catalyst were also considered. Since the activity of the mercuric ion derives from its Lewis acid activity toward the halogen, in principle, other Lewis acids could have been used. The consideration of acetonitrile as a solvent brings to mind the fabulously high solubility of silver nitrate in that medium. It is possible that a procedure could have been developed in which the silver ion was a reactant with a stoichiometric relationship corresponding to the following equation:

$$(5) \quad Ag^+ + \underset{H_2C}{\overset{H_2C}{\diagdown}} CHCN + SH + Br_2 \rightarrow$$

$$AgBr + SCH_2CHCHCN + H^+$$
$$\underset{Br}{\mid}$$

in which SH = a minor hydroxylic constituent of the mixture such as water.

Measurement of Rates of Displacement Reactions of 1-X-2,4-Dinitrobenzenes

It will perhaps be instructive to consider a problem that, in retrospect, was probably not handled as expeditiously as it might have been. For other purposes it was necessary to follow the kinetics of the following displacement reaction.

$$(6) \quad O_2N \overset{NO_2}{\diagdown} \hspace{-0.3em} \text{—X} + 2 \langle \rangle \text{—NHCH}_3 \rightarrow$$

$$O_2N \overset{NO_2}{\diagdown} \hspace{-0.3em} \text{—N(CH}_3) \text{—} \langle \rangle + \langle \rangle \text{—} \overset{+}{N}H_2CH_3 \; X^-$$

The reaction was to be carried out in nitrobenzene and ethanol as reaction media. The halides involved were fluoride, chloride, and bromide. It is possible that the very fact that a veritable wealth of potential solutions exist, led the authors to investigate an unprofitable method first. The following can be listed as outstanding characteristics of the products and the reactants that could be analytically useful.

1. The displacement product is a deep-red color as might be expected of an aromatic nitroamine.

2. An extreme decrease in the basicity of the amine should occur because of the interaction between the basic nitrogen and the nitro substituted ring.

3. The reactivity of the arylamine moiety toward nuclear substitution reactions, such as bromination, is decreased for the same reason that the basicity is reduced.

4. Ionic halide (or undissociated hydrogen halide) is produced in the reaction.

All these characteristics were studied before the completion of the work, and a logical approach would have involved at least a cursory survey of the possibilities of each at the outset. However, the initial concentration was on spectrophotometry. The reaction product was found to have rather intense absorption in the visible, which was actually a "tail" of an absorption band with a maximum in the near ultraviolet (Chapter 10). Two complicating factors were found immediately. The nitrobenzene solvent has some absorption in the visible, and this is increased measurably by addition of N-methylaniline, probably because of molecular complex formation. Furthermore, the dinitrohalobenzenes form colored molecular complexes with N-methylaniline immediately upon mixing of solutions of the two substances. Study of all the spectra showed that the absorption due to the complexes fell off substantially faster than that of the reaction product at long wavelengths. For this reason a wavelength (540 mμ), where the absorption by the product was relatively weak, was chosen for analytical purposes. It was found that this long wavelength end absorption followed Beer's law nicely in nitrobenzene solution and was not subject to interference from N-methylaniline or the dinitrohalobenzenes. The complex between the latter two had measurable absorption at this wavelength, but this was conveniently minimized at the concentrations chosen for measurement because of the breakup of the complex on dilution of the reaction mixture. In the preliminary program *the role of the second product, hydrogen halide or its equivalent, was neglected.* The reactions were carried out in individual tubes at 120 to 130° and, except for the dinitrofluorobenzene, produced homogeneous solutions at that temperature. However, the analysis was found to be inapplicable as it was originally conceived because of the slow precipitation of the N-methylanilinium halides after the solutions were cooled to room temperature.

As would have been anticipated, it was possible to titrate N-methylaniline as a base, using 0.1 N perchloric acid in acetic acid as a titrant (see Chapter 3). The end point was determined potentiometrically. It was found that N-methylanilinium fluoride was titrated as a base under these conditions, but fortunately the salt could be removed by a rapid filtration of the reaction samples. The amine hydrobromide and hydrochloride did not interfere in the titration of unreacted amine.

The reaction in ethanol could not be followed by the same analysis because of the leveling effect due to the basicity of the solvent. Titration curves for N-methylaniline showed only very poorly defined breaks reminiscent of those found in titrations of aromatic amines in aqueous solution. The determination of free halide was investigated next and found to be satisfactory for the chloride and bromide displacements. The reaction samples were washed into a separatory funnel which contained both benzene and an aliquot of standard, aqueous silver nitrate. The aqueous layer was drawn off, the benzene layer was washed twice with water, and the washings were added to the silver nitrate extract. Excess silver ion was determined directly by titration with standard potassium thiocyanate solution. It is interesting to note that this procedure depends upon the fact that the displacement reactions of activated aryl halides are not subject to silver ion catalysis. The same procedure would not have been equally successful with most aliphatic halides.

At this point the problem remained of monitoring the reaction of 2,4-dinitrofluorobenzene in ethanol solution. The determination of displaced fluoride by precipitation of a metal fluoride is uninviting. For the solution of this problem the authors turned to the aromatic bromination reaction. N-methylaniline reacts very rapidly to consume 3 moles of bromine, as shown in reaction 7. However, the product of reaction

(7)   [benzene ring with NHCH$_3$] + 3Br$_2$ → [benzene ring with NHCH$_3$ and three Br substituents] + 3HBr

6 is completely inert. The progress of the reaction of the fluoro compound was, therefore, followed by the conventional bromination procedure (Chapter 5), using standard bromide-bromate solution as a source of bromine. Much pilot work was eliminated by the appearance of a paper in the literature [5] describing the application of the procedure to study of the reaction of aniline with 2,4-dinitrofluorobenzene.

Polynitro Compounds

It may be entertaining (and perhaps, ultimately, embarrassing) to discuss plans for investigating a method that has not yet been brought to fruition, since it is always easier to speak with wisdom concerning problems that have already been studied experimentally. There is a real need in the explosives field for a reliable method for the determination of all the nitro groups in a polynitro compound. Various reductive procedures are available, and several are discussed in Chapter 5. However, these often do not yield good stoichiometric results when applied to compounds that have two or more nitro groups attached to the same or adjacent carbon atoms. This must be a consequence of interactions between the groups in partially reduced stages. For example, if a *gem-* dinitro function is reduced reaction 8 may occur. Such reactions

(8)   [structure: C with NO$_2$, NO$_2$] → [structure: C with NH$_2$, NO$_2$] →

[structure: C=NH] + HNO$_2$ → [structure: CHNH$_2$] + NH$_3$

would lead to the consumption of more reductant than expected. Alternatively, if cleavage products, such as nitrous acid, are not reduced rapidly under the conditions of the reaction, less than the stoichiometric amount of reductant will be required. What is needed is a procedure that will not be sensitive to subtle variations in reaction conditions.

[5] N. B. Chapman and J. L. Levy, *J. Chem. Soc.*, **1953**, 1673.

It is furthermore undesirable to require empirical calibration of the reducing equivalent of particular compounds, especially if they must be determined as constituents of mixtures.

The authors hope that it will prove possible to carry out exhaustive reduction which will convert all the nitro groups in a mixture to basic functions; that is, either ammonia or amino nitrogen. These units could then, in principle, be determined by acid-base titration. Such a procedure would place no special requirements on the stoichiometric aspects of the reductive step except that it would require sufficiently drastic conditions to ensure cleavage of all reduction with a reagent such as Ti^{III}, which requires the presence of a large excess of acid. The most attractive drastic reduction would seem to be catalytic hydrogenation since the excess of reductant would be of no consequence in the ultimate analysis. The choice of solvent for the hydrogenation would depend upon the plans for the final acid-base titration. It will certainly be appropriate to plan to carry out the titration in a non-aqueous solvent (Chapter 3). The solvents that are commonly used in nonaqueous titration of bases are acetic acid, acetic acid with added acetic anhydride, nitromethane, acetonitrile, and dioxane. There would be a real advantage in carrying out the hydrogenation in one of these solvents. However, nitromethane and acetonitrile would be immediately discarded for such a purpose since either would be itself reducible to an aliphatic amine. The presence of acetic anhydride would also be intolerable as it would acylate the basic reduction products. Acetic acid and dioxane would be worth trying with the object of following the hydrogenation by direct titration with a solution of perchloric acid in acetic. The first attempts will be made with acetic acid since it will be better suited to the retention of volatile bases such as ammonia and the lower aliphatic amines. The procedure for estimating the potential of the method can be outlined in the following steps.

1. Choose a representative polynitro compound that can be obtained in a high state of purity for use as a model.

2. Weigh accurately samples calculated to give several hundred milliequivalents of basic nitrogen compounds on complete reduction.

3. Dissolve the samples in glacial acetic acid, and dilute to a volume of 100 ml. in a volumetric flask.

4. Remove 10 ml. aliquots, and reduce over 20-mg. platinum (from PtO_2). The reduction should be carried out in an apparatus such as that described in Chapter 6. The progress of the hydrogenation should be followed in the conventional manner since it is desired to do an exhaustive reduction.

5. The hydrogenation flask should be removed, and the contents should be washed into a titration flask with acetic acid. The solution should then be titrated with standard $0.1 N$ perchloric-acetic titrant, using crystal violet as an indicator. Alternatively the trial titrations may be carried out potentiometrically in order to gain possible clues as to the strength of the various bases present.

6. The results obtained will dictate further action.

a. If the theoretical results are obtained with good reproducibility, the method should be further tested with other pure compounds and with typical mixtures.

b. If the results are variable, they will be studied to ascertain the direction of error. Low results are by far the most probable. These might result from either incomplete reduction or from the acetylation of the bases to form acetamides. If the former is the cause of difficulty, a trend toward higher results should be observed as longer reaction times and larger amounts of catalyst are used. It is possible that acetylation of the amines and ammonia will give weakly basic amides sufficiently rapidly to cause error. This will be detectable as a trend toward lower values at long reaction times. This error would be rectified only by change of solvent. The next choice would probably be purified dioxane. Incidentally, the traces of peroxides in the dioxane. would be destroyed by the hydrogenation.

PROBLEMS

1. It is claimed that the following equilibrium is established slowly. Devise analytical procedures for the measurement of the reaction rates and the equilibrium constants

$$
\begin{array}{ccc}
\text{R} \quad \overset{\displaystyle \text{OH}}{\underset{\displaystyle |}{\text{C}}}\text{—CO}_2\text{H} & \xrightarrow[\text{aqueous}]{63\% \text{ KOH}} & \text{R} \quad \overset{\displaystyle \text{O}}{\underset{\displaystyle \|}{\text{C}}}\text{—CO}_2\text{H} \\
\diagdown\diagup & & \diagdown\diagup \\
\text{C} & & \text{C} \\
\diagup\diagdown & & \diagup\diagdown \\
\text{R}' \quad \text{CH—CO}_2\text{H} & & \text{R}' \quad \text{CH}_2\text{CO}_2\text{H}
\end{array}
$$

2. How would you determine the composition of a mixture containing the following:

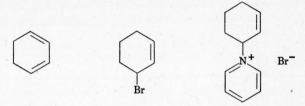

3. Devise a suitable procedure for determining the composition of the mixture:

$$CH_3CH_2Br$$

[benzene ring]—CHCH₂Br with D on the CH carbon

[benzene ring]—CH₂CHBr with D on the CHBr carbon

4. Devise a suitable procedure for determining the composition of the mixture:

[phthalic anhydride structure]

[3-nitrophthalic anhydride structure with NO₂]

[4-nitrophthalic anhydride structure with O₂N]

[dinitrophthalic anhydride structure with O₂N and NO₂]

5. Choose any five reactions from *Organic Syntheses*, and devise a procedure for (1) following the rate of the reaction, and (2) measuring the yields of the principal product and the most important by-products.

14.

LABORATORY PROCEDURES

INTRODUCTION

The procedures given in this section are intended for the laboratory part of a course in quantitative organic analysis. The aim of this laboratory work is to give the student firsthand experience with some typical quantitative determinations. The procedures presented here have been selected with the following points in mind:

1. It should have some practical value as an analytical method.

2. If possible, the method should illustrate some important analytical principle(s).

3. The procedure should not require the use of elaborate equipment.

Additional laboratory methods are conveniently available from several sources. Books by Siggia [1] and by Smith and Shriner [2] are designed primarily to give a series of working procedures for determining organic compounds. The collected work, *Organic Analysis*,[3] contains a gen-

[1] S. Siggia, *Quantitative Organic Analysis via Functional Groups*, 2nd ed., Wiley, New York, 1954.

[2] W. T. Smith and R. L. Shriner, *The Examination of New Organic Compounds*, Wiley, New York, 1956.

[3] J. Mitchell, I. M. Kolthoff, E. S. Proskauer, and A. Weissberger, Editors, *Organic Analysis*, Interscience, New York, Vol. 1, 1953; Vol. 2, 1954.

erous quantity of laboratory procedures. Finally, the current periodical literature abounds in organic analytical procedures.

Unknown samples for student analysis may be pure organic compounds, or they may be solutions of pure compounds in a nonreactive organic solvent. Mixtures of solid or liquid organic compounds may also be used, but care should be taken to choose substances that will not interact on standing. Chemicals for unknown samples may be obtained from commercial suppliers. Such compounds are usually 98% to 100% pure and can be used as received or may be further purified. Organic preparations that are known to be very pure are frequently available from university research laboratories.

In the authors' course, students are given samples for analysis that, except for the functional group to be determined, are unknown to them. Either the equivalent weight or the per cent of the functional group present is reported, although the latter is preferred. The students also analyze one or two mixtures. Here the type of compounds present are stated, and the student must devise his own plan for analysis, using procedures available in various books or journals.

1. HYDROXYL GROUPS BY ACETYLATION

Equations:

$$CH_3C \overset{O}{\underset{O}{\big\langle}} + ROH \rightarrow CH_3CO_2R + CH_3CO_2H$$

$$CH_3C \overset{O}{\underset{O}{\big\langle}} + H_2O \rightarrow 2CH_3CO_2H$$

Reagents:

Acetylating Reagent. Mix 1 volumĕ of A.C.S.-grade acetic anhydride with 3 volumes of reagent-grade pyridine. This mixture should be prepared just before use.

n-Butanol. Technical grade.

0.5 N Alcoholic Sodium Hydroxide. Dilute 28 ml. of saturated aqueous sodium hydroxide (carbonate free) to 1 liter with aldehyde-free ethanol or reagent-grade methanol. If methanol is used, the solution will not darken on standing. Standardize against potassium acid phthalate.

Mixed Indicator. Mix 1 part of 0.1% neutral aqueous cresol red with 3 parts of neutral thymol blue.

Procedure:

Weigh a sample containing about 5 millimoles of hydroxyl into a 250-ml. glass-stoppered Erlenmeyer flask or iodine flask, and add exactly 5 ml. of acetylating mixture. The glass stopper should be moistened with pyridine and seated loosely. Place the flask on a steam bath for 45 to 60 minutes. Remove the flask, cool slightly, and add 10 ml. of water. Replace the stopper and heat the flask for an additional 5 minutes. Cool the flask in ice or under running water, with the stopper partly open to prevent a partial vacuum from forming inside the flask. When cooled, rinse the stopper and sides of the flask with about 10 ml. of *n*-butanol. Titrate with 0.5 N alcoholic sodium hydroxide, using the mixed indicator. Alternatively, transfer the contents to a beaker and titrate to an apparent *p*H of 9.8, using a *p*H meter equipped with glass and calomel electrodes.

Run a reagent blank by adding 10 ml. of water to exactly 5 ml. of the acetylating mixture and heating a minute or two. Add 10 ml. of *n*-butanol, and titrate with 0.5 N alcoholic sodium hydroxide as above. If there is any free acid or base in the sample, dissolve a weighed sample in 5 ml. of pyridine, add 10 ml. of *n*-butanol, and titrate to a *p*H of 9.8 with standard acid or base.

Discussion:

The acetylation procedure given here is adapted from that of Ogg, Porter, and Willits.[4] Acetylation by this procedure is quantitative for

[4] C. L. Ogg, W. L. Porter, and C. O. Willits, *Ind. Eng. Chem., Anal. Ed.,* **17,** 394 (1945).

primary and secondary alcohols, most phenols, polyhydric alcohols, and polyhydric phenols. Some highly hindered phenols do not react completely. Sugars, cellulose derivatives, fats, and essential oils may be determined by a modification of this method in which the sample and acetylating reagent are allowed to stand for 24 to 48 hours at room temperature.

Primary and secondary amines, thiols, and thiophenols also react quantitatively with the acetic anhydride-pyridine reagent. Other interfering substances include tertiary alcohols, many aldehydes, α-amino acids, and all compounds that condense in basic media to yield a compound containing a hydroxyl group.

If the sample is known to contain only primary and tertiary alcohols, good results can usually be obtained by heating for only 15 minutes. The tertiary alcohol reacts to the extent of only 1 or 2% during this time whereas the primary alcohol reacts completely. Secondary alcohols react to the extent of 60 to 70% during the 15-minute heating period; phenols react even less during this time.

n-Butanol is added to the water-pyridine solution to ensure homogeneity during the titration and thus allow a better end point. If two layers form during the titration, more n-butanol can be added until a homogeneous solution is obtained.

Heating the solution after adding the water is recommended to speed the hydrolysis of the excess acetic anhydride and to ensure the hydrolysis of any mixed anhydrides that may have formed owing to free acid present in the sample. However, certain less stable acetates are partially hydrolyzed by this heating. In such cases the hydrolysis must be carried out at room temperature, and a longer reaction time is required for hydrolysis.

Considerable care should be taken in handling the heated solution because acetic anhydride is appreciably volatile. Acetic acid is complexed with the pyridine and does not volatilize. For more prolonged periods of heating, a reflux condenser instead of a pyridine-moistened stopper is recommended.

Water present in the sample will not interfere with the acetylation reaction, but it will consume the reagent by hydrolyzing the acetic anhydride. If considerable water is present in the sample, the amount of acetylating reagent should be increased to ensure the 100% excess recommended for complete reaction.

2. SAPONIFICATION OF ESTERS

Equations:

$$RCO_2R' + KOH \rightarrow RCO_2K + R'OH$$

$$RCO_2K + R_s\text{—}H^+ \rightarrow RCO_2H + R_s\text{—}K^+$$

$$KOH + R_s\text{—}H^+ \rightarrow H_2O + R_s\text{—}K^+$$

Apparatus and Reagents:

Ion Exchange Column. To a column that is approximately 20 mm. in diameter, add 6 grams of Dowex 50-X8 resin, 20 to 50 mesh, slurried with water. Drain off the excess water, and wash with 2 or 3 small portions of methanol-water.

Isopropyl Alcohol. Reagent grade.

Methanol-Water. Mix equal volumes of distilled water and reagent-grade methanol.

0.05 N Sodium Hydroxide. Prepare a carbonate-free aqueous solution, and standardize against potassium acid phthalate.

2 N Potassium Hydroxide. Prepare an aqueous solution.

Procedure:

Weigh a 100-to-200-mg. sample into a 15-to-30-ml. round-bottom flask. Add 2.5 ml. of 2 N potassium hydroxide and 7.5 ml. of isopropyl alcohol. Attach a small reflux condenser, and digest for 1 hour at the boiling point of the mixture. Cool the flask, dilute to approximately 40 ml. with methanol-water, and pass the solution through the ion exchange column. Wash the column with three or four 15-ml. portions of methanol-water. Heat the combined column effluent to boiling, and boil vigorously for 1 minute. Cool and titrate with 0.05 N sodium hydroxide, using phenolphthalein indicator.

In the same manner as above run a blank on each batch of alcohol and potassium hydroxide used.

Discussion:

This procedure was designed for simple esters that are fairly easily saponified. Methyl salicylate is a typical example of an ester that may be analyzed by this procedure. For esters that are more difficult to saponify, a higher-boiling alcohol (to increase the reflux temperature), alcoholic potassium hydroxide, and a longer reaction time might be necessary.

The resin in the ion exchange column should be replaced or regenerated after each determination. A convenient method is to add fresh resin for each determination and collect the used resin in a rather large container. When a sufficient quantity of used resin has been collected, place it in a large column, regenerate with 3 N hydrochloric acid, and wash with water. The regenerated resin is then ready for further use. This method reduces considerably the resin regeneration time per ester determination.

Many ion exchange resins contain appreciable resin that is finer than the mesh size indicated on the label. This fine resin may slow down the flow through the column. A good way to remove these fine particles is to agitate the resin with a large excess of water. Allow the resin to settle for a minute; then pour off the fine suspended particles. Repeat several times until the ion exchange resin settles rapidly and the supernatant liquid is clear and free of suspended particles.

In column operations with ion exchange resins, care should be taken that the column does not run dry. This may trap air bubbles and cause channeling which will reduce the capacity of the column and may prevent part of the sample from being washed through the column. When washing a column, allow each portion of liquid to drain just to the top of the resin before the next portion is added.

3. TITRATION OF AMINES IN NONAQUEOUS SOLUTION

Reagents:

0.1 N Perchloric Acid. Mix 8.5 ml. of 72% perchloric acid with about 200 ml. of glacial acetic acid, and add 20 ml. of acetic anhydride. Let this solution stand overnight to permit complete reaction of acetic anhydride with the water present; then dilute to 1 liter with glacial acetic acid. Standardize against potassium acid phthalate by titration in glacial acetic acid.

Methyl Violet (or crystal violet). Dissolve 0.2 gram of methyl violet (or crystal violet) in 100 ml. of glacial acetic acid.

Potassium Acid Phthalate. Primary standard grade.

Procedure:

Dissolve a sample containing 2 to 4 milliequivalents of amine in 50 ml. of glacial acetic acid, nitromethane, or acetonitrile. Add 2 drops of methyl violet indicator, and titrate potentially with 0.1 N perchloric acid. A pH meter (or other direct-reading titrimeter) equipped with ordinary glass and calomel electrodes is employed for this titration. Note the color of the indicator at each potential reading taken in the vicinity of the end point. Plot the potentiometric curve (millivolts against milliliters of perchloric acid), and titrate all additional samples of the same amine to the color exhibited by the indicator at the inflection point of the potentiometric curve.

Discussion:

The scope and limitations of nonaqueous acid-base titrations as well as the factors involved in choosing a suitable solvent are discussed in Chapter 3. Nitromethane and acetonitrile have a higher dielectric constant than glacial acetic acid and, therefore, frequently permit more stable potential readings. If the pH meter and electrodes used are in good condition, however, steady readings can also be obtained in glacial acetic acid. Glacial acetic acid is a much better solvent than the others for salts and for certain heterocyclic compounds such as caffeine. Potassium acid phthalate is difficult to dissolve in organic solvents but will go into solution in boiling acetic acid. Nitromethane should not be heated to help effect the solution of an amine sample.

A fiber-type calomel electrode is satisfactory for use in nonaqueous solvents only if the fiber contact is not clogged with any precipitate. When this happens, the potential becomes very unsteady. When not in actual use, keep both the glass and the calomel electrodes in distilled water. Just before a titration, remove the water from the electrodes by wiping them with absorbent paper. A sleeve-type calomel electrode gives much better contact between the electrode electrolyte and the nonaqueous solution, but diffusion of the aqueous potassium chloride into the solution being titrated frequently has an adverse effect on the titration. A sleeve-type calomel electrode filled with a 0.2 M glacial acetic acid solution of lithium chloride as the electrolyte appears to be satisfactory for titrations in glacial acetic acid.

4. NONAQUEOUS TITRATION OF ACIDS AND ACID MIXTURES

Equations:

$$R_4N^+OH^- + HA \rightarrow R_4N^+A^- + H_2O$$

Reagents and Apparatus:

0.1 N Triethyl-n-butylammonium Hydroxide or Tetra-n-butylammonium Hydroxide. Prepare triethyl-n-butylammonium iodide by refluxing equivalent quantities of triethylamine and n-butyl iodide. Tetra-

n-butylammonium iodide is available commercially from several sources. Convert the air-dried tetraalkylammonium iodide to the hydroxide by dissolving 30 grams of the salt in 90 ml. of absolute methanol, adding 27 grams of powdered silver oxide and agitating the mixture for 1.5 hours. Filter off the precipitate (preferably under nitrogen), and dilute the filtrate to 1 liter with anhydrous benzene. Standardize every few days by titration against reagent-grade benzoic acid.

Acetone. Reagent grade.

Acetonitrile. Matheson or Eastman.

Dimethylformamide (DMF). Technical grade. Purify by passing through a column of activated alumina.

Electrodes. General-purpose glass electrode (Beckman No. 1190-80). Fiber-type calomel (Beckman No. 1170) or sleeve-type calomel (Beckman No. 1170-71). Replace the aqueous electrolyte in the calomel electrode with a saturated methanolic solution of potassium chloride.

Buret. 10 ml.

Titrimeter. Precision-Shell Dual Titrometer or any sensitive pH meter that has a millivolt scale.

Magnetic Stirrer.

Procedure:

Dissolve a sample containing 0.4 to 0.8 milliequivalent of acid in 40 ml. of acetone and titrate with 0.1 N triethyl-n-butylammonium hydroxide or tetra-n-butylammonium hydroxide. Follow the titration potentiometrically, plotting the potential against the milliliters of titrant. Determine a solvent blank, and subtract from the total volume of titrant at the end point. When two or more inflections are observed, use the difference between successive end points to calculate the volume of titrant equivalent to each acidic constituent. Subtract the solvent blank from the last interval.

Discussion:

Pyridine, dimethylformamide, acetonitrile, and ethyleneglycol dimethyl ether are also good solvents for the titration of acids and mixtures of acidic compounds. Dimethylformamide is especially good for dicarboxylic acids and for other compounds that are difficult to dissolve in acetone. The magnitude of the end-point break is slightly less in dimethylformamide than in acetone. Strongly basic solvents such as ethylenediamine and butylamine are not well suited to differentiating titrations of acids because of their leveling properties for acids.

The procedure above can be used for the titration of carboxylic acids, enols, imides, phenols, thiophenols, sulfonamides of primary amines, and probably for other types of acidic compounds. Very strong acids such as sulfonic acids do not give stoichiometric results when titrated in acetone. Separate end points can be obtained for acid mixtures provided that the strength of the acids is significantly different and that the titration curves of the individual acids are reasonably flat. A few of the mixtures that the authors have been able to differentiate are the following: 2,4-dinitrophenol and any mono-substituted phenol, *o*-nitrophenol and methyl salicylate, phthalimide and dibenzoylmethane, sulfathiazole and sulfapyridine or sulfanilamide, salicylic acid and methyl salicylate, dichloroacetic acid and acetic acid, benzoic acid and dibenzoylmethane.

5. OXIMATION IN ALCOHOL-PYRIDINE

Equations:

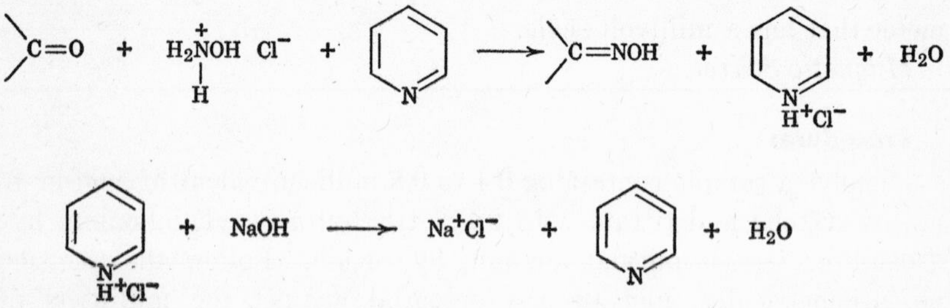

Reagents:

0.5 N Hydroxylammonium Chloride. Dissolve 35 grams of hydroxylammonium chloride in 160 ml. of water, and dilute to 1 liter with 95% ethanol (aldehyde-free).

Solvent Solution. Dilute 20 ml. of reagent-grade pyridine to 1 liter with 95% ethanol.

0.5 N Alcoholic Sodium Hydroxide. Dilute 28 ml. of saturated aqueous sodium hydroxide (carbonate free) to 1 liter with aldehyde-free ethanol or reagent-grade methanol. Standardize against potassium acid phthalate.

Procedure:

Measure 30 ml. of 0.5 N hydroxylammonium chloride into a 250-ml. glass-stoppered Erlenmeyer flask containing 100 ml. of solvent solution. Weigh or pipet a sample containing about 7.5 millimoles of carbonyl into the reaction flask. Stopper the flask, shake, and allow to stand for the prescribed time (see discussion below). If heat is required, moisten the glass stopper with pyridine, seat it loosely, and heat the flask on a steam bath. If extensive heating is necessary, a condenser should be used. After the reaction is complete, cool the solution to room temperature, then titrate with 0.5 N sodium hydroxide to an apparent pH of exactly 3.80, using a pH meter with glass and calomel electrodes.

Discussion:

The reaction time required depends on the type of compound to be oximated. Most aldehydes and unsubstituted ketones react completely on standing 0.5 hour at room temperature. Compounds with steric hindrance around the carbonyl group react more slowly. Ketones with one α-substituent require heating for 2 hours on the steam bath and very highly hindered ketones require 2 or 3 hours' heating on the steam bath, followed by standing overnight at room temperature. The times required for quantitative oximation of 30 aldehydes and ketones are given by Bryant and Smith.[5]

A visual indicator such as bromphenol blue is frequently used to detect the end point in the titration of pyridinium chloride with sodium hydroxide. However, the use of this indicator has disadvantages that are serious enough to encourage the use of the potentiometric method. Bromphenol blue has a poor color change in this titration and requires careful adjustment of a blank to the same volume as the sample solution in order to obtain the color match. Pyridine and appreciable amounts of other organic solvents also affect the indicator color change adversely. Furthermore, bromphenol blue is heat sensitive, undergoing a color change which is reversible during short heating periods but which becomes irreversible during prolonged heating. Directions for oximation, using bromphenol blue, are given by Bryant and Smith.[5]

Acidic and basic materials in the sample will interfere in the titration and must be corrected for by titration of a separate portion of the sample. Esters, acid chlorides, and anhydrides form hydroxamic acids with hydroxylamine and will interfere to varying extents with the

[5] W. M. D. Bryant and D. M. Smith, *J. Am. Chem. Soc.*, **57,** 57 (1935).

oximation of aldehydes and ketones. Iron and other metallic ions interfere with the reaction, and so samples containing metallic salts or oxides should be distilled before oximation.

6. OXIMATION IN GLACIAL ACETIC ACID

Equations:

$$\text{>C=O} + \left(\text{H}_2\overset{+}{\text{N}}\text{OH}\right)\left(\text{OAc}^-\right) \rightarrow \text{>C=NOH} + \text{HOAc} + \text{H}_2\text{O}$$

$$\left(\text{H}_2\overset{+}{\text{N}}\text{OH}\right)\left(\text{OAc}^-\right) + \text{HClO}_4 \rightarrow \left(\text{H}_2\overset{+}{\text{N}}\text{OH}\right)\left(\text{ClO}_4^-\right) + \text{HOAc}$$

Reagents and Apparatus:

0.5 M Hydroxylammonium Acetate. Dissolve 47 grams of hydroxyl-ammonium acetate in A.C.S.-grade glacial acetic acid, and dilute to 500 ml. with glacial acetic acid. The preparation of solid hydroxyl-ammonium acetate is described by Higuchi and Barnstein.[6]

0.1 N Perchloric Acid. Prepare a 0.1 N solution in glacial acetic acid as described in procedure 3, page 265.

pH Meter, or other direct-reading potentiometer equipped with glass and calomel electrodes.

Procedure:

Pipet accurately a 10-ml. portion of 0.5 M hydroxylammonium acetate into a 100-ml. volumetric flask, and add the sample, which should contain 2 to 3 millimoles of carbonyl compound. Let the solution stand for 20 minutes at room temperature if the carbonyl compound is an aldehyde or simple aliphatic ketone, longer for less reactive compounds (see discussion below). Dilute to exactly 100 ml. with glacial acetic acid and titrate a 5- or 10-ml. aliquot potentiometrically with 0.1 N perchloric acid. For the assay of compounds that form non-titratable oximes, prepare a blank and titrate in the same way as the sample.

Discussion:

This procedure is taken from the work of Higuchi and Barnstein.[6] Using oximation times of 20 to 30 minutes (except where noted), they

[6] T. Higuchi and C. H. Barnstein, *Anal. Chem.*, **28**, 1022 (1956).

obtained very good results for the following compounds: acetone, acetonedicarboxylic acid, acetophenone (2 hours), anisaldehyde, benzaldehyde, p-hydroxybenzaldehyde, benzil (24 hours), n-butyraldehyde, cyclohexanone (4 hours), diethyl ketone, diisopropyl ketone (24 hours), furfural, methyl ethyl ketone, piperonal, and vanillin. From this information, it appears that the method should be applicable to a very wide variety of carbonyl compounds.

The chief advantage of this method is in the sharpness of the end point obtained. Other oximation methods give a potentiometric inflection at the end point which is scarcely detectable. In favorable cases, such as benzaldehyde, oximation and titration in acetic acid gives a sharp break of approximately 250 millivolts in the immediate vicinity of the end point. With compounds such as methyl ethyl ketone, the oxime is slightly basic and is titrated in glacial acetic acid. In this case two end points are obtained; the first occurs at approximately 480 millivolts and is for the titration of the excess hydroxylammonium acetate, and the second is for titration of the oxime and occurs around 620 millivolts.

7. PURITY OF GLACIAL ACETIC ACID

Basis of Method:

In relatively pure samples of glacial acetic acid or other organic liquids, there will be a lowering of the freezing or congealing point which is proportional to the amount of impurities present. By referring to a suitable calibration curve, the freezing point of a given sample will give directly the purity of that sample. In glacial acetic acid the major impurity is water; hence, this method may be used to estimate accurately the water content of glacial acetic acid.

Procedure:

Place about 10 ml. of the sample in a dry 20-mm. test tube, and cool rapidly to about 5 degrees below the suspected freezing point. Place the tube in a larger tube through a cork so that an insulating jacket is formed to prevent the temperature from rising too rapidly. Stir the liquid with a standardized thermometer until solidification begins; then discontinue the stirring, and note the temperature rise every few seconds. Take the freezing point as the highest temperature that remains constant for about 1 minute. Calculate the purity of the glacial acetic acid from Fig. 39 on page 229.

8. TITRIMETRIC DETERMINATION OF SULFUR IN ORGANIC COMPOUNDS

Equations:

$$\text{Organic S} \xrightarrow[\text{KClO}_4]{\text{Na}_2\text{O}_2} \text{Na}_2\text{SO}_4 + \text{NaOH, etc.}$$

$$\text{Na}_2\text{SO}_4 + \text{NaOH} \xrightarrow[\text{H}_2\text{O}]{\text{HCl}} \text{Na}^+ + \text{HSO}_4{}^- + \text{Cl}^- \xrightarrow{\text{Alumina}}$$

$$\text{Alumina} \cdot \text{HSO}_4{}^- + \text{Cl}^- + \text{Na}^+$$

$$\text{Alumina} \cdot \text{HSO}_4{}^- \xrightarrow[\text{H}_2\text{O}]{\text{NH}_3}$$

$$\text{Alumina} \cdot \text{OH}^- + \text{SO}_4{}^= + \text{NH}_4{}^+ + \text{NH}_3 \xrightarrow{\text{H}^+\text{-Resin}}$$

$$\text{NH}_4{}^+\text{-Resin} + \text{H}^+ + \text{SO}_4{}^=$$

$$\text{Ba}^{++} + \text{SO}_4{}^= \rightarrow \text{BaSO}_4$$

$$\text{Ba}^{++} + \text{Thorin} \rightarrow \text{Ba-Thorin}$$

Reagents and Solutions:

Alcohol. Absolute ethanol, 2-propanol, methanol, or mixed ethanol and methanol as purchased commercially.

Barium Perchlorate, 0.01 M. Dissolve 3.9 grams of barium perchlorate trihydrate in 200 ml. of water, and add 800 ml. of ethanol. Standardize against 10 ml. of 0.005 M sulfuric acid.

Sulfuric Acid, 0.005 M. Prepare a 0.005 M solution, and standardize against 0.02 N sodium hydroxide.

Thorin, [2(2-hydroxy-3,6-disulfo-1-naphthylazo)benzenearsonic acid]. Prepare a 0.2% solution in water.

Methylene Blue. Prepare a 0.05% solution in water.

Potassium Perchlorate and Sodium Peroxide. Sulfur free. Produced by Parr Manufacturing Co., 211 Fifty-third Street, Moline, Illinois.

Sucrose. Grind reagent-grade sucrose in a mortar.

Ammonium Hydroxide. Reagent-grade.

Hydrochloric and Perchloric Acids. Reagent-grade.

Apparatus:

The alumina column and the apparatus used for its operation under reduced pressure is shown in Fig. 45. Add some chromatographic alumina, 80 to 200 mesh, to a beaker, wash with water, and allow to settle. Decant the supernatant liquid, and repeat the washing process until the very fine particles have been removed, as evidenced by the wash water remaining clear. Transfer the alumina to the column, and wash with 5 ml. of 1 M ammonia, several 5-ml. portions of 0.1 M ammonia, and finally with approximately 50 ml. of water. Lastly, wash with 10 ml. of hydrochloric or perchloric acid of the same strength to be used in the sulfate sample that will be passed through the column.

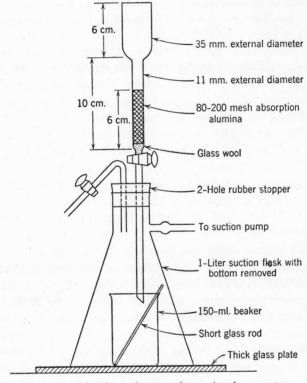

Figure 45. Alumina column and associated apparatus.

The column is now ready to receive the sample. In all operations with the alumina column, avoid letting the column run dry.

Use an ion exchange column which is approximately 1 inch in diameter, and fill with a 3-inch bed of cation exchange resin (Dowex 50-X8, 20 to 50 mesh) in the hydrogen form. After passage of each sample through the column, transfer the resin to a used resin container and add fresh hydrogen-form resin to the column. When a sufficient quantity of used resin has been collected, place in a large column, regenerate with 3 M hydrochloric acid, and wash with distilled water.

Use a macroperoxide bomb of the type manufactured by the Parr Instrument Co.

Procedure:

Weigh 0.2 to 0.3 gram samples into the macroperoxide fusion cup, and add 0.5 gram powdered sucrose, 0.5 gram potassium perchlorate, and 12 grams of sodium peroxide. Mix thoroughly with a tiny spatula or wire. Place 3 grams of sodium peroxide on top of the mixture. Assemble, screw tight, and ignite by placing the bomb over the sharp blue tip of a bunsen flame for 90 seconds. Quench the reaction by immersing in cold distilled water. Open the cup, and dissolve the fused contents by laying the cup in a 400-ml. beaker containing sufficient water to cover the cup. Cover with a watch glass and heat to near boiling. When the melt has dissolved, rinse the cup with water, and remove. With cover glass in place, add sufficient concentrated hydrochloric acid (28 to 30 ml.) to make the solution distinctly acidic. After allowing the carbon dioxide to escape, transfer the solution (with filtration if necessary) to a 500-ml. volumetric flask. Dilute to volume, and pipet 50- or 100-ml. portions into 150-ml. beakers. Dilute to approximately 125 ml. Pass the solution through the alumina column in the perchlorate form at the rate of 2 drops per second. Rinse the beaker with a little water, and pass this through the column. Rinse the column with 10 ml. of water added in two portions; then place the original 150-ml. beaker beneath the column. Elute the sulfate by passing through the column 5 ml. of 1 M ammonia and 20 ml. of 0.1 M ammonia added in four portions. Finally, rinse with 10 ml. of water. Pass the eluate through the cation exchange column, and collect in a 100-ml. volumetric flask. Dilute to volume. To 10-ml. portions, add 40 ml. of ethanol, and titrate with 0.01 M barium perchlorate to the first permanent pink color, using a drop each of thorin and methylene blue.

Discussion:

The Carius, Pregl combustion, or sodium peroxide bomb procedures are the most widely used for the analysis of pure organic compounds for sulfur. Of these, the peroxide bomb fusion is basically the most simple and rapid method for decomposing the sample. The chief disadvantage of this method is that a very large excess of sodium peroxide and potassium perchlorate must be used, and these foreign salts make the subsequent sulfate determination less accurate and more difficult to carry out. This is especially true if a direct titrimetric method is used to determine the sulfate.

The procedure given above [7] avoids these difficulties through a separation of sulfate on a column of activated alumina. The alumina column acts as an anion exchange column which has much greater affinity for some anions than for others. In acid solution the alumina column takes up sulfate (actually bisulfate at the pH used) avidly; it has a somewhat lower affinity for phosphate and fluoride and a much lower affinity for chloride, nitrate, and perchlorate. Sulfate will be taken up quantitatively from a solution with a chloride, nitrate, or perchlorate concentration many times that of the sulfate. The alumina has a greater affinity for the hydroxyl ion than for any of the other anions mentioned, thus permitting easy elution of sulfate from the column following the separation. Some chloride accompanies the sulfate but not enough to interfere with the final barium titration.

9. DETERMINATION OF UNSATURATION BY BROMINATION

Equations:

$$>C{=}C< + Br_2 \rightarrow \overset{\displaystyle Br}{\underset{\displaystyle |}{-}}\overset{|}{C}\overset{\displaystyle Br}{\underset{\displaystyle |}{-}}\overset{|}{C}-$$

$$Br_2 + 2I^- \rightarrow 2Br^- + I_2$$

$$I_2 + 2S_2O_3^{=} \rightarrow 2I^- + S_4O_6^{=}$$

Reagents:

0.1 N Bromate-Bromide. Dissolve 2.8 grams of dry reagent-grade potassium bromate (weighed accurate to ± 0.3 mg.) in water; add 10 grams of potassium bromide, and dilute to exactly 1 liter. Calculate the exact normality from the weight of potassium bromate taken.

0.2 N Mercuric Sulfate. Dissolve 30 grams of mercuric sulfate in a solution containing 28 ml. of concentrated sulfuric acid and 950 ml. of water.

0.05 N Sodium Thiosulfate. Dissolve 25 grams of sodium thiosulfate and 0.2 gram of sodium carbonate in 2 liters of water. Standardize against potassium bromate, potassium iodate, or iodine.

Carbon Tetrachloride. Reagent grade.

Glacial Acetic Acid. A.C.S. grade.

[7] J. S. Fritz, S. S. Yamamura, and M. J. Richard, *Anal. Chem.*, **29**, 158 (1957).

Procedure:

Prepare a solution of the sample that is approximately 0.08 N in unsaturation by adding a weighed sample to a volumetric flask that is approximately half full of carbon tetrachloride; then dilute to the mark. Use water in place of carbon tetrachloride if the sample is water soluble. The carbon tetrachloride solution may be quantitatively pipetted with the aid of a rubber pipetting bulb.

Add a calculated excess (10 to 15%) of 0.1 N bromate-bromide solution from a buret to a 300-ml. bromination flask (Fig. 11, page 81). If the amount of unsaturation in the sample is unknown, make a preliminary analysis, using a large excess of bromate-bromide. Evacuate the flask by means of a water aspirator; add 5 ml. of 6 N sulfuric acid, and allow to stand for 2 or 3 minutes while bromine is being liberated. Add 10 to 20 ml. of 0.2 N mercuric sulfate and exactly 25 ml. of the solution to be analyzed. Rinse the sample into the bromination flask with about 15 ml. of carbon tetrachloride (or water). If the sample is not water soluble, add 20 ml. of glacial acetic acid. Wrap the flask with a black cloth, and shake for about 7 minutes. Add in succession 15 ml. of 2 N sodium chloride and 15 ml. of 20% potassium iodide, and continue shaking for another 30 seconds. Release the vacuum and titrate with 0.05 N sodium thiosulfate, using starch indicator. Concurrent with this analysis, run a blank containing no sample and one-third the amount of bromate-bromide solution used in the analysis.

Discussion:

This procedure is essentially that of Lucas and Pressman.[8,9] It gives accurate results for most olefins and acetylenes, although some compounds require a somewhat longer reaction time. Mercuric sulfate generally speeds bromination, but it may actually slow down the reaction in the case of certain conjugated systems (see discussion on page 80).

The dark cloth is used to reduce the possibility of substitution bromination. If the titration is not to be carried out in the bromination flask, it is convenient to exclude light by painting the flask or by covering it with black tape. A large excess of bromine will also cause substitution. If the bromine excess is less than 10 to 15%, however, the bromination is likely to be incomplete in the time specified.

[8] H. J. Lucas and D. Pressman, *Ind. Eng. Chem., Anal. Ed.,* **10**, 140 (1938).

[9] S. Siggia, *Quantitative Organic Analysis via Functional Groups,* 2nd ed., Wiley, New York, 1954, p. 69.

10. DETERMINATION OF ALKYL SULFIDES AND DISULFIDES

Equations:

$$BrO_3^- + 5Br^- + 6H^+ \rightarrow 3Br_2 + 3H_2O$$

$$R_2S + Br_2 + H_2O \rightarrow R_2SO + 2HBr$$

$$RSSR + 5Br_2 + 4H_2O \rightarrow 2RSO_2Br + 8HBr$$

Reagents:

0.1 N Bromate-Bromide. Dissolve 2.8 grams of dry reagent-grade potassium bromate (weighed accurate to ± 0.3 mg.) in water; add 10 grams of potassium bromide, and dilute to exactly 1 liter. Calculate the exact normality from the weight of potassium bromate taken.

Glacial Acetic Acid. A.C.S. grade.

Hydrochloric or Sulfuric Acid. Concentrated, reagent grade.

Procedure:

Weigh a sample containing about 2 millimoles of alkyl sulfide or 0.3 millimoles of alkyl disulfide into a 250-ml. Erlenmeyer flask. Dissolve the sample in 40 ml. of glacial acetic acid, and add 10 ml. of water. If the sample is an alkyl sulfide, add 3 ml. of hydrochloric acid; if the sample is an alkyl disulfide, add 25 ml. of either hydrochloric or sulfuric acid. Warm the solution to 30 to 50° C., and titrate with 0.1 N bromate-bromide until the bromine color persists. The end point can be noted within 2 drops of reagent. Run a blank to correct for the excess bromine needed for the end point.

Discussion:

This procedure is taken from the work of Siggia and Edsberg.[10]

Thiols are also titrated with bromine, first to disulfides, then to alkyl sulfonyl bromides. Thiols should, therefore, be determined separately and the amount present taken into account when calculating the results for sulfide or disulfide analysis. Other types of compounds that consume bromine readily will, of course, interfere with the bromometric determination of sulfides and disulfides.

[10] S. Siggia and R. L. Edsberg, *Anal. Chem.*, **20**, 938 (1948).

11. DETERMINATION OF PEROXIDES

Equations:

$$ROOR + 2HI \rightarrow 2ROH + I_2$$
$$I_2 + S_2O_3^= \rightarrow 2I^- + S_4O_6^=$$

Reagents:

Potassium Iodide. Prepare a saturated aqueous solution.

0.1 N Sodium Thiosulfate. Dissolve approximately 25 grams of sodium thiosulfate and 0.1 gram of sodium carbonate in 1 liter of distilled water that has been boiled for several minutes and allowed to cool. Standardize against potassium dichromate, potassium bromate, or potassium iodate.

Starch Solution. Prepare a 2% aqueous solution.

Dry Ice.

Glacial Acetic Acid. A.C.S. grade.

Sulfuric Acid. Concentrated, reagent grade.

Procedure A—Determination of Benzoyl Peroxide:

Weigh a sample estimated to contain 0.25 gram of benzoyl peroxide, and dissolve it in 25 ml. of glacial acetic acid. To this add 2 ml. of saturated, aqueous potassium iodide and a few pieces of Dry Ice. Allow the mixture to stand for 10 minutes. Titrate with 0.1 N sodium thiosulfate until the end point is approached, as indicated by the fading of the brown iodine color. Add 25 ml. of water and 1 ml. of starch solution. Continue the titration until the familiar starch end point is reached.

Procedure B—Determination of tert-Butyl Hydroperoxide:

This procedure is the same as Procedure A except that 5 drops of concentrated sulfuric acid are added after the addition of potassium iodide. Gentle warming, under a blanket of carbon dioxide, may be used to accelerate the reaction.

Discussion:

Easily reducible peroxides such as benzoyl peroxide require no added mineral acid in the reduction, and Procedure A is used with such compounds. Other peroxides, notably alkyl hydroperoxides, are reduced better by Procedure B, in which mineral acid is added to accelerate the reaction. Dialkyl peroxides, such as di-*tert*-butyl peroxide, are not reduced easily by either procedure.

The order of addition of reagents is of particular importance. If either the potassium iodide or the peroxide precipitates, the reduction in the heterogeneous system may become very slow.

12. KINETIC ANALYSIS OF A MIXTURE OF TERTIARY CHLORIDES

Equations:

$$(1) \qquad R_3CCl + H_2O \rightarrow R_3COH + HCl$$

$$(2) \qquad R_3CCl + H_2O \rightarrow olefins + HCl$$

$$(3) \qquad HCl + NaOH \rightarrow H_2O + NaCl$$

Reagents:

"80%" Ethanol. Mix four volumes of absolute alcohol with one volume of distilled water.

0.05 N Sodium Hydroxide. Dilute 3 ml. of saturated aqueous sodium hydroxide to 1 liter with distilled water which has been freshly boiled to expel CO_2. Standardize against potassium acid phthalate or by comparison with an accurately known solution of standard acid. Store protected from CO_2 by a tube packed with soda lime.

Chloride Mixture. Place an 11-gram sample of 2,3,4-trimethyl-3-pentanol [11] in a 250-ml. separatory funnel and shake with 150 ml. of concentrated hydrochloric acid. Allow mixture to stand with occasional shaking for an hour. At the end of that time, draw off the acid (lower) layer and add a fresh portion of concentrated hydrochloric acid. Shake the mixture vigorously, and allow to separate into layers. Remove the upper layer, and dry over calcium chloride. The products may be vacuum distilled but for the purpose of this experiment it is sufficient to remove samples directly for the kinetic analysis.

Procedure:

Place 100 ml. of the ethanol-water solvent in a long-necked flask such as a 125-ml. volumetric flask. Place this flask in the 25° thermo-

---

[11] This alcohol is made by the addition of methyl magnesium bromide to the commercially available diisopropyl ketone. F. C. Whitmore and R. S. George, *J. Am. Chem. Soc.*, **64**, 1241 (1942). Because of the time saved by distillation of large batches, it is recommended that a large supply of the alcohol be prepared as a stock for this experiment.

stat [12] to attain temperature equilibrium (about one hour). Add a 1-ml. sample of the chloride mixture, mix the contents of the flask rapidly by inversion, and return to the thermostat immediately. At intervals remove 5-ml. samples with a volumetric pipet, and deliver into 100 ml. of ice-cold, absolute ethanol.[13] Then titrate the samples with 0.05 N standard sodium hydroxide to the methyl red end point.

Infinity Titer. Remove a 5-ml. aliquot from the reaction vessel, and deliver into 25.0 ml. of the standard base. After standing for one-half hour, back-titrate the sample with standard 0.05 N acid. Replicate determinations are recommended.

Discussion:

We recommend that students prepare their own chloride mixtures for analysis. This is done by the reaction of hydrochloric acid with 2,3,4-trimethyl-3-pentanol.

$$
(4) \quad
\begin{array}{ccc}
CH_3 & CH_3 & CH_3 \\
| & | & | \\
CH_3CH\!-\!C\!-\!\!-\!CHCH_3 + HCl \rightarrow \\
| \\
OH
\end{array}
$$

$$
\begin{array}{ccc}
CH_3 & CH_3 & CH_3 \\
| & | & | \\
CH_3CH\!-\!C\!-\!\!-\!CHCH_3 \\
| \\
Cl \\
\text{(I)}
\end{array}
\; + \;
\begin{array}{ccc}
CH_3 & CH_3 & CH_3 \\
| & | & | \\
CH_3CH\!-\!CH\!-\!CCH_3 \\
| \\
Cl \\
\text{(II)}
\end{array}
$$

The analysis illustrates principles discussed in Chapter 9 and is slightly adapted from a published procedure.[14] Figure 46 shows the run rate data as plotted by Brown and Fletcher, and Fig. 47 shows the data resolved into two components. The first figure shows that data taken after 11 hours fit the first-order plot with accuracy, indicating that the change in titer is contributed, within experimental error, by a single reacting species from that time.

There is no need to distinguish between the displacement and elimination reactions (equations 1 and 2) because both produce hydrochloric

---

[12] Thermostatic control is virtually indispensable for the success of this experiment. If no thermostat is available, it is possible to maintain reasonably constant temperature in a water bath in a large Dewar flask which is kept *near room temperature* by periodic addition of small amounts of warm or cold water.

[13] This quenches the solvolysis reaction by slowing down the rate. The titration should be carried out as soon after sampling as is possible.

[14] H. C. Brown and M. S. Fletcher, *J. Am. Chem. Soc.*, **73**, 1318 (1951).

acid.   The production of acid is monitored by periodically removing aliquots which are titrated with standard sodium hydroxide solution. The data are analyzed by the use of the first-order rate law since it is virtually certain that the hydrolysis of each chloride would indi-

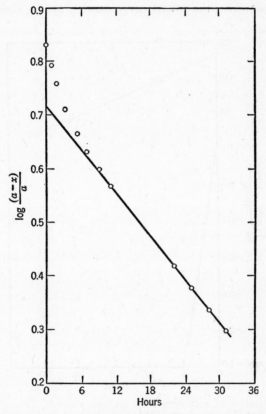

Figure 46. Rate of solvolysis of a mixture of *tert*-halides.

vidually follow that law.   The integrated form of the law is used, and the experimental data may be plotted directly.

$$(5) \qquad\qquad -2.303 \log \frac{a - x}{a} = kt + c$$

where a = initial concentration of reactant $\propto$ ml. NaOH at t_∞,

   x = amount of reaction at time $t \propto$ ml. NaOH consumed at t,

   c = integration constant = 0 if a = concentration at t_0.

$$(6) \qquad -2.303 \log \frac{(\text{ml. NaOH})_{t_\infty} - (\text{ml. NaOH})_t}{(\text{ml. NaOH})_{t_\infty}} = kt + c$$

The data are plotted according to equation 6, and the best straight line is drawn through the latter points. The intersection of this line with the $t = 0$ axis gives the initial concentration of the slower reactant,

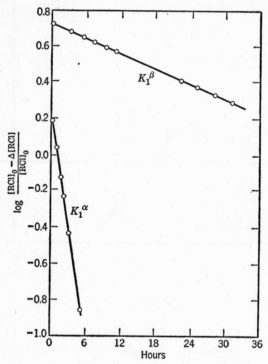

Figure 47. Separation of solvolysis rates for two isomers. [From H. C. Brown and R. Fletcher, *J. Am. Chem. Soc.*, **73**, 1318 (1951).]

designated as the β isomer.[15] The difference between the total β isomer and infinity titer gives the initial concentration of the α isomer. The results should be checked further by constructing a plot such as that in Fig. 47. To do this, subtract from the experimental values for the early points the calculated values for the amount of β isomer reacted during the interval. The difference is the amount of α isomer solvolyzed

[15] Brown and Fletcher[4] assign structure I to the α isomer on the basis of its greater reactivity and the theories of steric strain as a factor in determining relative reactivities.

during the interval. These values are then plotted according to equation 6. If the results yield a good straight line, this is evidence that the kinetic separation is satisfactory.

The times involved in this experiment are necessarily long. If conditions were chosen to be conducive to faster solvolysis, the rate of reaction of the α isomer would become so rapid as to be difficult to measure by the simple technique described above. It is necessary to plan the work to cover a period of up to 36 hours although it is not necessary to monitor the progress carefully throughout the period (see Fig. 46). One should plan to take some 8 to 10 points during the first 10 hours; and a similar number should be distributed, to suit the convenience of the student, over a further 25-hour period. The infinity titer is critical to the success of the method and is determined by adding an aliquot of water to accelerate the hydrolysis.*

* It may be desirable to carry out this experiment on a partnership basis in order to implement the planning of an extended time schedule. The measurements require little time in themselves, and other work can be profitably carried out in parallel with the kinetic measurements.

AUTHOR INDEX

GENERAL INDEX *

Absorbancy, 169
Absorption spectra, 168
  correlations with molecular structure, 191
Accuracy, 246
  of acid-base titrations, 56, 57
Acetals, 10, 15
Acetic acid as a solvent, 29, 32, 238, 257, 265
Acetic anhydride, effect on nonaqueous titration of bases, 36, 37, 43
Acetone as a solvent, 44, 54, 267
Acetonitrile, as a solvent, 29, 32, 41, 44, 57, 265, 267
  purification, 45
Acetophenone, rate of oximation, 12
Acetylation, interferences, 263
  of alcohols, 59
  procedure, 261
Acids, conditions for titration, 43
Acid-base theories, 24

Acid catalysis, 11
  of oximation reactions, 12
Acid mixtures, differentiating titration of, 54
Acidity, effect on chelate formation, 121
Acids, determination of dissociation constants by spectrophotometry, 178
Activation energy, 148
Active hydrogen methods, direct, 106
  indirect, 107
Activity coefficients, 10
Acylation, 59
Adsorbents, see Chromatography
Alcohol, effect on nonaqueous titrations, 36
Aldehydes, absorption spectra, 193, 195
  separation, 202
Aldol condensation, 15
Alizarin sulfonate, sodium salt, 142
Alkali error, 46

* For references to the determination of specific compounds or functional groups, see the Index to Methods, p. 299.

291

INDEX TO METHODS